Carmen María Montiel

STOLEN IDENTITY

A STORY OF LOVE, VIOLENCE AND LIBERATION

CARMEN MARÍA MONTIEL

DISCLAIMER

This book is a fictional memoir based on my recollections of actual events, locations and conversations. Some names and identifying details have been changed to protect the privacy of individuals.

To all women that are suffering abuse in silent, those who have already been able to free themselves and those who did not live to tell their stories.

Dedication

To my family, for showing me once again what unconditional love is.

To my successful lawyers, for having had faith in me and for fighting for my children and me.

To my children, for teaching me the innate integrity that human beings have. At their young age, they gave me daily lessons that allowed me to continue. Thank you for having been able to smile despite the darkness and for giving Mommy those little glimpses of happiness in the worst moments. Thank you for being able to get ahead and for taking the positive of this experience to get your lives on track. Alexandra, Kamee and Juan Diego: you saved me. I love you more than anything in life.

Introduction

MARRIAGE CAN BE the safest relationship or the most dangerous one. Toward the end of my marriage, I knew I was living the second option, but could not dare do anything about it.

Domestic violence is a silent killer. It happens behind closed doors at home. In fact, every nine seconds a woman is the victim of domestic violence. In my case, killing me was too obvious! The next best thing was burying me alive by sending me to prison.

Like most women, I did not know I was a victim of domestic violence. The abuser starts with a combination of mental and psychological abuse to destroy the victim's self-esteem and confidence first, then progresses to physical violence.

My abuser husband was able to diminish me with years of emotional, psychological, physical and substance abuse. He thought he finally had me out of the way, so he could enjoy life as he wanted, spending our money and indulging his sex addiction.

But despite being nearly destroyed, I managed to retain my dignity even while being forced to allow him to lead a double life as a respected family man with a successful medical practice and a husband who cheated on his wife with prostitutes, often in their own home.

I loved my husband and worked hard to build a family and our business. I never imagined he could hurt me, much less try to destroy me. Like most abuse victims, I never thought when he hurt me that it was intentional. After every assault, I recreated the incident to see what I did that caused him to react violently.

Stolen Identity goes beyond domestic violence to expose how difficult it is to recognize abusers, even for the authorities. This is the story of an abused immigrant woman who had no place to go or hide. A Catholic who believed in family and fought to save it for her children's sake. In the end, however, because of her children, she had to get out of that vicious marriage to save herself.

CHAPTER 1

Fear

"**Y**OU ARE CHARGED with a single count of 'intimidating a flight attendant.'" I am standing with my hands handcuffed and feet shackled—this is beyond humiliating. The judge continues: "The charge has a prison sentence of up to 20 years and a fine of $250,000!"

I can hardly hold my body up. My legs are shaking. I whisper to my lawyer that I am afraid in the quietest voice I can manage to get out of my lips. I can hardly speak. My life is passing by inside my head, all the light and happiness, my three beautiful children. And now my world has come to this? How? Why?

After all the shining moments in my life, after all the hard work, always helping others and holding my head high—because "doing the right thing" was the motto my parents raised me with—I am ending my life in prison! Will I become a felon? Me? The maximum that had happened to me before this was a traffic ticket. Will Alejandro succeed in setting me up?

My feet can hardly support my now extra tiny body; though tall, I now only weigh 110 pounds. I cannot control my shaking. I am hoping no one can notice.

My lawyer whispers in my ear to be calm.

The prosecutor addresses the judge and asks for my passports to be turned in—mine and those of my children.

"Her husband says she is a flight risk, Your Honor, and she will take his children away."

At that moment, I realized that Alejandro was trying hard to block my release. It was as if he had something to do with the charges. In time, I would understand how all of it was planned.

It has happened in the "best" of families. Sons have killed their fathers to become kings. Henry VIII executed two of his six wives. And Henry II sent his wife, Eleanor of Aquitaine, to prison for ten years.

My attorney protests, "Your Honor, her husband took her Venezuelan passport from the house and it cannot be found. Her family lawyers have requested it numerous times since the divorce proceedings began. These are more of his abusive tactics. She has been the victim of domestic violence for years."

Tears started to roll down my cheeks once I realize my love story has turned little by little into this nightmare.

"I am subpoenaing the husband to produce the passports," the judge said. "A big strong marshal will make sure he comes on Thursday."

At the end of the hearing I am taken back to a cell. I lost track of time because it took so long that it felt like an eternity. It was so long I thought they were not going to release me that day. I was afraid I was going to be taken back to the Federal Pen, as they called it.

Finally, someone came for me and took me to a room where one of my criminal lawyers was on the other side of the window. While I was walking, I passed other cells with men who were talking even though they could not see each other. One of them said to the other: "¡*Esta bolilla debe ser una mula!*" meaning "This white woman must be a drug trafficker."

"What is going on?" I asked my lawyer. "I have not done anything."

"It is a stupid charge, Carmen, but it is a federal charge. You need to answer these questions for your release. However, I need to tell you that the prosecution is fighting hard. They said your husband called the FBI agent several times to warn them that you are a flight risk."

"I will not go anywhere without my children! How is it that Alejandro has the FBI agent's direct number?"

"They are saying he is almost crying, saying you will take the children and he will never see them again. He is even saying that you have TWO Venezuelan passports."

"He is the one with dual identity in Venezuela. He is insane, accusing me of HIS crimes. He is behind all of this—you know it's a lie!"

"Ssssshhhh! We will talk later. Just answer the questions."

I answered all the questions, for my attorney. They were mostly financial questions.

After that, I was taken back to the little cell where I waited to be called again, hoping to be taken home.

But suddenly I thought: "Oh my God! Another night in this place?"

I had never felt so insignificant. In a place I did not know, with people I never imagined I would ever spend time with or even be close to. There I was with alleged drug traffickers, murderers, illegal immigrants, and prostitutes! Criminals, real criminals, and then me!

When they asked me what I had done and I explained, they were all incredulous. I did not look as though I belonged there. They called me "the Virgin" because they said my face was so beautiful and I wore no makeup.

"She is a Virgin," one said. "Oh! A doll," said another.

Before that, the only time I had seen a prostitute was from a distance while driving in Caracas by Libertador Avenue. They looked as if they came from an alternative world. I never imagined our lives would end up being so similar: Abused, drugged and taken to a criminal court. In a way I was part of today's slavery of women.

Alejandro had brought a different set of prostitutes into our lives, Houston prostitutes. They dance in men's nightclubs.

Once while insulting me, Alejandro said: "You think you are different from the rest of the world because you have light eyes. Don't you? Well those prostitutes I am involved with that you hate also have light eyes. See, Carmen. There is no difference between you and them!"

He managed to label me like this the day of the first setup and after that, I became his prisoner, just like prostitutes become imprisoned by their pimps.

My fellow prisoners probably thought I was lying. The federal officers told me not to say who I was or where I lived. It felt like they understood an injustice had been done, and they wanted to protect me.

They said: "No one here is your friend. Be careful what you say. Be careful with every word. It is better if you limit your communication with them. Do not tell them you live in Memorial. They don't understand where you come from."

Memorial is one of the wealthiest neighborhoods in Houston.

"Great! Now what?" I thought to myself. It was too late. I had already told a couple of people, including my cellmate.

How could I not say anything when I could not stop crying? Of course, these women were asking.

The officers explained that this was not a jail; it was prison, federal prison. I did not understand the difference. I had never cried so much.

I expected my lawyers to come see me in that place and explain where I was. The marshals had picked me up around noon. I thought my lawyers would show up to tell me what was going on. I spent the whole afternoon waiting for them. I was hopeful until quite late.

I had to be nice to these women. But I did not know how to act with them. How should I talk to them? I smiled but mostly stayed quiet.

The girl who was my cellmate had a weird suggestion. She said she had a sugar daddy. And she was in prison! How did she manage a sugar daddy while in prison? It is a bizarre world.

"You should get a sugar daddy, too," she said. "You are pretty and have a nice figure!"

She asked more about what had happened. Although the officer had already told me not to talk, how could I not? I told her everything my husband had done to me, and how he kept calling the flight attendant until I was arrested.

After that, she said: "I can solve that for you!"

When I asked her how, she replied: "Better for you not to know too much."

Then I understood what she was talking about.

"Oh my God!" I said. "No…do not! Don't even talk about it, please!"

In time, I came to understand that this was probably a setup, that the girl was a mole. They were really trying to get me for something real—not this trumped up charge of "intimidating a flight attendant."

Even when I had arrived earlier that day, one of the officers was puzzled and said it was not a federal charge. If anything, it was "contempt of court"—a misdemeanor state charge.

"Why are they bringing you here?" he asked in a low voice, looking angry.

I prayed to get out that day. I was worried about my children. They were home when I left. They stayed with the housekeeper and did not know anything about me after that. I am everything for them.

My lawyer never showed up. He later explained that he could not find me in the system, and he was not allowed in the prison because of it. I did not even exist there! Apparently, people get lost in the system all the time.

I spent the longest night in federal prison with that girl who checked me all night to see if I was sleeping.

"Why are you here?" I asked her.

"I witnessed my brother killing someone. Since I knew about it, that is why I am here. They went to my home at 6 a.m. and took me in my underwear."

I could not help but think that every conversation with this girl was bizarre. But probably she thought the same about me.

Finally, they came for me.

I was taken to a room, where the chains were removed. Then I was passed to another room. Every room was behind locked doors, extremely secure. Finally, I got to a hall where my lawyer was waiting for me. He explained that my release was approved with the condition that I had to turn in both passports, Venezuelan and American, by Thursday. Alejandro was to appear in court with the Venezuelan passport. And my family lawyers were to appear, too, with evidence that the Venezuelan passport had been formally requested in the divorce proceedings.

My attorney walked me to an office, where my daughter Alexandra was waiting, along with one of my family lawyers. I ran and hugged her. I cried because I thought I was never going to be able to hug her again. I am thinking while hugging her: "My baby has to be a responsible adult now at only 17 years old, for her and for her siblings. This is so wrong. Why? Why? Why do my children have to be going through this experience?"

My family lawyer tells Alexandra to make sure her father does not go home, because I am going there. She texted him, "*Mami* is out." He answered, "I know." She showed the text to me and I could not believe it. How does he know?

He is in close contact with federal officials and I asked myself: "Do they know he has dual identity in Venezuela? Do they know about his patient that died in unusual circumstances?"

At that moment, I was informed that Alejandro was planning to move into the house. I refiled for divorce a month after the airplane incident, and divorce proceedings started officially over a month ago.

The court had granted me a "kick-out order," meaning he had to leave the house, and a protective restraining order whereby he had to stay away from me after the last beating he gave me put him in jail. I had been living at the house with the children and the housekeeper ever since.

Alexandra told me that Alejandro went to the house once the FBI took me away. He was there in less than 15 minutes. It is obvious he knew I was going to be arrested. (He works 40 minutes away from the house.) It was a Monday around noon, and he was with his younger brother. They obviously did not work that day.

When I got back home, I hugged my other two children. I cannot cry. They cannot see me weak—I am their strength. Kamee knew where I had been, but not JD. My computer tech was at the house at the time of the arrest and he went up to JD's computer to entertain him.

I went to my bedroom and took a shower. I felt filthy. Once in the shower, I started to cry: "Daddy, come help me please," I cried out, screaming. I started to sing "*Muñequita linda*" (beautiful doll), just like he used to sing to me. I felt so lonely and lost. And I have three children who depend on me. Their father is an alcoholic and drug addict who is "dating" prostitutes. He cannot take care of the kids. He was never able to even take care of himself. I prayed: "God, please do not let them lose me."

After the shower, we all sat down to have dinner. I could not eat. My daughters tried to make me. "*Mami*, eat please. You look like you lost ten pounds." In fact, I had. I can lose weight when stressed out or sick so fast.

"I will gain it back," I replied.

Alejandro had taken my Blackberry and more documents. The housekeeper told me he was looking for my American passport. If I did not have the passports to turn in, I would never have been freed because he said I was a flight risk. He was also looking for my jewelry. He wanted to leave me with nothing, without any means of support. However, after he finished look-ing, he left, leaving the children with the housekeeper. He did not care to take them with him. And now I have to pay for a lawyer to defend me.

When I finished dinner, I went to my closet to try to figure out where my American passport was since it was not where I kept all the passports. My daughters had already taken the rest of them in. I searched my two-story closet but could not find it. I was getting desperate. I still had tomorrow, but was not going to sleep well if I did not find it now. I decided to look inside every handbag, when it occurred to me that the handbag I used the day of the flight to Colombia was the pinkish Prada. There it was along with my passport! Thank God! Thank you, Jesus. Thank you. I kissed it.

I wonder what Alejandro would think if he knew he was so close but could not find it.

That night I slept with my son, the youngest of my chil-dren. I hugged him hard. Ever since his father left, JD moved into my bedroom. Once he was sleeping, I started to cry. I was in my bed, in my house. I never wanted to ever again sleep in that place. But a thought came to me: "My God! I could end up there for years!"

I cried harder and suddenly started to call for my mom. I needed my mother.

Is there ever a moment in life when you stop needing your mother? I thanked God I still had her. My father has been gone since 1999. At that moment I decided to bring her over to stay with us.

The next day I rested. I was exhausted. My lawyers called to make sure I had the American passport for Thursday. My brother also needed to go there to sign as a responsible per-son for me.

I spoke with my family lawyers and informed them of what Alejandro had taken from the house. They told me that

Alejandro now wanted the children and the right to live in the house. My lawyers wrote a letter requesting everything and advising his lawyers that Alejandro was not to be at the house ever again. However, he never respected court orders. He acted like he was above the law and maybe he was because no one ever punished him.

On Thursday, all of my lawyers (criminal and family), my brother and Alejandro went to court. I waited at my lawyer's office.

Alejandro said he did not have the Venezuelan passport. To which my lawyer said, probably he already shredded it! His lawyer insisted to the judge that I was a flight risk and should not be left free—that I should be back in prison to await trial there!

How could he? He knows I did nothing and I am the mother of his children.

The best way to defend yourself is by staying free. You find a way. You are free to talk with family and the lawyers; you are free to find ways to pay for your defense. Alejandro withdrew all the money from our bank accounts, leaving me penniless.

Ultimately, I was free to brainstorm with my lawyers. But in prison? Forget it! And prison was a card he was going to wave at the family judge every second. As he did with this charge.

And that is what Alejandro was trying to do. Trying as best as he could to lock me up. But God was on my side and the side of the truth. My lawyers turned in the American passport and that was enough for the judge. I proved I did not have the Venezuelan passport with all the motions presented by my family lawyers.

José, his brother, also was there. Funny, because they had not had a relationship ever since he got married. Now, they are best buddies. And José is missing work often to be with Alejandro. As usual, José was hitting on one of Alejandro's female criminal lawyers. The people in his family are all the same. My brother told me everything in the afternoon, including how Alejandro and his lawyers—even after everyone left court—were working in the Federal Building trying to get me locked up.

One of his lawyers on a previous occasion told me: "Carmen, get out of this marriage. I have seen many women ruining their lives because of a man like him."

Not only did she know whom she was defending, but also now she was helping him ruin my life and wrongfully put me in prison just as she had warned me about. Today 75% of women in jail are victims of domestic violence. Many do not live to see another day.

By Friday I met with my legal team. That is everybody: family lawyers and criminal lawyers. "My God, this divorce is becoming so expensive. Where am I going to get the money to pay for this?" I asked myself while sitting there. It was all part of Alejandro's master plan. If I could not pay the lawyers, then I could not defend myself from prison or get what was rightfully mine in the divorce. In the end, what he wanted was to keep it all and not have to split the marital estate with me. All we have made together. He was a medical student when we met and he did not come from money. His father was a Lebanese immigrant and his mother was his father's secretary.

Once in prison, I would lose all my rights and, while I was locked up, he would leave me with nothing, not even my credibility. I knew too much about him. Alejandro could not risk that, because he did not know where his illegal Venezuelan passport was. My own children would never see me again. And he would destroy them. My oldest daughter said Kamee would commit suicide in her father's "care," and she and JD would end up in juvenile prison. Alexandra saw it clearly. It broke my heart that my beautiful children had to go through this.

I prayed and prayed, asking God to help me.

My family lawyer looked at me in the meeting and said: "Well, this divorce just hit the target of half a million dollars or more with the indictment. Carmen, do you have the funds for this or a rich boyfriend or some money stacked somewhere?"

"I will find a way," I whispered.

Some money stacked somewhere? All he wanted was to get his hands on it and leave me with no means—as he ended up doing. He took over $400,000 for less than three days in court and six months of work. When he got all of the money he could from me, he fired me. Could he be part of Alejandro's master plan?

With all that happened to me, I came to realize how people lost respect for me. Not only that, they felt they could abuse me. Because they knew that if I acted out, it could prove Alejandro's version of the story.

My lawyer talked about the case. He told the team it was a silly charge and more than likely he would be able to get it dropped. He also said that if it fell in the court of one of those older male judges, it would be dropped. However, I ended up in the court of a female judge for whom every case merited a trial—she never let a case go away. Everyone had to go to court or settle with the government. How scary!

I started to deal with my divorce and this charge at the same time. My life was so complicated.

I wondered what would have happened if I had not filed for divorce. The answer came months later when listening to recordings I made before my divorce of conversations with Alejandro to have them translated into English. In one of them he said: "You are going to prison, Carmen. You are a felon. Don't worry —I will take the children to visit you once a year."

"What are you talking about?" I said. "I did nothing!"

"Tell that to the judge," Alejandro replied laughing.

This happened right after the airplane incident, when my lawyers thought there was never going to be a charge. It was a discussion between Alejandro and me. My lawyers said it was a domestic dispute and the maximum the airline could do was fine us. But that was even before everybody knew the airplane returned due to weather. They were never going to fine me. I then understood that Alejandro was already talking with someone at the FBI. That is why two months before the indictment he already knew I would be indicted. Had he planned this?

Later, I read his interview with the FBI, full of lies. He even said I had mental problems. How could he? He was my husband. Was not he supposed to protect me?

I was lonely and weak. I was full of fear. I was even afraid of my shadow. I had lost all confidence and hope for living. I was afraid to drive. I could not afford to get pulled over. One day, I got pulled over for changing lanes. Oh, my God, no! I was on my way to meet my lawyer with my daughter Kamee. I almost had a panic attack. Kamee was trying to calm me down while the officer took my driver's license. "This is it," I thought to myself. He is going to see in the computer I am on bond. The officer came back to the car and told me a long story of his sacrifices as an officer and gave me a warning.

I arrived at my lawyer's office devastated. When I showed him the warning, he said, "This is nothing. Calm down. You are a cry-baby."

"Calm down? Do you know what I am risking here?"

"But this is nothing, Carmen."

Well, it was something to me while it was happening.

I had lost so much weight that I looked sick. But I had to be strong for my children. My mother came, and finally I had a shoulder to cry on. She did not know anything about the abuse because I had never told her. Just as I had never told anybody. How could I? My mother and friends would hate him. Victims always stay silent.

I was trying to fix my marriage for my family's sake. I could not reveal such a thing because I was expecting this to go away.

I just told my mother once that I was having problems with Alejandro. We were both in Venezuela. I told her about the cheating—that, I could tell her! I wanted her advice on what to do. My mother told me to fix it.

"Carmen María, this is probably a phase. It will pass. Are you going to destroy your family for that? Fix it!"

It was the common consensus for cheating…fix it! Even my friends told me that. But they did not know about the abuse.

In fact, the cheating and abuse went hand in hand. The more he cheated, the worse the abuse got. The more I told him his behavior was going to end in divorce, the worse his abuse got.

As soon as my mother was in Houston, I sat down and started explaining everything that had happened: the abuse, the plane incident, even the first and second setups.

My mother, who knows her children and how she raised us, started to cry.

"I cannot believe this has happened. What happened to him? Why does he want to hurt you so badly? You are the mother of his children. You two were so in love when you got married!"

Finally, she said: "Honey, God is good and knows the truth. He will help you, and you are going to be free, and a testament for many other women."

My mother always expected me to be this bigger-than-life person. Every time she said something to cheer me up, it was a prophecy. Just like when I lost the Miss Universe pageant but came so close. When I encountered her after the event, she hugged me and said: "You were the winner, but our country needs you more!"

My days passed slowly and were very boring. I have worked since I was a kid right up until I filed for divorce. Alejandro fired me two days after the court ordered him to get out of the house.

All I did during the day was meet with lawyers. They were preparing for the first hearing in family court. Alejandro now wanted to take the children away from me. As soon as I recovered from the shock, and with my mother making sure I was well fed, I started going to the gym again. I had exercised all of my life doing spinning, yoga, weight lifting and playing tennis. I always kept in shape, which helped me to maintain my body as it was the day after the Miss Universe pageant, even after having three children. Exercising made me feel good physically and mentally.

I lost most of my friends in Houston during the divorce. They just stopped talking to me! The people who embraced me were the ones I least expected. Friends who were not close to me before became my most loyal ones. And people I did not know at all embraced me when they learned what was going on. They reached out to me. I discovered what true friendship is all about at this point in my life. I realized that I wasted years in Houston with these "friends" who ran away at the time I needed them the most. Friendship should be just like marriage: "for better or for worse."

I met wonderful, loving people during this time. Real people! I also discovered in this difficult time the value of family more than ever. My family surrounded me and covered me with love. My two sisters put their lives on hold to travel and be with me. My brothers were very protective. My children became closer to me than ever. I began to enjoy time with them that I was not able to before, when my time was dedicated to their father. And they liked it that now I was 120% with them. I did not have to sit on that black sofa with Alejandro from the time he came home until we went to bed. That sofa was my punishment! Not even my own children could talk to me during that time. I was his prisoner in my own home.

I learned many life lessons during that dark period. This proved to be the worst time of my life but also the most beautiful one!

CHAPTER 2

Maracaibo

H<small>E IS WALKING</small> toward me. I can see him through the bars. His face is familiar and I am happy to see him. He is shaking a baby bottle. My mouth melts…uhm! It is my favorite, Toddy (Venezuela's chocolate milk by excellence). He is whistling. As he gets closer, he stops whistling and starts singing "*Muñequita linda*" and he has this beautiful bright white smile. The sound is familiar to me and I am soothed by it. I am on my back and cannot stand up. I am so happy to see him. It is a new day. He looks clean and smells like he always does…fresh. This is all familiar to me. He must have been getting my first bottle of the day, my favorite!

My dad is wearing his silk burgundy robe and his slippers. He looks like a king. His face is of pure love when he sees me. I get the bottle with my hand as he says, "*Buenos días.*" He smiles while looking at me and then disappears from my eyesight.

This is my first memory of life with my dad, whom I loved so much. I always felt safe with him. I must have been a baby since I was in my crib and could not stand up.

He is the reason I trusted men and never thought anything bad could come from them, because I expected all men to be like him.

There are many memories of my first years. They come to mind like flashes, always the same, always surrounded by family starting in Maracaibo.

Maracaibo is the oil region in Venezuela.

Maracuchos are proud people. We are called "regionalists," people that like and defend their region.

The country is named for the houses or *palafitos* in the nation's biggest lake, Lago de Maracaibo, which is the oldest lake on earth. The *palafitos* are in the water. When Américo Vespucio saw them, he called us "Little Venice." That is why my country's name is Venezuela…Little Venice.

Maracaibo is flat and of course is hot all year around, much like Houston in the summer time. My mother used to look through the window in the morning while having breakfast and say, "Today is going to be hot." Like there was any difference. What she meant was "hotter." She said that whenever the trees did not move at all, that meant there was no breeze, a hotter-than-usual day. For her that was a killer. She is from Altamira, Barinas, an Andean town located where the Cordillera Andina starts. The Cordillera Andina is the longest mountain chain in the world and extends all the way down to Argentina, across Colombia, Ecuador, Bolivia, Peru and Chile.

Back then, school was all day. We went in the morning, came back home for lunch, then returned for the rest of the day.

Our favorite was when Mom could not pick us up for lunch and uncle David, my father's older brother who never got married and had no kids, was sent to get us.

The instructions from my mother were the same every time: "David, please no ice cream before getting home. Remember, they will not eat their lunch."

But as a rule, as soon as we got in his car: "Ice cream, kids?"

It was paradise. My uncle David always had little wooden spoons in his pocket, because ice cream for him only tasted good with them.

"David, again? Really? They are not going to eat lunch," my mother said as soon as she found out we did indeed have ice cream. It was impossible to hide.

"But I am hungry. I will eat," he used to say.

I was the smallest of the "yours, mine and ours" pack. My parents were divorced and remarried, each bringing children from the previous marriage, and then having my sister and me. At that time, we were as modern as can be, for not too many people were divorced and remarried then. That was the modern family of today. We were the *Brady Bunch* before they ever existed!

I felt like I was living among giants, all of these grown people around, surrounding me. My older sister (from my mother) and the boys (one from my mother and the rest from my dad) were teenagers. My house was always full with family, friends and their friends. And they all wanted to hug me and hold me and carry me.

I imagine I must have been cute and irresistible…hahahaha! They all wanted my kisses.

I kissed and kissed until I got tired, then I would say, "That is it, no more kisses. I ran out."

"You must have more," they would say.

"I have to make them."

"Well, go make them."

And I went and made more kisses.

The table was the best in our house, especially for dinnertime. At lunchtime it was fast; everybody had to get back to school and Dad to work. However, we all managed to squeeze in a nap. That was the time life was relaxed and beautiful.

But dinnertime was so much fun! The table was full with all the kids and my parents. My mother only allowed us to have a soda at lunchtime and only one, but not for dinner. For dinner, she would make a nutritious drink. That could be *chicha*, *avena* (made with oats) Toddy, milk or a fruit shake.

The problem was when the drink was a favorite one! Ah…
Chicha! Venezuela's rice drink. Or…Toddy!

The pitcher was full in the middle of the table. The boys looked at it like beasts watching their prey. Laura, my older sister, so beautiful, skinny, elegant, and the two little girls could not care less about it.

The boys wanted to drink the whole pitcher.

"I will serve everybody," Perucho said.

"No. I will do it," David insisted.

"Whoever said first that is the one that is serving!" my mother said.

Perucho started to pour in every glass, just about half way full, but when he got to his, he almost spilled it over the top.

"That is such bad manners," Mom said. "You don't do that. I will not allow that at this table. You serve up to two fingers from the top."

They were always the smart ones.

One night it was time for *chicha*. I could see the boys' faces; they were almost jumping at the pitcher.

"Perucho, remember we were told two fingers from the top."

As David started to serve, Perucho said: "Let's measure with my fingers!"

My dear and beautiful brother has the fattest fingers in the world. Nobody was complaining, but when it was time for his glass to be filled, he chose the fingers of my sister, María Eugenia, to measure his glass. She has the thinnest fingers of all of us. We were crying of laughter!

"*Perucho, voz si soz vivo!*" David said. ("Perucho, you are a smart ass").

Those were our fights!

We grew up with the Americans that lived at the oil camps. That was fun for my brothers; they always went to the camps to meet girls.

In my house, my siblings' friends came to dance, play board games, talk and laugh. Just as it was years later when we, the two little ones, were teenagers, our house was a clubhouse always full of people. My father preferred to have an "open house" where everybody was at home and he knew what we were doing to not knowing where we were. He was a fun-loving dad that all of our friends loved and he was proud of the "Montiel Club," which is what our friends called our home.

I was so little that I used to walk between my father's legs every morning on our way to breakfast. I do not know how he managed to walk and not fall, but he did. It was one of the things I hated about growing up, not being able to do that anymore. I could not fit within his legs.

My older sister wore some fun stuff in the '70s! The day she graduated from high school everybody that arrived at her party was greeted with a shower from a bucket of water. My God! I have never seen women so mad! The boys, as usual, did not care.

Fake eyelashes were on their cheeks and partial wigs were falling off. I used to look up to my sister. I was five years old when she graduated from high school. She went off to college and moved to Caracas. A hole was in my heart; I missed her so.

She used to fool people, telling them the youngest two of us were her daughters. That lasted for many years. Not anymore! She loved to see the expression on people's faces when she said with her baby face that she had a daughter.

She was full of energy. I will never forget the day man landed on the moon because of her. She ran all around the house excited, screaming, "Come, come see it!"... "Man on the moon, man on the moon!"

She gathered everybody around the TV set to watch the first steps on the moon. I ran too and watched, but was too little to understand what was going on. I was then four and a half years old. Later in my life I understood. I had watched history in the making. While too little to appreciate what was happening at the time, it has become one of my most valuable memories.

In 1994, as an anchorwoman for Telemundo, I was invited to the dinner celebration for the 25th anniversary of the day man first walked on the moon at the Astrodome in Houston. There, I met astronaut Neil Armstrong! My past became present, and I landed on the moon the moment we shook hands.

Without knowing, I have always been walking in many of mankind's first steps.

CHAPTER 3

Divorce and Plane

My daughter told me to be careful with my lawyer.

I asked her which one because I had a lawyer for every possible specialty. She said my criminal attorney was a friend of her dad's criminal lawyer.

"Baby, they are all friends," I told her. "They all know each other. They work together in those courts."

"This is different, *Mami*," she replied.

Alejandro had hired an attorney known for representing serial killers, murderers and psychopaths, many of them well known in the community, and saving them based on technicalities. However, it was his female associate who handled Alejandro's case for him, the same woman that year and a half before had told me to get out of that relationship. Is not that a conflict of interest? She should have not been able to represent Alejandro and actively help him destroy his wife. But nobody cared.

What my daughter saw or heard I do not know. But time will prove that something wrong happened. This warning and my suspicion later saved me.

Alejandro had moved to the Four Seasons Hotel when the court ordered him out of the house. Alexandra said his female attorney came there to talk to her. What else Alexandra saw or heard during that time, she never told me. But her warning stayed ever present with me.

In reality, these attorneys should not have represented Alejandro, because they represented both of us before. I was so scared and confused I did not realize it at the time. But my lawyers should have. I told them about it. They should have tried to get his legal team disqualified.

As time passed and I healed, I not only saw things clearer, but also realized how all these attorneys took advantage of me.

I am brushing my hair while looking at the mirror. I am finally able to see myself in it. I am tall enough now. My very excited sister María Eugenia came running to get me because the New Year is almost here. My family is in the living room, Mom, Dad, siblings, aunts, uncles and cousins. I know them; they are all familiar to me. I did not know what they are talking about, but suddenly everyone starts hugging and kissing each other Happy New Year. They are eating grapes so fast. I do not understand how they can manage to kiss, hug, eat and drink champagne all at the same time. But this is who we are!

I am suddenly awakened from my daydream when I heard that my lawyer was ready for me. But he wanted to see my daughter first.

My lawyers want to talk to my second child because she was the only one of my children on that flight when the incident occurred. Kamee is still wearing her school uniform, which makes her legs look ever so long. I had picked her up at school and headed downtown to my lawyers' office. She does not like to miss school, not even for ten minutes, so I arranged this meeting for after school. I kept waiting outside.

My mind lately often goes back to the beautiful years of my childhood and teenage time. Suddenly, I remember the day Alberto gave me a ride on his motorcycle.

Caracas is a valley, so beautiful and green with mountains everywhere. The day was clear and blue, a perfect day for a motorcycle ride. There I am holding Alberto's waist and feeling free, enjoying the view while we were going up the mountain to my house when suddenly I see my dad's car coming down.

"No! My dad!"

"So what?" Alberto asks.

"He forbids all of us to ride motorcycles."

"Well, he is leaving."

"But he saw me and tonight I will hear about it. I am in so much trouble!"

As soon as we stopped in front of my house, my dad was right behind us.

We could hear his car running. I was petrified. Should I get off? My father is already walking up to us.

"Alberto, I would much appreciate it if you do not get my daughter on a motorcycle. They are very dangerous."

My dad looked serious and worried. He meant what he said.

We were pale and scared, but Alberto managed to say yes to my father.

"*Mami*, you can go in now!" Kamee said.

This woke me up from the half dream I was having.

"Well, Carmen, her story is just like yours. This is good," my attorney said.

The judge had forbidden me to talk about the case with potential witnesses, so, I did not know what my daughter was going to say. At the time it happened, we never talked about it. She was mad at her dad as I was and had the same reaction toward him that I had. That is why I never wondered about it.

But once I was charged, I started to wonder about the conversation we never had.

"It is the exact same story," he continued. "Your husband kept on calling the flight attendant for no reason."

The trial was set for October. However, they informed me it would be moved, which was good because we needed more time to investigate.

"It will be moved to January, which is also good, because guess what? The prosecutor is retiring and this case will be assigned to another. Nobody loves his children more than their own parents. This case is becoming a foster child case."

"What do you mean?"

"People do not like to inherit cases," he replied. "Especially this one when the consensus in the Federal Building is that if your husband gave you his shoulder, none of this ever would have happened. Plus, the prosecutor that is taking the case is my friend. I saw him at the grocery store the other day, and he told me to talk to him after the first of the year. He sounded not at all happy about this case."

I was starting to realize how important whom you hire was in this process. It was all about who you know. It was all about negotiations. However, this could also backfire. Lawyers even negotiate among themselves and owe each other favors.

"I have been doing my research and we need to request the flight log and the black box," I told my attorney. "This is important for the case. Plus, I think we also need the manual for the airline's personnel. The flight attendant must have broken all the rules that night."

"All of that has been ordered," he said. "Now we will have more time to get it. My investigator has already spoken with the female police officer and will do more interviews. Now, Carmen, you know that comes at an extra charge! But I guess all of this will be solved in the temporary orders hearing."

Another one of my attorneys asked: "What is it that you were fighting for on the airplane—peanuts?"

"Who did you hear that from?" I asked.

Alejandro was the one who was fighting for peanuts. But no one heard that. He wanted my peanuts, and I told him to eat his food. That was it! This happened a lot of times before the incident.

No one heard this. Unless they were talking with Alejandro. Were they?

In the meantime, we were getting ready to go to the temporary orders hearing where they set the spousal support and child support payments that Alejandro has to make while the divorce is pending, along with who pays what within the estate. There are credit cards, mortgages, loans, etc.

My legal team is expecting that Alejandro's lawyers are going to play hard ball on the plane situation and they do not want me testifying under oath about this issue before trial. As a matter of fact, according to the research I had been doing, it is always recommended that the person accused not testify. One friend told me, "If you talk, you don't walk!" That reminded me of OJ Simpson's famous trial for his wife's murder, when he did not testify.

Everything in my life was so scary now. I pray every day! God, why? Why did you allow this to happen? If I had never come to this country, this never would have happened. I wished to be back home, in my home country! Until one day while praying a thought came to my mind: "If you were in Venezuela, you would be dead."

Oh My God! That is true. In Venezuela, the situation had gotten so bad that over 25,000 people a year are killed in robberies that go unsolved. People are so desperate for money; they sell themselves for very little as long as they can feed their families. It would have been so easy for my husband to have me killed as another victim of crime in Venezuela, just another statistic.

A few months later, Mónica Spears, Miss Venezuela 2004, was killed just like that in a robbery with her daughter and her ex-husband. Her infant daughter survived the assault.

When I heard the news, it was not only heartbreaking, but also a close call for me.

The emotional outpouring and protesting in my country were enormous. People were asking for violence and crime to stop in Venezuela. But all I kept thinking was: "It could have been me first!"

A day before the hearing, we all met at my family lawyers' office. They had been working on who to get as witnesses for the hearing. The first thing I asked was whether they had talked with the female police officer who was in the back of the airplane when the whole thing happened. When I was taken back, she offered to help. My lawyers' investigator interviewed her before the indictment, when she reported what happened exactly as my daughter and I had said.

"Carmen, she changed her story! What she's telling us now has nothing to do with what our investigator's report says."

"God! How can people lie and destroy someone's life? But the investigator has a recording of the conversation; we will get her lying under oath."

"We better not use her," my lawyer said.

"Why not? We have evidence and a recording of what she originally said."

It was as if I was talking to the wall about very good evidence my own lawyer was dismissing. Incredible! That was not good. Apparently in family court, people can lie and create evidence. Anything plays there.

While we were there, Alejandro's lawyers withdrew the motion to take over the house and my children. I was thankful that I did not need my friends to help me with that after all.

The friends I had asked had refused to testify in my favor—my friends who knew the whole story, who knew I was both mother and father to my children, who themselves said, "He is not the Father of the Year. He never has been." But I was tainted now and they wanted nothing to do with me.

We went to court and the female police officer was there with the prosecutor. My family lawyer said it was Alejandro who subpoenaed her. Years later, Alejandro said it was *my* lawyer. What I learned at this time of my life was that no one was telling the truth. I learned to never trust anybody. That feeling started once I realized my husband had been lying to me for years, and now in the courts with all the lawyers and judges, I confirmed that I was better off not trusting anybody.

Through the morning, my family lawyer scared me with the plane thing: "Carmen, people are gathering outside. It must be everybody from the plane."

I felt this was good, so they could tell the court that they heard and saw nothing. They could tell the truth. The truth is: nothing happened and the other passengers were mad that this incident stopped their flight. In time, I learned that it was related to bad weather in Bogota.

Once again in my life, I was in the hands of a bully...my family lawyer. He negotiated for me the worst temporary orders in history. He should have known that Alejandro was not only going to destroy my credit, but also let every service be disconnected under this agreement. For the first time in my life, I lost control of all my finances, which were given to Alejandro, who had never written a check.

My family lawyer had negotiated the same type of agreement for another famous person in town, the wife of the late hand doctor and my former neighbor.

I was given the standard Texas child support of $2,500 a month for two kids, when Alejandro makes over a million dollars a year. He claimed my oldest daughter and $2,500 for my support. After working for him for almost twenty years, he fired me two days after he was kicked out of the house by the court.

Alejandro had to pay all utility bills, mortgages and charge cards. The charge cards were all in my name. He failed to pay all the bills as ordered, my credit was ruined within months, and all the charge cards were lost. I had no means to access money. I could not afford the maid that I needed to help me take care of my children. I was spending a lot of time in court with my lawyers, plus we had a house of over 18,000 square feet with terraces, patio and pool space that needed to be cared for.

However, my attorney walked out of court acting like he got the deal of the year, while Alejandro was high fiving his lawyers outside. This was my lawyers' second failure. The first was when they withdrew the protective order that the judge granted me on July 23, 2013.

I had hired supposedly the best attorney in town. However, he brought another lawyer into the case because he and the judge assigned to hear my case hated each other. My attorney needed to take a step back, so his presence would not negatively affect the outcome of the case. The second attorney had left on vacation when we had to go to the protective order hearing on August 6 in another court, the domestic violence court. This was a big ace in our hand because it was going on Alejandro's record and would give us the upper hand. However, my attorney withdrew the protective order a day before the hearing without my authorization or a signed agreement. He said the deal he negotiated was much better than any granted in court.

However, he agreed to let Alejandro in the house the day we were supposed to be in court in order for him to pack his possessions—something he did not do when the court ordered him to leave. By my maid's account, he only packed enough for two weeks because he said: "She is just mad; she will get over this in two weeks maximum. I am coming back."

Once the pressure from the protective order was gone, Alejandro felt secure that he was back on top of the situation.

He came home with the Suburban. He had crashed his Mercedes CL63 Turbo driving while drunk, but of course paid off or reached an agreement with the other person not to call the police. Later, he ended up in a punching fight with the owner of the Ferrari since insurance did not cover the car's full repair because the insurance had already paid a total loss for his car in January 2013, for another drunk driving accident by himself. Alejandro showed up with two of his employees from the office with each driving a pickup truck. They came to ransack the house. What Alejandro was not counting on was that my lawyers had put a 6'5" tall bodyguard inside the house.

Alejandro came in all confident, but stopped and went pale once he saw the bodyguard. Obviously, his plan changed when he saw that I was protected.

"Good afternoon, sir," the bodyguard said.

"Good afternoon, Carmen María Montiel," Alejandro said without a word to the bodyguard, like calling me by my unmarried name was a way to hurt me.

In fact, I was looking forward to gaining my name back. I had asked for it in the divorce lawsuit.

He went straight to the study to get papers. The bodyguard advised him: "Sir, you are here to pack your clothes. That is it."

Alejandro's face told it all. He was not accustomed for anybody to tell him what to do. He always does as he pleases.

He went to where I put the mail.

"Sir, again, you cannot take anything but your clothes."

Once again, he was furious this was happening in front of his employees. I can only imagine how he planned this with them ... and now he has been humiliated in front of them. The Boss!

His employees looked at him like they were waiting for an order. It was not possible that he brought his office employees to pack his underwear. Alejandro was agitated and furious. He was perspiring and very pale. His Middle Eastern coloring had disappeared from his face.

"I only have two hours. How can I pack in such a short time?"

"That is why, sir, you should not waste time on things you cannot take, and pack your clothes," the bodyguard said.

I walked out of the room and advised the guard I had outside the house ever since Alejandro left not to let anybody put anything in those three vehicles that I had not approved first.

Alejandro had never packed before. He asked for luggage. I sent his secretary to get the bags in the attic. He packed his underwear and socks with his secretary and billing specialist. When he went downstairs, so did I. His billing specialist said he needed the computer.

"Sir, please do not address her," the bodyguard said. "You are here to get the doctor's clothes and that is it."

Alejandro left in less than an hour without most of his clothes still. It is obvious he came for something else and, once he could not get it, he left angry.

This irresponsible move from my lawyers messed up the temporary injunction orders that freeze all the financials. Every time I left town, Alejandro broke into the house with the excuse that he did not have all of his things. It took a court order in his criminal case for assault charges to stop that in January 2014.

Alejandro had a falling out with his first lawyer, the one during my deposition who paid a lot of attention when I started talking about the physical abuse. He changed from being relaxed, lying back in the chair, to an upright position. He believed me!

Months later, a friend of mine interviewed this lawyer for her divorce. She was married to another Middle Eastern man, and he told her: "I know the ways of these men."

The attorney in charge of Alejandro's divorce case filed a motion to postpone the divorce trial from January to March, and another to move it from March to later in the year. After taking all the money I had, my family lawyer fired me, forcing me to find a lawyer in an emergency move. I hired an African American woman. I liked the idea of getting someone who was not part of the "Good All Boys Club," a wild card.

I did not know at the time the game that was played in family court. As soon as Alejandro's attorney knew about my change of lawyers, he did not want to move the trial further out. He was blocking his own motion. He called my new lawyer and tried to sweet talk her into a bad, I mean really bad, settlement. Her answer was: "Give me the discovery and we settle."

By the time I got a new attorney, I had already hired a forensic accountant to look into Alejandro's financials after the separation. Because of Alejandro's extreme mishandling of his financials, she got suspicious and referred me to a bank investigator that could find any bank account Alejandro had by himself or with any entity. And bingo! We found several.

Since they did not want to move forward with the trial date change, my lawyer agreed to go to mediation. I was mad, because how can you have a real mediation when we are missing so many parts of this puzzle? But we went.

On the day of the mediation, it was the women against the men. Alejandro, his lawyer and the mediator were all men. The mediator was from Cuba, or at least his parents were. He came and told me that Alejandro was talking about all of my supposed issues.

"Really?" I said. "Has he mentioned his? Because he has assault charges, anger management therapy, double identity in Venezuela and more. We can sit here all day and talk about it, along with prostitutes or dead patients, for example."

"No," he said. "But I told him that you do not do what he did. Getting his wife in trouble. You don't call the police on your wife. I can see the picture."

I do not know if he meant it or it was a way to make me believe he was on my side. The day came and went. At around

6 p.m. or later, the mediator came with a settlement proposal. Of course, when we were all tired!

I could not believe what I was reading! At what point had Alejandro decided I was an idiot, dumb and stupid? I was the one who ran all of our business in the office and for us personally, and suddenly he thought I was going to fall for a trick.

The mediator presented me with an offer in which Alejandro was to keep 100% of his medical practice and our commercial building, which was way over 50% of our estate. From the rest, I was to get 60%, about 20% of our estate in reality for me.

"I know my math," I said. "Why am I going to get 20% when the law gives me 50%?"

However, I wanted to end it and asked the mediator if I could make changes to it. As I started to work on my changes, the mediator came back and said Alejandro had left!

Alejandro always cheated people out of money. Why was I expecting any difference? He cheated a woman that invested in Sleep Labs out of over $200,000 when they got together to do sleep studies in Dallas. She did not have the license. Alejandro flew there every Thursday and read the studies, and our office did the billing. When she wanted to end the deal, he never paid her what he owed her.

The same thing happened when we took back the billing from a vendor to which we owed money. Alejandro never paid it. It always amazed me how none of them ever sued him—maybe because it was going to be dirty for both. Alejandro walked away with a lot of money that belonged to other people. His excuse: I am tired of people taking advantage of me!

So, we went to court on March 28, 2014, for the final trial for divorce. We walked into the courtroom and the associate judge was there, the same one that allowed my children to keep having visitation with Alejandro after all the testimony and the one accused of campaign fraud. I knew Alejandro had something to do with this since she was always going in his favor.

After my lawyers showed proof of why we needed more time, the associate judge ruled we were to be divorced that day. Alejandro high fived his lawyers. I had no idea what they were planning, but it must have been something where I was ending up very badly. Alejandro wanted me to be broken and penniless in jail or prison if possible.

We were supposed to be back in court at 1:30 p.m. I cried! What was going to happen to me? I went to the cathedral and prayed at lunchtime.

When we got back, the sitting judge was there, not the associate judge. She reviewed the evidence, including inventories where Alejandro had changed the numbers in the millions of dollars and bank accounts not put in any discovery.

"Millions are added and subtracted. What is this?" the judge said.

The judge ruled to delay the trial and Alejandro stormed out the courtroom, insulting my lawyer, his lawyer and me. He also accused me of opening his bank accounts. Like I am some kind of idiot opening bank accounts to hide money and hiring an investigator to find them, then turning them over to the court.

That victory gave my lawyers an opportunity to file a motion for a change of temporary orders to increase my support. Twice we went to court and expended two full days in cross-examination, but the judge did not rule. She was retiring and it looked as if she did not want to mess with it, or she was bought out? By whom?

Two years later, Alejandro said his friend, the car salesman nobody liked, introduced him to a judge that helped him. Was that for the hearing about the drugs or the spousal support? Was that real or did he just not want to say he paid for it? Four years later, in an interview, he said he had dinner with a judge and that same judge connected him with my family lawyer.

After two hearings about the change of spousal support that ended with no decision, his lawyer fired Alejandro. Like me, he was looking for a lawyer at the last minute and got a man with no scruples in the summer of 2014.

With the new lawyer, Alejandro did not show up in court ever, and it was impossible to enforce anything on him. He should have been thrown in jail many times. But what happened with the system? Well ... the law only applies to poor men. Rich people, doctors, lawyers, CEOs, etc., have a different set of rules that no one knows. They are the breadwinners of the family and are treated differently by the court even if it means leaving their families starving.

By summer 2014 I had a third lawyer. The situation with Alejandro and his new attorney got worse. He was not paying anything. My credit was ruined and I had no money. It was so bad that my lawyers decided to request a receiver, which was granted. But the judge changed our choice from an unknown receiver to one that worked at the same building where Alejandro's lawyer had an office.

The idea was to freeze Alejandro's business account and make sure the children and I got paid.

Along with this battle, I was scheduled to go to trial in federal court every three months. And every three months, the trial was rescheduled. I did not meet with my criminal lawyers more often than every three months when the trial was close and we had to go to court. There was always an excuse from the prosecutor or my lawyer to move the trial.

Every three months I asked about the flight log, flight attendant manual and everything else. The answer was always the same: It is coming.

Time passed and the case was not getting dropped. I learned that Alejandro's female criminal attorney was at the Federal Building often, making sure this case did not go away.

In January 2014, I had my first court appearance with the new prosecutor. Of course, he requested to move the trial again. I appeared in court with my lawyer and the new prosecutor did not show up. Another prosecutor took his place while the first one was in another trial. This prosecutor was inclined to drop the case, but he did not prosecute it at the end. One more of those last-minute things that makes you wonder.

After the hearing, the three of us—the prosecutor, my lawyer and I—waited for the elevator when the prosecutor asked my attorney: "So, has this been the H. prosecutor's case all along?"

"No," he replied. "It was the D. prosecutor's case."

His face showed disapproval and he added: "So, D. did this? Unbelievable!"

I could feel this seemed to be the sentiment in that Federal Building. My attorney said the new prosecutor was not interested in this silly case either; after all, he was dealing with bank robbers. That was his specialty.

By October 2014, over a year after the indictment, I was not feeling confident about my case. And my daughter's words kept ringing in my mind: "Be careful, Mommy. He is a close friend with Dad's lawyers."

It felt as if my lawyer had lost interest in the case. At first, he was all pumped up and ready to go with ideas of what to do, how to do my defense, who should be interviewed, and what needed to be requested. But now he looked as if he was not interested. He had no more ideas, and I felt he was just going with the flow. And all documents requested never arrived at his office. That was the most uncomfortable point for me. It felt as if he was ready to let me go, as if I was being presented as a sacrificial prey.

Around that time, I met this incredibly beautiful young Houston native. She is someone who knows everybody in town. We were talking about mishaps in life. Suddenly I felt comfortable enough to tell her what was happening to me.

After I finished my story, she acted very normal (to my surprise) and asked who my lawyer was. When I told her, she said: "Oh, no, no, no. You need to change your lawyer. After his daughter died, he is just not interested."

That is something I hated to hear. That meant more money, a lot more? Is it really necessary? But a voice inside of me was telling me that not only was it necessary. It was imperative.

It was now September and even though I was supposed to go to trial in October, I had already been informed that was not going to happen.

CHAPTER 4

The Road Back to God

Everything I did, whether good or bad, my husband always used against me. I did not realize how much it irritated me. But it did!

I am a practicing Catholic and that, too, was cause for his demeaning comments: "*Te la pasas dándote golpes de pecho, pero no haces nada*" (All you do is beat your chest with your fist). Now look at me. I am really a good man. I am a doctor. I save lives and take care of people every day."

Whenever he accompanied me to Mass with the children, which he only did if we had one of those abusive fights, he walked out making fun of me, even during the service.

So, the normal happened: I limited my attendance and distanced myself from the church. I went to Mass only on some Sundays just to keep my children within the faith. However, he made fun of it in front of the children.

Alejandro was transformed toward the end of the marriage. I hardly recognized him. He was talking nonsense. He would engage in conversations for a full hour or more, saying things like: "I have killed many people in my previous lives." Or, "In my next life, I will be an enlightened because I have gone up the whole ladder of progression. I have reached the maximum level."

Alejandro lost respect for the family and for me. For a while, he was careful to make sure no one knew about his cheating, but I know he really did not care. Eventually, he openly made comments even in front of the children having to do with sex and women. He would talk publicly about the women he had sex with, embarrassing me in front of everybody.

He would say over and over that he had sex with an actress from Venezuela, but his real fascination was going through my magazines from my famous past in Venezuela. As he went through the pages, he would say, "I did this one and this one, ah! Also, this one…" right in front of me and everybody else.

He went as far as bringing women to our garage, hoping to be able to get them inside the house when I was out of town, but the children were there and cut him off before he succeeded.

Alexandra, my oldest, saw one of the women. Her father came back from having dinner one night while we were still married and walked around the house looking for a good time to sneak in the woman, as it turned out. But Alexandra, sensing something was wrong because he had said he was going to the pharmacy after dinner, decided to come downstairs to see what he was doing. She was surprised to see a woman with black hair inside her father's car. As soon as Alejandro realized Alexandra saw her, he got in the car and left. Even my maid saw this woman.

Toward the end, whenever Alejandro looked at me, he had fury in his eyes, which were disoriented and different. I felt that it was the devil or evil looking at me, not the man I fell in love with. But I wanted this to work for my children's sake. Maybe I could get my husband back and make him realize that this path of destruction was a mistake.

He played the victim, the person that did not do anything, and made me feel everything was an accident or my fault. He acted like he did not mean anything bad, and I, with my hopes up and trying to protect my family, believed him. Or did I believe him because I wanted to so badly.

I was a woman of faith even against my husband. As a person who believed in evolution, he said there was nothing after life and did not believe in creation, only evolution. Many times, we fought about it and I would end the discussion, saying: "Fine, you come from the monkey, but God made me. You will never convince me that I come from the monkey." This was my way to avoid conflict, as he meant for these discussions to get heated.

When Alejandro wanted to sound respectful, he used God's name. His hypocrisy had no limits.

Many times, when I went to Mass, I felt as if the sermon was directed at me. But never like the Sunday after the plane incident. My love for Alejandro was in a free fall as a result of his actions. But in that plane, when he did what he did, it was as if my heart was cut open and whatever love was left within me was surgically removed in a second.

That Sunday I got up and told the children to get ready. We were going to Mass. I did not include Alejandro, but he heard me and hurried up to get ready for Mass. When we got to the church, he laughed and joked, distracting everybody and showing a total lack of respect. I was annoyed but trying to pay attention to the sermon when I heard the priest say: "God sends you messages or warnings and you need to understand them in every situation, whether it is to change jobs, move to another city or end a marriage!"

That got my attention. The priest was talking about divorce, something the Catholic faith forbids. Why?

The priest continued: "You need to be attentive. He can send you a couple of messages. You could miss the first one and the second, but at some point, they will stop coming. It is just like the story of the castaway. You know he prayed for God's help but died. When he arrived in heaven, he told God: 'But I prayed for your help, why am I dead?' God answered: 'I sent you a tree branch and you did not take it. I sent you a log and you did not take it. And finally, I sent you a ship. I sent you help, but you did not take it.'"

At that moment, I understood! It dawned on me! Alejandro had hurt me and got me in trouble a couple of times. It was getting worse and worse. Why am I trying to fix my marriage? What if the plane incident was the worst? What am I waiting for? What if this is the last message God is sending me?

The sermon that day was directed at me and only me, I thought. I looked around as if people could see and understand the priest was talking about me. I looked at Alejandro to see if he was getting this as I was. In the meantime, Alejandro was trying to distract me from the sermon, asking me to explain the passages of the Bible that depicted every painting in the church. Only evil does that.

I grew ever more silent with my husband. I finally understood that I had to get out for good. I just needed to find a way. My husband became increasingly more abusive with the plane issue and what was going to happen in Colorado. He felt he had me in his hands.

Alejandro mistreated me more than ever, verbally, mentally and physically. I tried to stay away since I knew God's message could have been the final one.

The last time he hit me, the police took him into custody by himself for the first time. It was as if God put the officers there. The two officers that came to the house were totally different from the ones before. They had never been to our home and they disliked Alejandro. They saw him for who he really is and understood what they were facing. The officers wanted to find more evidence to increase the charges. They looked in his medicine area. But Alejandro, knowing the police were coming, cleaned everything up. I later found a bag with all his prescription medication that he self-prescribed in his own name and that of his alter ego, Eduardo Martínez.

With Alejandro in jail, I was able to refile the divorce for the second time and get ready to take him to court to get him out of the house.

I felt that God was with my children and me. Finally, evil was going to be removed from my house.

Once Alejandro was out of the house, I was able to light candles and put up an altar at the entrance of the house with Saint Michael, Sacred Heart, Virgin Mary and more. I started to pray many times every day and to read the Bible with the help of my childhood friend Gustavo Hernández. I even prayed the rosary every day. I needed to rid my life, my house and my children from evil.

But evil's work was on the go, and I never imagined I was going to be charged for the plane incident until they came to get me at my house. However, my faith was untouched by this incident. I trusted that God was going to get me out of jail and help me fight this, as he did.

I prayed every day with faith and trusted my life and my children's lives to God. But the most faithful proof was when my first lawyer's office made the mistake of turning in during the first discovery the only bank account I had for my expenses, against my advice to wait.

I was frustrated and afraid that now Alejandro was going to get all the money out. I sent many emails to my lawyers and had phone conversations about it with them. I used to make notes in my cell so I would remember what to talk with my lawyers about when suddenly this appeared in one of the notes: "God wanted it to be like this."

I could not believe my eyes. I knew I did not write this. At that moment, I knew I would know in time. But this message gave me peace.

It was not until year and a half later—when Alejandro filed a motion accusing me of fraud, forgery and stealing—that I was finally able to thank God for that note. And that was not the only message.

Suddenly, I started to get texts on my cell phone with Psalms and other Bible pieces, each one providing what I needed for the day. They helped me heal and gain strength. I had never signed up for Bible verses, so I did not expect the texts. As time went by and I regained mental strength, the texts stopped coming.

My childhood friend helped me to reconnect with God. Every night through Skype, we read the Bible and prayed the rosary. As a man of faith, he explained many things to me that either I had forgotten or never saw that way before.

It became our daily routine, a routine that would become a new way of life for me, one I never should have stopped. While praying and asking for the truth to come out, I did an internal cleansing and study. I wondered what I could have done to deserve this, although no one should ever deserve any of this. God does not punish people. But I felt this was an opportunity to better myself.

I also asked God to use me as a tool if my experience was something that could help others. I started to see that everything was better moving forward the stronger my faith became. Of course, it was still difficult, but it did not look impossible anymore as it had at the beginning. My house, which had become a place I was afraid of, was now my temple and I felt secure inside it. I was calm and so were my children.

I learned to pray in many different ways. I established a relationship with God I never had before. I was speaking words of wisdom and was proud of myself. The person that had been afraid to walk out of the house now felt protected as long as God was by my side. This faith gave me strength, and I used it to make many decisions. I was able to ask with faith for answers and trusted that what came to mind was the right one.

Of course, my faith was put to the test many times during this period, but the results always proved that every step and every fight fraught with delays and problems were the right ones. I learned to have patience. Patience in God.

CHAPTER 5

Caracas, Here We Come

WHEN I WOKE UP, there were a lot of people in the house putting everything into boxes. They worked like termites. They were fast. It felt like an invasion.

I looked for my *mami*. I did not understand what was going on. Who are these people? I was only eight years old. *Mami* was in the kitchen with the maids also packing and giving instructions. María Eugenia was having breakfast, so I sat next to her quietly and asked *Mami* what was happening.

"We are moving to Caracas," she said.

The boys were already in Caracas for what I thought was their summer vacation.

That day after everything was packed, we stayed at my aunt Norah's, my dad's older sister and my favorite person in the world. She was so full of life and had an incredibly funny story for every event in her life. She made me feel that a life like that was worth living. Aunt Norah played the castanets like she was a native Spanish woman. Funny thing, because she was married to a man from the Basque Country and they hated flamenco and everything Spanish like, even though that is part of Spain.

But my aunt did not care. When she put on the castanets and started to sing and dance, everything came to life. I think uncle Manolo forgave her because of that. She was naturally elegant, and I always viewed her with wonder and admiring eyes hoping to be like her when I grew up.

Many times, when my parents traveled, they left me at her house. It was my favorite thing. They did not have children so they spoiled me rotten. I was so spoiled by them that I started to think of ways I could stay with her forever. I think I was probably five years old when I decided that I could help in her house. One of her maids, Rita, used to work for my grandparents, and aunt Norah "inherited" her when they died. It is customary in Venezuela for the help to stay with the family.

I started helping Rita, and one day I dared to wash the dishes. Rita was not around, so I pulled a chair up to the sink so I could reach it and started washing everything. I did not break a thing and felt so accomplished. When my aunt came into the kitchen, I was just finishing. She sounded worried when she said in that wonderful *maracucho* accent of hers: "*Niña, ¿qué haces?* (Baby, what are you doing?)."

"See, *tía*, you don't need Rita. I can do all of her work!"

She just started to laugh at my childish idea with a look of love.

Uncle Manolo, whom I adored, called me "*Frijolillo,*" which in the Basque language means "little, pretty thing." Years later, when I was full grown at 5'9," he still called me *Frijolillo*, but would add: "¡*Frijolillo! De Frijolillo lo que te queda es lo de bonita, porque de chiquita ya no tenéis na'* " (*Frijolillo*, the only thing you have as *Frijolillo* is the pretty, because little you are no longer).

They always took us with them to the Basque Club, where I experienced their culture, food and sports. I loved it there. We were treated like family. They played jai alai, which was so different for me, but I loved the game and the passion they had for it.

I was sure going to miss them all and the life we had in Maracaibo. Not been able to see them as often as we did was definitely going to hurt.

Caracas for me was the place where my grandmother and the rest of my mother's family lived, even though they were from Barinas.

We do have fun memories of our times together there or when they came from Caracas to visit us in Maracaibo. When we went to Caracas, we always stayed at my grandmother's house. She spoiled us rotten, cooking our favorite dishes and just being that lovable *abuelita*.

One summer while driving to Caracas, my father found out that both María Eugenia and I had lice. My mother was already in Caracas. They were terrorized by that because lice were not that common in Caracas back then due to the cooler weather.

"Girls," he said, "don't you dare tell anyone that you have lice. And if anybody asks to borrow your brush, do not let them have it."

As luck would have it, sure enough Grandma could not find her hairbrush and asked us to lend her one of ours.

We were terrified, whispering to each other, and did not answer her. My mother was not there. She and my father were out searching all over Caracas for that magic lice shampoo.

"Girls!" she repeated later. "Really! Please let me use your hairbrush." Once again, we whispered and giggled but still did not answer her.

"Come on! What is your problem that you cannot lend your grandmother your brush?"

We had actually ran and hid our brushes. We did not want our *abuelita* to get lice. Finally, she said: "I do not have lice if that is what you are worried about."

We could no longer hold it in and broke out in laughter: "*Abuelita*, it is us who have lice!" We were crying, laughing and embarrassed at the same time.

In the meantime, *Mami* and *Papi* went from pet store to pet store all over Caracas. In one store, the salesperson was too nice and replied to my parents' question about the shampoo with: "Help me to help you. What do you need?"

My embarrassed parents said: "We have a couple of dogs with fleas."

The gentleman replied: "Oh, well I have the solution for you. We have these collars that are wonderful for that. It will kill all fleas. Guaranteed!"

My parents looked at each other, just managing to contain their laughter until they left the store. "Can you imagine the girls with those collars?" my father asked my mom.

In the summers, my mother's sister always visited us from Caracas with our cousins, two boys our ages and a baby girl. We love each other to pieces. It was the best time when they came over. We played all day long.

One summer, our generosity was tested. We were playing in the backyard when we heard someone on the front porch. Little and full of energy, we ran to the front and found an old man, a *guajiro*, asking for something. *Guajiros*, an indigenous people from the area of Venezuela that we share with Colombia, have their own language. When they speak Spanish, it is difficult to understand them.

We tried our best, asking him again and again what he wanted. Finally, we came to the conclusion that he wanted "lemons."

"Oh, lemons!" We all said at the same time looking at each other." "¡*Claro, señor!* (Yes, sir!)" we all screamed. "We can do that!"

After all, we had a lemon tree in the house. So, we told him to wait and we would be back. We went into action with a purpose: we needed to get enough lemons for this old man. We felt like warriors.

Armed with a chair and a bat, we started getting lemons from the tree like monkeys hanging there. We filled up a bag, laughing, giggling and loving it. We were so proud of ourselves because we were helping an old man who needed a cane to walk. Once the bag was full, we run to the front porch and handed it to the old man with a smile.

Instead of the praise and thanks that we had expected, he was furious and started hitting the iron fence hard with his cane as he screamed, "¡Limona, limona!" We were like, "Yes! Here you go, a bag full of lemons (limones)." But he kept screaming limona.

Scared, we ran back into the house screaming, finally understanding he wanted limosna (alms). My mother and aunt came running, then went outside and gave him alms. To this day, we laugh when we remember that story.

I was sure I was going to miss my Maracaibo. But I knew we would go back because it is our hometown.

Caracas meant a new neighborhood, new friends, and seeing more of the family we had there. Of course, it was nice that we could enjoy the Caracas weather, open our windows, and wear a sweater in the morning and in the evening. Maracaibo is so hot that we keep the doors closed and use air conditioning all the time.

But the biggest challenge was starting a new school with girls we did not know. My mother took us to get the uniforms —a gray jumper with a white shirt underneath worn with black shoes and white socks. We got our books, and the first day of school finally arrived.

I was starting second grade. For some reason, my sister was off to her classroom but I was held at the principal's office, along with another girl who also was starting second grade and attending that school for the first time. She was a redhead. We sat together.

The school is a magnificent building that looks more like a castle than a convent. I felt ever so small inside it. The ceilings are so high that I feel minuscule sitting there. Rumor has it that the last right-wing dictator, Marcos Pérez Jiménez, built the school because his daughters attended it. Like anything he did, this was perfect, beautiful and magnificent. The time of Pérez Jiménez was a time of building. Most of the freeways and buildings in Caracas were erected during his dictatorship.

I looked at the girl sitting next to me, but we did not talk. We kept looking at each other timidly and somewhat mischievously. My eyes showed I was scared; she must have been scared also. We were new and inside this spectacular building. We might get eaten by it! My childish brain was spinning.

At Santa Rosa de Lima School, the sisters belonged to the Dominican Order. Their white habits were so well pressed they were almost shining. Some had black veils and some had white. It was the way hierarchy was determined.

Finally, a nun came to the office to get us. As we started to walk together behind her, we held hands. Although we had just been introduced, she was the first person I met at the school and that created a bond. The nun opened the door of the classroom where they had already started to introduce themselves. She said to the teacher, "These girls—Carmen María Montiel and Amarilis—belong to this classroom and they are both new."

Life would prove that was not the only day we would walk together. Our lives mirrored each other for many years.

The following days proved to be the first challenge of my life. I had a heavy *maracucho* accent, something that was the butt of jokes made by the rest of the girls. There is nothing more cruel than children, not because they are naturally cruel, but because they have no filter. Children always tell the truth and say what they feel. They made fun of every word I said, my natural expressions, everything!

It got to the point where I hated to go to school. I missed my friends in Maracaibo. Until one day I decided this accent of mine had to go! And in no time, I was talking like a *caraqueña* and the jokes ended.

What I did not know at the time, there was another possibility of embarrassment. I am dyslexic. Back then, there was no knowledge of it. I was able to get good grades in all subjects, but I was not able to read. At the time, everybody just thought I was lazy or dumb.

I had all types of tutors in Maracaibo to teach me how to read and my father tried. They all failed. When my mother signed us up at the school, she wanted to put me in first grade because of this, instead of second grade where I was supposed to be, but I was too tall for my age. The nuns told my mother that it would not be a good idea for my self-esteem. La *Madre Superiora* (Chief Nun) assured my mother that their teachers were specialized and if I was not able to read by December, they would put me in first grade then.

My God! What could have been worse? But sure enough, I was reading by December, not perfectly but much improved.

It was not until I was in college when reading an article waiting to see an ophthalmologist that I learned what my problem was…I am dyslexic! That article described me. Every word, every symptom was talking about me.

However, I went on to graduate *magna cum laude* from college and worked as a news anchor reading a teleprompter. Who would have ever thought I could accomplish that? I think the move to Caracas, with all the changes and challenges that came with it, made me more aware and secure in myself.

Once my accent became more like the other girls, school life was normal, learning, studying, playing kickball, learning ballet and being with friends. However, the girl that sat behind me did not like me or my hair, which was long, down to my waist, and honey colored. My mother took care of us, and the three girls had beautiful long manes. My sisters had golden hair.

But this girl had black short hair barely to her shoulders. She always pulled my hair, but acted like she did nothing when I would look at her. It started when we were sitting in class, but progressed to her pulling my hair whenever she passed by me.

I asked her to stop, but her answer was: "What? What did I do?"

My dad was the problem solver for all of us. I told him what was happening and he suggested that I tell my teacher and then the principal, if the problem persisted. I did as he told me. But the problem continued. I went to the principal. The hair pulling got worse. So, I told my dad that I had done as he had said, but the problem was worse.

"Well, honey, you did the right thing," he said. "The teacher and principal know what is going on, you also talked to her and nothing has happened. Now you have to take things into your own hands. The next time she pulls your hair, you pull hers but even harder than she has ever done to you."

So, I did! A few days later, at dismissal time, while talking to friends, this girl passed me running and pulled my hair. This was the hardest of all. I dropped my backpack and followed her. She was running up the stairs. I caught up with her right in the middle of the staircase and pulled her hair so hard her head bent backwards. I turned around and picked up my backpack. That day was the last time she ever pulled my hair. Bullies have to be stopped.

Two years later, I faced another challenge when I started suffering from asthma. I missed a lot of days at school, and the teacher had already advised that if I missed another day, I could lose the year. By then I was in fourth grade. I was really worried because I did not want to get behind in school.

One morning right before we left for school, I was sitting in the living room arranging my books, when I heard my mother's high heels coming down the stairs. "Oh no!" I thought. The routine was that when my mother came down, we were supposed to be having breakfast and I had not even started. I got up and ran to the kitchen when my feet got entangled and I fell, hitting the wall with my face. It was a matter of seconds but I saw how I was going to hit the wall. In a split second, I decided to turn my face sideways so I would not get disfigured since our walls were made of concrete. I turned to the right and heard my face crack when I hit the wall.

My father was in his study and came running when he heard the noise. That is how loud it was. My mother came running down the stairs and found me on the floor crying. My face was as red as a tomato and it hurt so badly.

My dad could had been a doctor. He examined me, touching my face to make sure no bones were broken.

"Your bones are good, but you had a good hit and cannot go to school," he said.

"No! I cannot miss another day of school or I will lose the year. I have to go!"

"You cannot, plus I have to take you to have an x-ray."

"No!" I cried harder. "I will lose the year. I have to go."

My dad called one of his best friends, Filiberto. They grew up together and Daddy spent a lot of time with Filiberto while he was in med school. My father responded to his questions and when they finished talking, he said: "Okay, I am taking you to school, but this afternoon Filiberto is going to check you out."

He took me to school with a bag of ice and instructed the nuns to make sure they got fresh ice every so often. By the time

I got there, I had missed Mass and the classroom was locked. I sat down outside and waited for the class to come back. I could only imagine how bad I looked when I saw the faces of my friends as soon as they spotted me.

"What happened?" the teacher asked while all the girls stared at me with horror.

"I fell and hit the wall."

"Why are you here? You should not be here."

"You said if I missed another day, I would miss the year."

"No, no. This is bad. You need to go back home. If you are well tomorrow, come, but you are not going to miss the year for today."

I was taken to the principal's office and my mother took me for x-rays later. No broken bones but my face turned purple, so ugly to the eye.

For a year or so I had a clot of blood inside my cheek that felt like a rock. It dissolved by itself over time.

Years later, my face would be almost disfigured again when my husband ran a red light in Tennessee. Nearly wintertime, we were driving to have dinner on a Saturday night in the icy rain when he ran the red light. He thought he could make it, but suddenly a pickup truck appeared in front of us. With the weather conditions, the brakes did not stop the car and we hit the truck. I hit the windshield. It did not hurt at the moment, but an iron-like smell started immediately and a hot liquid was coming down my face. I looked down and saw blood was everywhere. I started to scream.

Alejandro pushed me back in the seat and touched my forehead. I later learned he had put his fingers inside the wound.

"It is okay, Carmen. You do not have a fracture."

Within seconds, fire trucks, police cars and ambulances surrounded us. I could not see much because I could not move as per instructions from my husband and the paramedics who arrived so fast. The blood flowed nonstop like it was coming from a water faucet. The smell was unbearable.

I was taken by ambulance to the hospital. Once we got there, Alejandro asked me if I wanted to have Theresa, my best friend, called. I was at the emergency room for hours, having x-rays, exams and eight stitches on my brow where my hairline starts.

Theresa got both of us home. The car was a total loss. The pain was killing me. I went to bed and Theresa put my sweater in water. It was full of blood. Alejandro was going to trash it, but she said that if we wash it now, the blood will be gone. I had a sedative and slept, but when I woke up the next day and saw my face in the mirror, I was scared. I was completely disfigured.

The accident was mentioned on the news that night. My friends informed me on Monday when I showed up for class with a beret to cover my now disfigured forehead. Once again, I had a bruise coming down my head but now on the left side. Funny how bruises on faces roll down!

I was the director of the news station at East Tennessee State University and many times was out filming. One day while looking in the lens of a TV camera, a fellow student realized I had a terrible bruise on my left side. The forehead bruise was now on the lower part of my cheek and neck.

"My God, girl! Who is hitting you?" she said.

Little did I know that possibility was going to become reality later in my life.

The bruise kept on coming down at the same time it was disappearing to the point that it looked like a "hickey" on my neck. Everybody, people at school and the gym—the only places I frequented in that college town—commented that I had a "hickey"! It was embarrassing but what could I do? After all, I was married.

Thank God the pageant taught me to deal with false accusations, something I had to endure later to a greater magnitude while protecting my children.

CHAPTER 6

Miss Congeniality

IT WAS A BORING regular day of work for her. Every day she must have asked herself what happened to that popular blond girl from school. She was beautiful, popular, dedicated, always the beauty queen... But now?

She hated her post, hated that regular small office at the airport, where she sat to eat and her ass got bigger on a daily basis. Houston is not that important in the USA, not even for the weather forecast or for terrorists, but she requested this position because it allowed her to have a side job... Real estate!

Is she allowed to do that with a federal job?

Just like every other day, the days passed without anything happening to make her feel like a real FBI agent. All that sacrifice, study and training were reduced to a small office desk job.

However, that morning when she got to work, there was a notice of an incident on an airplane earlier that day, the plane that had arrived at around 4 a.m. Miss Congeniality is happy. Finally, something to do. She was hoping it was something good. Could have not been anything major since she was not called when it happened. That was the only requirement of her job that made her feel like she was a marshall: she could be called at all times.

She read the report about a domestic disturbance on a flight from Houston to Bogota, Colombia. The plane returned to Houston. It did not make sense!!! The woman was with her husband and her 14-year-old daughter. No charges were filed. The pilot did not want to file charges. The police listed public intoxication. But both she and her husband had been drinking on the plane. And the flight attendants have a responsibility not to serve alcohol to passengers to the point of intoxication. Was she really drunk?

The woman arrested in this incident was only 115 pounds. What was she really arrested for? But then she thinks if only she could have kept her weight down like that. She remembered when she was that skinny, tall, blond and beautiful.

She checked her belly and her dark cheap suit. The only thing that resembled something from her past was the hair…a little!

She decided to Google this woman.

WOW!!! She was a walking Wikipedia. She saw that Carmen was her age and had pages and pages of achievements and awards. She was Miss Venezuela, Miss South America and second runner-up in the Miss Universe pageant for 1984. She is a journalist with a successful broadcasting career. And she still looks beautiful. She has kept herself well and is active in numerous charitable organizations in Houston. Recognized in Houston and abroad for her work and dedication, she is a woman who had earned respect and love. But now this?

She is a public figure that people still follow as if it were yesterday when she won the crown. She has Facebook, Twitter and Instagram accounts all open for her many fans. From the comments, it sounds like people still love her, even though she was a beauty queen nearly 30 years ago.

Her social media posts are full of recent pictures of herself and with her family. She still looks stunning! How has she done it? Miss Congeniality thinks to herself: "Everybody has a dark side. I will find this woman's dark side…or this is it? Is she Miss Little Goody Two Shoes?"

She started her investigation. She searched and searched, finally finding that this woman was arrested for DWI in Colorado. Bingo! However, none of this was public. She still enjoyed popularity and love from her fans. No one knew about it. But what if this got out? Little Miss Perfect and Beautiful is not that perfect after all!

She was jealous! She kept thinking, "What if I not only was the queen in my high school, but went beyond and became like her, Miss USA! My life would have been different, like hers. Not like this. Not these ugly four walls. Not this boring job. Not this ugly dark suit. I could be a real FBI agent, out fighting terrorists."

But Miss Congeniality was never at the top of her class and not smart enough for that type of position.

"But this woman was Miss Venezuela and a journalist. And now she flies first class while I am here in this hole."

She bet there was more and she was going to find it.

She later learned that the night of the incident, weather was the reason the plane returned. But the truth was not going to stop Miss Congeniality from making a case out of this. After all, she had nothing else to do.

She launched her investigation, calling Colorado and speaking with everybody she could there. Then she talked with Carmen's husband, who was surprisingly cooperative…Why?

He actually was very interested in helping her. He said Carmen had been a problem always and told her things that could not be found anywhere else. They could be true or lies, she thought, but who knew her better than the person who had spent 28 years with her. As he said, she had been with him longer than with her own parents. She assumed he knew more than anybody else, but it never crossed her mind why. What was his motive? As a husband, was not he supposed to protect her? Did she check with Harris County for divorces filed and other reports that stay in the system even if nothing happened after all?

This will show how ineffective the FBI is. A husband trying to get rid of his wife successfully uses the system, and the innocent woman ends up facing criminal charges, while terrorists like the Tsarnaev brothers and Omar Marteen, responsible for the Boston bombing and the Orlando massacre, respectively, fall through the cracks of the FBI and end up killing many innocent people. But she could not think about why that man wanted to hurt a woman who had loved him for 30 years and was the mother of his three children. Really, she did not care. After all, it served her purpose.

She further investigated social media posts, for lack of anything else to do. She went back to comments and tweets made, and bingo! She got something she repeated on Facebook and Twitter: "President Obama is the American Chávez." She hated Obama. Then she sees social media comments against Hillary. It was obvious this woman was conservative and a Republican. If this woman ended up in prison, it could mean a great advantage to Miss Congeniality's career whether or not Carmen was guilty. It did not matter what really happened on that plane. This would at least lead to a photo opportunity in *People* magazine since she is a beauty queen from the country with the most crowns in the world.

After all, it is almost impossible to win over the US government once you face federal charges. Less than 2% of people charged by the government wins.

CHAPTER 7

My Daughter, the Victim

IN LESS THAN two months, I got my daughter back. But she was destroyed!

My oldest daughter was always a challenge to raise. She is hard headed and a negotiator. "No" never meant "no" to her. It meant there was room to negotiate her way into anything. I called her my 70-year-old daughter. She was like an old lady, very entertaining to talk to. And she has an insight into things that only mature people have. However, she inherited her father's compulsive and experimental personality. At the time I did not even know my husband had an addictive personality. I just thought he was compulsive.

The divorce was very hard for her. She adored her father, so much so that when she turned six years of age, she asked me to have a wedding with her dad as the setting for her birthday party. Venezuelans like parties big and orchestrated, especially parties for the children. We have themes for our parties and go all the way with decorations, tablecloths, piñatas, party favors, the cake, entertaining, etc. So, this special birthday party was like a mini wedding; even my friends cried like a real wedding. It was hilarious, fun and beautiful.

But now, for her to see and understand the person her father had become was difficult. She could not understand that he had changed or she could not accept it. She was hoping for him to be who he once was. Even for me, it was hard to see who he had become. I definitely did not fall in love with this person.

She went through periods when she was mad at him and would not talk to him. Then she would tell him off and describe what she did not like about the situation. But she loved him so much. And his personality changes made her feel like he did not love her. She was just a teenager dealing with too much... not understanding and thinking "*No me ama, Mami!*" ("He does not love me, Mom.")

After two months of not talking with her dad, she decided to see him, because she needed money or maybe it was simpler than that: she missed him. She took her brother and sister to dinner with him, but she came back changed. Every time he saw the children, they came back mad.

Especially mad at me. He filled their heads with hate toward me. He told them it was my fault. I was breaking the family apart, like they did not see what had happened. But they are children and easy to manipulate.

This was on a Sunday. By Monday, she was very rebellious. It was Labor Day, and she said she was going out after dinner. It was nearly 10 p.m. I told her no because it was a school night and it was late.

"But I don't have school tomorrow," she said.

"I don't care. It is a school night and too late. Only prostitutes go out at 10 p.m."

"Well, I am moving in with Dad. He said he would let me do whatever I want!"

"Please don't do that."

"I can do whatever I want, Daddy said."

She became some other person. She had that look her father got. It felt like the devil. Her eyes were different. I was still very weak from what happened with my husband. I did not have any dignity left and begged her not to leave me. I went on my knees and begged her. But she left anyway, feeling all mythic and powerful.

I knew her father would not watch over her, especially at this difficult stage in adolescence. After all, he had never watched over them. Everything was always "him" first. So much so that once we got out of the car to see a house across the street. It was just him, our son Juan Diego, and me. We parked in a place where the road was uneven. I was in heels and had to walk carefully. As always, Alejandro did not even care that I could fall. He started walking across the street, not paying any attention to Juan Diego following him. I started yelling at him to pay attention to Juan Diego because I could not run to keep up. Alejandro crossed the street with Juan Diego behind him, and the worst almost happened. A car came and nearly ran over my son. If it was not for the guard in the parking lot, Juan Diego would have not been saved.

It was left for me to always care for my children. I always knew they were my responsibility. I love them so much that they have never been too much for me.

Alejandro was now living in a hotel. There was no space for her. While here in our house, she has her own bedroom and all the space she needed. She was a senior, and we had so much to do: applications for college, the SAT, graduation.

I always had to be on top of her making sure she studied or finished her homework. I texted and called her every day to say "good morning" and "good night." For weeks she did not reply.

Within two days, we were in court working on the worst temporary orders a woman can have with the most expensive lawyers in town. I am convinced Alejandro had bought them off.

Alejandro walked into court saying: "Alexandra does not want anything to do with her mother. She does not want to see her again. Therefore, I am keeping her."

The papers were drawn up, and Alexandra was his to keep. I did not even have the right to visit with her. She was not answering my calls or my texts, but I kept trying every day in the morning and right before bed. My house was gloom!!!

Alexandra's sister and brother missed her a lot. I missed her a lot. I missed my first baby! Kamee hardly ever saw her at school. They are on different floors, and Juan Diego is in another building.

On a flight back from Colorado, I wrote her. I poured my heart out. After two days, I got the worst answer ever. It was so hurtful and made no sense. It did not even look like her writing. She writes beautifully, but this was poorly written. It looked more like something Alejandro would write in his five-year-old style.

Within a few weeks, she started answering my texts. She was sick. Ah!!! A sick girl needs her mummy. Alejandro left for work and did not give her medicine or food. There she was in a hotel one-bedroom apartment alone. I offered to take her chicken soup, but she refused. Of course, her father had forbidden her to let me in into his hotel room. Anyway, the important thing was ... she was talking to me.

From there on she sent me her paintings, via text ... WOW, what incredible pieces they were. She started to get out of the car when she came to drop off or pick up her brother and sister. I enjoyed seeing her. But I noticed how she was deteriorating. She was not taking care of herself. She looked dirty with greasy hair. It looked like she was losing her beautiful hair. She did have such a beautiful mane. But she was volatile. She could be in a good mood one minute and suddenly be mad. It was so hard to deal with her, to talk to her. She was like her dad at times. She would walk in happy saying hello to all, be sweet to my mother, and suddenly in a split second, get mad and walk out. She had no respect for anything, just like her father. She was becoming him!

I checked her Twitter and Facebook accounts. She was not making much use of Facebook, but doing a lot on Twitter. And that is where I started to see that something was wrong. She was tweeting about marijuana and using words I did not know. With the help of my sister, we went online and searched for these words. They were all drug related. Words that of course I did not know. I saved all of the tweets and sent them to my family lawyer. I told them I needed to get my daughter back. Something was terribly wrong. Little did I know.

On Friday, October 18, 2013, she called and said she was sick. She had nausea and was vomiting. I got worried. I thought she was pregnant. She knew where I was coming from and said, "¡*Mami!* I am not pregnant." Of course, she knew what was wrong with her.

On Sunday, two days later, she came home to drop off Kamee and Juan Diego. She was so dirty. It hurt me to see her like that. She stayed for a short time and then left.

Then came Monday. The school called me at around 2 p.m., asking about her whereabouts. I said she should be at school, but they informed me she was not. I told the school, "I don't know if you know, but she is not living with me; she is with her father."

They said, "Yes, we know, but her father is not answering. The problem is she has missed so many days at school that it is getting into the danger zone. She can lose the year."

I hung up, and called and texted her. She did not answer. Finally, she did answer and asked, "*Mami*, what happened?" in a sleepy voice.

"Where are you?"

"Home."

"Home??? Aren't you supposed to be at school?"

"I am sick."

"Sick again? You were sick last Friday."

"Well, I am sick."

"Why didn't your father call the school and let them know you were sick?"

"I guess he did not realize I was still here."

"What? He does not know if you are home or not?"

"Come on, *Mami!*"

We finished the conversation and hung up. Frustrated and desperate, I called my lawyer and explained what the school had just told me. My lawyer said they were going to subpoena her attendance records. So, the wheels were in motion to get my daughter back.

I knew my daughter was not doing well. But at the same time, I did not want to force her to come back. I wanted for her to come back willingly.

Tuesday was a quiet day. I did not hear from her or the school. Like they say with children, silence is not good, right? Or is it no news is good news?

On Wednesday, Alexandra called me at around 3 p.m. "Mommmmm" She has this way of saying *Mami* when she needs me. That melts my heart still.

"¡Hola, mi amor!" (Hey, Baby!)

"Mommmmm, I have to tell you something. You know they take the dogs to school..."

The dogs? I know what that means, and it is trouble. The school randomly and unannounced brought in drug dogs to search through the school and student cars. I interrupted her: "The dogs? You got expelled, Alexandra?"

"No, *Mami*, no. They are not expelling me. It was not mine."

Here we go. The old story of "It is not mine. It is my friend's."

"Alexandra...who is going to believe that?"

"*Mami*, it is true! Anyway, I told them to call you, that even though I am living with my dad you need to be informed. Please, wait for his call."

Oh my God! She is delusional. She is getting expelled. The school has a zero-tolerance policy on drugs. I know about cases in previous years when kids got expelled even with all of the excuses they made. Why was it going to be different this time?

The principal called. I know he has a sincere appreciation for Alexandra. This man knows the psychology of the teenagers he deals with and manages them very well. You cannot ask for a better head of the high school. After explaining what happened, he said the incident occurred on Tuesday and that this morning they had a meeting with her father, which Alejandro never told me.

He said Alexandra collaborated and was believable. And the school was not going to expel her, but there were going to be consequences that would be explained to me on Monday. She and another boy were suspended until Monday. I did not know yet why the school was protecting Alexandra and I will be forever grateful for that. Expelling her would have destroyed her, and I would have lost my daughter completely and forever. She would not have been able to recuperate from that. It would have been too much for her. She had enough with everything that had happened in our family.

Ok…this is it! I called my lawyers again and told them they needed to speed up filing the motion to get my daughter back. That it was obvious she was under no supervision by her father and this had gone way too far. My daughter was on the verge of losing the year for missing days or getting expelled.

Thursday went by quietly until around 7 p.m., when Alexandra called me again.

"Mommmm…!!! You know my car got towed. I need you to go with me to get it. Since the car is under your name, I cannot go alone."

"Alexandra, have you noticed that something wrong has been going on with you every day of the week?"

She started to scream: "*Mami*, you need to…!"

I hung up. She called again.

"Did you hang up?"

"Yes, I did. I am your mother and until you respect me, I will not talk to you."

She started screaming again: "*MAMI*…"

Click. I hung up again.

Just like with other people, I have even lost my daughter's respect.

I had an appointment on Friday at my lawyer's office. I am working to get on the stand. I have never done that before, and the lawyers from the opposite side will try to destroy me, to get to me, so I needed to learn how not to let them. In other words, I was coached on how to be on the stand.

Yes, you got that right! You have to be coached for that. Family court and any other court is a theater. The best show wins! You would think the truth always wins. Well, you need the truth and a good show, too. So, I figured that I had the truth already and now I am training to win.

On that day in the afternoon, around 2 p.m., Alexandra called me.

"Mommmmm, can you take me to get my car?"

This time she is sweet, but also sounded sad and depressed.

"Of course, Baby. I am in a meeting. As soon as I finish, I will pick you up."

I hang up and asked the coach how much longer it would take. He said about an hour. So, we continued. About half an hour later, she called again.

"Mommmmm, can you come get me, please?"

It sounded like she was crying. I told them that I needed to go. I did not like the sound of her voice.

Ever since my problems started, I have been the perfect driver. I keep to the speed limit and do not make a misstep. I cannot afford that. So, even though I wanted to run get her, I did not go over the speed limit. I got to their building and called to let her know I was downstairs. By now, her father had moved to a luxury high rise downtown.

She got in the car. My God, she was like hobo, filthy, smelly, greasy hair. I cannot stand this!!! She looked awful!

I asked: "Are you okay?"

"No, *Mami!*"

Her eyes looked lost. She was crying, her eyes red. She pulled up the sleeve of her blue jean jacket, showing eight cuts on her left arm.

"I was going to jump from the balcony when you called to tell me you were down here!"

I did not know how I was able to be composed and calm because I wanted to scream and cry.

My poor baby. God gives you strength in the most important moments. Only God could have helped me through that time and so many others.

I did not cry. The shock was such that I could not cry. I was speechless. It felt like a lifetime, but probably seconds passed. I was looking at her and thinking what would be the best possibility at that time for my daughter... Definitely not the emergency room. It would take hours and be in her record as a suicide attempt.

This would prove to be a mistake that haunted me and saved Alejandro from losing his medical license. I called my psychiatrist. Yes, I have a psychiatrist. I needed one to help me recover. After all, I had post traumatic stress disorder and battered wife syndrome, plus I had to clean myself up from the medication Alejandro had been giving me. Years of abuse did this to me.

No answer. I left a message.

"Dr. Gus, I hope you are at your office. I want to bring my daughter to you."

Within a couple of minutes, his secretary called me back. I explained, and she told me to come right in. The cuts are fresh. She has blood on them. I do not know how I can drive! The tears started to burst out of my eyes. And I do not want her to see me crying. I am shaking!!!

We get to his office, and he is with a patient. When he came out and saw her, he instructed his secretary to clean the cuts. We went to the bathroom, washed her arm, and applied peroxide and Neosporin.

While we were waiting, Alejandro called her. I took the phone and told him what was happening.

"Why is this happening to her?" I asked him.

We have not spoken in three months. But he is the usual victim. He always played the victim. He did not know anything.

"I don't understand. But Carmen, she is depressed. Come home and I will give you some medicine for her."

"Alejandro, you will never again medicate any of my children or me." And I hung up.

We went in to see the doctor and I explained what I knew. Then he asked me to leave, so he could speak with Alexandra alone. When I went back in, Dr. Gus told me: "Take her to Menninger. I am calling and they will wait for her."

Menninger is a mental health rehabilitation facility. This was all new to me. The doctor made it clear to me she did not need medication and that he will not give her any, that the more important thing now is to get her clean from all medication since she had taken Xanax.

"Xanax? Who gave her Xanax?" I asked.

Dr. Gus gave me a look which I understood to mean that it was better to leave it like that. When we got to Menninger, they would not let us in until they knew for sure that she was committed and we were ready to pay $28,000 for a three-week stay. My God! I do not have that kind of money now. Alejandro emptied the bank accounts and I do not have access to the money. Alexandra decided to call her father and said: "Let's see how much he loves me. His watch is worth that much."

She called: "Dad, I am at the hospital. Dr. Gus sent me to Menninger. But they need $28,000 in order to check me in."

He started to scream: "You and your mom think I am a bank."

"Dad, your watch is worth that much."

"Put your mother on the phone."

Then he started screaming at me: "I am not paying $28,000 or $1,000 for a spoiled girl that is just afraid of a drug test."

I hung up.

He kept on calling and I told Alexandra not to answer. I asked her what she wanted to do.

"You cannot stay at this hospital. Do you want me to take you back to him?"

"No, *Mami*, please, please, don't take me back to him. Take me home with you, *Mami*."

He called again and asked her to put me on the phone. When I answered, he started to scream. I said: "You do not scream at me ever again!" and I hung up.

What a powerful feeling to hang up on him! I thought. He cannot control me ANY more.

We decided to pick up her car since every day they were adding more fees and I was left with so little money. She has what her father gave her to pay for the car up until today. While I was at the lot dealing with the car—trying to restart it because the battery was dead—Alejandro called again.

"*Mami*, it is my *papi*. He said he won't scream again."

"Tell him I have nothing to talk with him about."

I thought... I do not want to talk to him and I do not have to. What an empowering feeling! He cannot control me anymore. We get the car and go home. Long day. A friend of mine picked up Kamee and JD from school. They are so happy to see Alexandra. She is so filthy! I told her to take a shower, and she did.

Within minutes my house was full of kids. They came up to me and said they were glad Alexandra was back with me. Alejandro called the house and demanded to talk to Alexandra since she was not answering her cell. I handed the phone to her.

"*Papi*, the doctor said I have to stay with Mommy."

I could hear his scream on the phone.

"Fine, *Papi*, if this is how you are going to be. I love you!"

But he had already hung up on her.

The mother of one of her friends came over. This is where she stayed the most while she was with her father. Yes, she spent more time at this friend's house than with her father. She brought Alexandra her favorite snack and started telling me how bad it had been. Alejandro would text Alexandra not to come to the hotel when he had company until later. She would hang out and wait and wait, sometimes until it was 2:00, 3:00 or 4:00 a.m. She slept in her car, many times parked on the streets or in the school parking lot. Then she had to wake up at 5:00 a.m. to get back to the hotel for her books and uniform to get to school by 7:45 a.m. Many times, when she arrived, the door to her father's room was open and she could see him in bed with a woman. No wonder she wanted to escape.

She was so mad at Alejandro's lack of responsibility with Alexandra that she offered to be a witness at the upcoming custody hearing.

Later a friend of Alexandra's came to visit and wanted to talk to me.

"Please, Mom L, do not let her go back to her dad's. That was bad. She does not want to go back; don't allow her to. Alexandra does not want me to tell you the truth. Promise if I tell you, you will not let her know I told you."

I hated to promise. What if it is something I really could not hide? But I was so in the dark during the time Alexandra was with her dad that I wanted to know, especially if it was something so important. I wanted to know what Alon needed to tell me, but was afraid of it.

I have known Alon since he was eight years old. He and Alexandra are like brother and sister. They care for each other.

Alon started to talk, "Alexandra was spending most of the time in the street when her father had company. But the worst part was when he brought prostitutes over and they stayed there for days. God knows what else happened there!"

By midnight everybody was gone. What a long day! I could have used a drink, but I did not drink alcohol anymore, not even a drop. I became afraid of it because Alejandro was drugging me to get rid of me. With time I was going to find out how often he did it.

Just as Alexandra did when she was a little girl and got sick, she slept in my bed with me that night. She needed Mommy. My children had slept with me every time they were sick or felt scared. I looked at her and saw my baby, not a 17-year-old girl. I still did not know the whole story of what she had gone through.

Next morning when I woke up she was still sleeping. It was Saturday so I did not mind. She slept most of the day. When she finally got up, she said she was not feeling well. It was October and the weather was changing, so I figured that must be it. She was catching a cold or the flu, I thought.

She had chills and fever. She was shaking and sweating a lot, to the point where the bed was wet. Chicken soup cures everything. I gave her lots of chicken soup and lots of love. Little did I know that I was nurturing my daughter through detox!

Saturday and Sunday, she stayed in bed. I fed her and continued taking care of her, changing the bed sheets because they were wet with sweat. On Saturday, her father kept calling her and arguing. She kept hanging up, until finally she blocked his number in her cell phone. She did not want to talk to him. I still did not know what this was all about.

I spent a lot of time with her in bed, keeping her company and talking to her. She needed to feel she had a mother who was always there for her. We watched movies together. Her siblings came and went. But I stayed there with her.

Finally, she said: "Why didn't you fight for me? Why didn't you fight for me in court?"

"Your father said you did not want to be with me."

"That was not true. I wanted you to fight for me. You always fight for us."

I started to cry. I saw then what she was expecting from me.

"¡*Mi amor!* I had so much on my plate at that moment and you were so rude when you left that I believed what your father said. I was weak, so weak, and I am so sorry."

She looked at me with tears in her eyes; I had tears in my eyes. I just hugged her and we cried together.

Finally, on Sunday she said: "You know, *Papi* is afraid that I am going to talk."

"Talk about what?" I asked.

She did not answer, and I did not want to push her. If she did not want to talk, that was fine. It would all come out in due time.

However, by Monday she started to talk. I had seen how on October 17, a school night, she was tweeting at 3:00 a.m.

"You are too old for this. I cannot believe this s…!"

We were in my bed. I was caressing her hair.

"*Papi* brought three prostitutes to the apartment," she suddenly said.

"What? When?"

I could not tell her I knew. I had promised her friend.

"Almost two weeks ago, *Mami.*"

"How did you know they were prostitutes?"

"They said it. They stayed for days. We talked a lot, *Mami.*"

She went on: "Dad left with *tío José* and they came back with three women. *Tío* told Dad something when he saw me there. He left after a while and said, 'Your dad is crazy.'"

He did not leave because he had a moral attack because he would have taken my daughter and dropped her at my house. He left because he was worried Alexandra was going to tell his wife what he was doing, but the damage was already done. He was there with one of the prostitutes who was hurt when he left. That girl was in the bathroom when he left by Alexandra's account.

"They pulled out cocaine and started using. My dad said she needed some white. Mom, he acted like a little boy with those women. Later, another woman came. So, now there were four. At the end, only three stayed overnight. Dad got sick. He was sweating and throwing up in his bathroom. I went and checked on him. He was white, *Mami*, so pale. So, I stayed with the women until I had to go to bed."

"By Thursday afternoon, when I came back from school," she added, "my dad was going to have breakfast with two of them and invited me. I did not go because I had homework. On Friday, when Kamee and Juan Diego arrived, only one of them was still there, and Dad told them she was a friend of mine."

Oh My God! How disturbed this is. Even my younger children spent time with a prostitute.

On Tuesday, I was with my lawyers, who had already filed the motion to get my daughter back and to restrict Alejandro's visitation with the children, when suddenly Alexandra called: "*Mami*, you have to withdrew the motion."

"What motion?"

"The one you filed."

"How do you know about that?"

"*Papi* just sent it to me and is threatening me. If you do not withdraw it, I am leaving and you will not ever see me again."

She hung up.

I told my lawyers he forced her to make that call and called her back. She did not answer. I called the maid and she said Alexandra had left. I went home with my lawyer and called her again. No answer. My lawyer told me to call the police.

I texted her: "Alexandra, the police are going to be looking for you. Come home, please."

The police came and completed a report, but said there was nothing they could do about it until 48 hours after she was gone. My lawyer left and I prayed: "God please don't let her do anything irrational."

She finally came back crying and apologized after three hours.

On November 20, 2013, we went to court to legally get my daughter back and have Alejandro's visitation with the children supervised. My lawyers had requested a drug test since Alexandra saw him using.

Alejandro drank water at the courthouse worse than a fish. This was very rare because he does not drink water; he usually drinks Coke. My lawyers were making fun of it.

I testified about what I saw when my daughter came back to me. However, Alejandro's lawyers diverted the court's attention by asking me about the plane incident, accusing me of being an alcoholic and a drug addict.

"After all, she takes after her mother."

With this, Alejandro had managed to accuse me of his ways. He is the drug addict and alcoholic, but now the tables were turned. The psychiatrist who saw Alexandra testified and gave an explicit account of what Alexandra had told him: drugs, prostitutes and sleeping in the streets. At lunchtime, my lawyers told Alejandro's lawyers to have him take a drug test. His lawyers refused, saying they had to work with their client. Work or go do another treatment to get him clean? I thought to myself.

The lab sent the technician to the court. It was a female. Alejandro refused to be tested by a woman. He said he preferred to wait for the male technician. Suddenly, he was all modesty. A man that walked naked around the house where all the maids, workers and children saw him.

When Alejandro got on the stand, he lied. He said none of it was true. After a full day, the associate judge dictated that I was to get my daughter back; Alejandro had to pay 100% of the medical bills, Kamee's horseback riding lessons and Juan Diego's tutoring; and we all had to attend a class of families in divorce, but Alejandro's visitation stayed as it was.

Alejandro never paid for anything or attended the class. We, my children and I, did. We were punished, not him. I was devastated, and so were my children. They did not want to go back to visit him.

After a week we got the results from the drug test back ... negative! My daughter looked at me with tears rolling down her cheeks: "*Mami*, I saw him! I saw him! Believe me, he uses."

"I know, *mi amor*. I believe you. I have seen also."

Two and a half years later, Alejandro proudly told me how a dinner with a judge from another court helped him get on the good side of the judge in our court. That is how he got away with this.

CHAPTER 8

The First Setup

As HAD BECOME our tradition, we spent Christmas and New Year's in Colorado at our apartment in Beaver Creek. The kids are now 15, 12 and 6 years of age. Juan Diego is still in ski school but the girls ski with us. All in the family are great skiers and we enjoy the sport. It was our first day of skiing and Alejandro, as usual, had a red face, as he does not use sunblock.

On Christmas Eve, we went to have drinks with friends before Christmas dinner with the children at the Hyatt Hotel. We sat in a space close to the bar and a bartender was taking care of us.

However, Alejandro went to the bar himself and got our drinks. I could not understand why. When he came back with the drinks, I said: "Why didn't you ask the waiter for them?"

"Ah! He was taking too long," he responded.

I thought he was being extra nice because we were not living together then. He should not have come on this trip.

After our friends left, we stayed a little longer and Alejandro went back to the bar for a second set of drinks. As usual, we started fighting. The therapist had recommended that we put distance between ourselves when fights started.

I left to get our car with the valet and noticed I could hardly walk. Why? What was happening to me?

When I got to the apartment, the children were walking out. Why? We had dinner reservations. Alejandro got there right behind me and started screaming: "Why did you leave me?"

"The therapist said to put distance between us when problems start, plus we have to get ready for dinner," I said.

"What dinner? You ruined everything."

"How? What did I ruin?"

I was dizzy. I could not understand what was he talking about. He came close and started hitting me. I already had bruises from a previous day. Once again, I decided to leave, to put distance between us.

I did not know where to go. It was Christmas Eve. Everybody was having family time. We had dinner reservations with the children; now we did not. I decided to get on I-70 toward Vail.

That was the night Alejandro called the police and told them I was driving drunk in a blue Hummer 3 with Texas license plates. This was his first success in getting me in trouble with the authorities. And that became his golden card. After this I was at his mercy.

I was scared and knew I was not well. I only remember having less than two glasses of wine. I did not finish the second glass, so why did I feel so bad and start to lose consciousness after the first drink? Alejandro even exaggerated this story knowing he had drugged me that day and purposely put me in that position, something he had been doing for a while I came to find out later.

When I went to court, I could not believe when I read the police report. Besides calling the police to report I was driving drunk and giving them the description of the car so they would get me, he told them I had hit him and used his "red" cheeks as evidence!

We just started to ski so, of course, his cheeks were red. He furthered his accusations by saying I had a history of mental problems, more of his lies.

What? I thought to myself. How could he come up with all these lies? And then act with me like he had done nothing? How could he ever imagine that I would never read this report? I realized then the power that doctors have. People take their word as if it was incorruptible, even if what he was saying sounded unreasonable. Who are you going to believe: the doctor or the beauty queen? Yes, he always told the authorities I was just a beauty queen and failed to mention that I was also a journalist who had graduated *magna cum laude*. Once he realized he had that power, he went on manipulating the authorities.

What was worse was to read the reaction I had. I could hardly remember what happened. But in the last months, I could not remember what happened on so many of occasions.

Alejandro arranged with the lawyer to get a deal for me. As a first offense, a lawyer could have fought the charge and had everything completely dropped. But that was not Alejandro's intention.

I was trapped in this situation.

"Carmen, this will teach you a lesson," he said. "You really need a lesson. After all, you were not properly raised."

And who is he to know how a properly raised person behaves when he had no family and was raised in a mall?

"I did nothing, Alejandro. You called the police and said I was driving drunk, something I do not understand. I only remember having one drink and then I was totally drunk. How did that happen? Not only that, you accused me of hitting you, when I escaped from you; I escaped from your attack."

"Carmen, do this. You have no other choice. Just follow the rules."

Somehow, he had a look of happiness on his face.

After that, I could never tell him anything. Every time I said something that bothered him, he would answer, "Well, sweetie, do you want me to call the District Attorney in Colorado?" especially when we were in Colorado. One day, we were having a fight and he said that. We were in Colorado with my son, just the three of us. I found out he was texting with one of his girlfriends and told him about it.

He started to scream: "Definitely you do not learn. I am calling the police now and having you locked up."

My son was only six years old. He came to hug and kiss me. "*Mami*, this is in case you go!" he said.

I started to cry and hug my baby. How did my family end up like this?

I called the police in Houston on three more occasions when he hit me and bit me or dragged me by my hair, like he did in a restaurant parking lot earlier that December. That day, a bystander, a US Air Force Colonel who later became a General, saw him in action. This investigation was what made him determined to stop it, and that is how Christmas Eve happened.

On those occasions I had evidence of his attacks. Once I had fresh teeth marks on my shoulder, hand and breast. Twice the Houston police were ready to arrest him, but he told them I had problems in Colorado.

That was it! They took us both in, and my hand got infected in jail. The doctor there could not understand why I was arrested when I had visible attack marks—just like that officer in Houston could not believe I was accused of a federal crime for what could be, if anything, a contempt of court charge. I was never able to prove he was attacking me until July 2013.

Alejandro always said: "The power that being a doctor gives you!" He knew it and used it.

I decided to start taking pictures of my bruises and scars as evidence, sending them to my best friend in Venezuela for safekeeping. I was worried that Alejandro would find out and destroy them. I lived in fear that something fatal would happen to me and told Gustavo to please keep the photos safe just in case.

Gustavo was desperate. My best friend since we were kids, he was helping me find a way to get out of this abusive relationship. But he knew that if I was in Venezuela the outcome could be worse.

It was not until the next fall that I realized Alejandro had been putting drugs in my drinks. And after we separated, I found out that all the medications he had given me for my asthma or colds were for mental problems. He had me on an emotional roller coaster.

CHAPTER 9

The Pageant

Miss Venezuela is... Miss Zulia, Carmen María Montiel!

Becoming Miss Venezuela was like a fairytale, one I never dreamed of or expected to experience, unlike many little girls in my country. But time, life and many of us facing reality had proved we do not live "happily ever after."

That moment felt like a dream that little by little had become part of my life since I had met Osmel Sousa, the president of the Miss Venezuela pageant and the "Maker of Queens," three years before. It felt like I was outside my body. Was that me? Was that happening to *me*? It was not until my father hugged me that I came back to reality and knew it was real.

Yes, I am Miss Venezuela! I said to myself and started to cry on his shoulder. In Venezuela it was very important to hold that honor. Like Osmel Sousa told my dad when trying to convince him to let me enter the Miss Venezuela pageant, we become part of our country's history.

Zulia state had only had one Miss Venezuela until then, so with me it was the second crown. Our state is very important to the country. It has the second most important city in Venezuela, after the capital of Caracas. We *maracuchos* are very proud and love our state. This was an incredible accomplishment for us, especially in 1984, when we were capturing all the honors: our baseball team won the Baseball Cup and went on to win the Series of Caribe; and Luis Aparicio, a *maracucho*, became the first Venezuelan player to be inducted in the Baseball Hall of Fame. To this day he is the only one to hold that honor for Venezuela.

My dad ran, jumped up to the stage and hugged me before Paola, Miss Venezuela until that moment, had a chance to put the crown on me. Miss Departamento Vargas' family, who sat in front of my family, called Dad "the athlete" after that because of that move. It took him a matter of seconds to get up on stage, and he came all the way from the last row of the theater. Candidates' families were assigned seating in alphabetical order, so our Zulia section was last.

After the ceremony ended, the press got on the stage to take pictures. It was an avalanche. I started to step back. I was only 19 years old, and I was scared. I was never in a position like that. The security for Venevisión Network, the owners of the pageant, surrounded me. They made a human chain to protect me. My dad was one of them!

In the days during the pageant, my father, being my father, befriended everybody. He got to know each security agent by name and everyone from Venevisión who was working for the pageant that week. We were all staying at the Macuto Sheraton Hotel at La Guaira, the beach that is 30 minutes from Caracas.

During that moment of terror with the human avalanche, my dad pushed against the people, protecting me, just like one of the security guards. Many of then started to tell him: "Do not worry, Mr. Montiel. We got it. She is safe."

"*Pero Pedro Emilio, es que me van a matar a la muchacha.* (But Pedro Emilio they are going to kill my baby.)"

My dad was really worried. Those were the moments I felt absolutely loved and protected. He had not wanted me to compete, but once I did, he supported me 100%. Dad ended up competing more than I did!

What an incredible life I was about to start. After the pageant we stopped to eat *arepas*. I had been on a strict diet for months and was craving one, plus I was very hungry. It had been a long day and night.

Héctor Beltrán, my new boss, also was there at *El Arepazo*, a restaurant specializing in arepas. As soon as he saw my dad, he asked him where I was. I was in the car with my mother and siblings still in my pageant gown with the Miss Venezuela sash on, holding the crown in my hands on my lap.

Héctor ran out and started singing the hymn from the pageant, "Miss Venezuela." "*¡En una noche tan linda como esta, cualquiera de nosotras podría ganar!*" As soon as you hear that song in Venezuela, you know what it means, especially on the night of the pageant. The country is paralyzed the night of the event. Everybody watches the competition.

That got everyone's attention, and people started coming close to the car. Poor *Papi*! My dad, always so worried, came running.

"*¡Héctor, qué broma me echaste!*" (Oh My God, what am I going to do now?) he said, while trying to overcome the people and get inside the car.

Looking at me, Héctor said: "Get used to this, *mi amor*. This is your new life! You won more than 50% of the vote."

I was exhausted after months of preparation for the pageant, a week at the Macuto Sheraton Hotel in rehearsals, interviews, and television shows, and finally the pageant. I wanted to rest because I knew the press would be knocking at my door first thing in the morning, as it happened every year with the new Miss Venezuela.

But everybody was so happy that when we got home the house was full of people, family and friends from both my mother and father's side. It was a Friday night and must have been after midnight by the time we were back home. Apparently, everybody just left wherever they were and went to my house. It was a party!

My dad's side of the family had a wedding that night in Caracas. They were all happy telling us that as soon as the result was known, the orchestra announced the groom's cousin had just become the new Miss Venezuela. Everyone started jumping and dancing. This was the best moment to celebrate with dancing!

In Maracaibo, some members of my family went to see a concert by Spanish singer Rocío Durcal. When she announced that one of their own, a *maracucha*, just became the new Miss Venezuela, all of my aunts started to scream, "She is our niece! She is our niece!"

My dear uncle Manolo was sick at the hospital. He saw the pageant but fell asleep right before the finale. However, he told my aunt that "*el Frijolillo*" was way ahead. "This title is hers."

Back home I was soaking my feet in cold water. I really wanted to go to bed, so I left the visitors and retreated to my bedroom.

The next morning at 6:00 a.m., the press were there. At that time, I had to get up and get ready. I dressed very simply and casually and wore no makeup. The headlines read: "She is more beautiful with a clean face."

The pageant was on a Friday. Saturday was the big marathon show on TV, *Sábado Sensacional*, from 3:00 p.m. until 10:00 p.m. According to tradition, Miss Venezuela and the competition's finalist had to be there. During the show, cars were given to the first runner up and me.

That meant I only had Sunday to rest because on Monday morning, I had to go meet with the President of Venezuela at the time, Jaime Lusinchi. This was the magnitude of what it meant to be Miss Venezuela.

I met Osmel Sousa at "Le Club," a private discotheque at the time. I was only 16 years old and never in my life imagined that I would be in the Miss Venezuela pageant. After all, I had never considered myself that type of beauty. I was the ugly ducky at school, too tall, too skinny, too pale. I earned many nicknames because of all those things. But I did not care then because no one was particularly pretty at that time; we were all teenagers going through the worst period of our lives. Yes, they called me names, but we all did that to each other. To be skinny in a Latin country was definitely not a sign of beauty.

All I cared about at the time was to have fun and exercise my brain, coming up with the best jokes with my dear friend Gustavo. And yes! Good grades were important, too. When Osmel came up to me and said he wanted me to participate in the pageant, I could not help but laugh. I said that I was not that pretty.

"You are Laura Álvarez's sister, aren't you?" he asked.

"Yes, I am, but I am nothing like her," I told him.

My older sister, thirteen years my senior, was the first woman from Venezuela that became a top model in New York in the '70s. She was well known at the time and the pride of the fashion world. Regardless of what I had told Osmel, deep inside I felt good. It was not that bad to be so skinny, pale and tall. But still I thought: "No way am I pageant material."

In reality, I was more worried that my parents were going to find out we were at the club! On Sundays, the club had matinees starting around 2:00 p.m. for the young generation. We used to say we were going to the movies, but really went to dance.

Osmel started calling the house and inviting me to participate in many fashion shows. I thought: "Good! Pennies from heaven! This I am. Skinny, tall, pale…yes! I am a model. That I can be."

"Miss Venezuela? No way!!!" That is how he met my mother. She was always with me, especially since my father did not want me to model.

Osmel told my mother right away that he wanted me to compete in the pageant.

"Osmel, that is not possible because her father is against it, plus she is not interested at all and she is too young now."

After a few fashion shows, Osmel insisted.

"Osmel, she still is not interested. Why don't you give her some time and see if she likes the idea later? But, anyway, her father's issue is still there. He will never let her participate."

"Noemí, girls like her marry young. If I wait too long, she will get married."

Of course, even my mother started to like the pageant idea thanks to Osmel's insistence. I do not know if she really liked it or was proud because of the attention, but she started telling her sisters that Osmel wanted me for the Miss Venezuela pageant.

I still resisted the idea. But after more than two years, I started to get curious. "What if?" I thought. What if I won the Miss Venezuela title and went on to win Miss Universe? It was well known when Osmel insisted on a girl, that meant something incredible would happen.

However, I had my doubts. Many things were said about the pageant by people that had nothing to do with it. They said it was arranged, fixed, bought, anything but fair, so I wondered.

Mother and I kept the modeling hidden as long as we could, until my niece, my mother's first grandchild, was born. My father not only did not want me in any beauty pageant, he did not want me to be a model. My sister tricked my parents to become a model, and Dad was very mad about that. He definitely did not want another of his daughters to become a model.

My mother and I were doing a great job hiding this from my dad, but once she left to meet her first granddaughter, I was on my own. To make matters worse, I was supposed to be part of a very important fashion show while she was gone. Bulgari was visiting Venezuela, and I was one of the models for their fashion show being held at Le Club.

When I asked my mother what I should do, she said: "Tell your father the truth. He is going to have to go with you in my place, anyway."

My sister, María Eugenia, knew about the fashion show and helped me deliver the news to Dad that I was one of the models for the famous fashion show with Bulgari that everyone in Caracas was talking about. This show was going to gather the who's who of Caracas where my father was going to learn not only that I was a model but also that Osmel Sousa had his eyes on me for the Miss Venezuela pageant.

Disaster was coming ahead!

In the end, I was glad my father knew beforehand because there was no way to hide from the newspaper stories. In fact, I already knew one article was coming up. It was far better for my father to find out about it from me than a newspaper.

The day came and we all got ready for the big night at Le Club. I was upstairs with the other models. When I came out to take a peek at my dad, he was talking with Osmel.

"Oh no! This is not good," I thought to myself. I could see that my father did not have a happy face. This was all too much to bear for him. I bet he must have been wondering why he did not lock me at home!

The fashion show was a total success. It was an incredible experience. We wore black leotards with our hair held back very tight. The idea was for the jewelry to be displayed with no distractions. Each model had a bodyguard assigned to protect the jewelry. Until between changes they could not remove a necklace from me in time to put the next one on, so I pulled my black leotard neck over that piece of jewelry and told them put the other one on top. I was ingenious! But now I have two bodyguards assigned to me.

When the fashion show finished, all the models went down to join the party. My father was proud but protective and I could see he was not that happy. He was always the friendly person.

Later I learned what he had told Osmel Sousa. When we were talking, Osmel came and asked my father to go with him. I followed them with my eyes. Dad was introduced to Irene Sáez, the second Miss Universe for Venezuela, who had recently come back to Venezuela after finishing her reign.

I saw my father talking with her. I knew he admired her, not only for how beautiful she is, but also the way she carried herself.

He started smiling, but I saw his smile fade quickly. It was not long before he stood up and left. I thought it was awkward.

He came back and stood next to me, saying: "After what she just said, there is no way you will ever compete in that pageant. I don't want you to become crazy!"

It was not until we got in the car that Dad told us the whole story. He said Osmel told him that he wanted me to compete. To which my father replied: "I don't want any of my daughters competing in the pageant. The only girl I admire out of all the pageant is Irene Sáez."

"Really?" Osmel said. "Well, I am going to introduce you to her."

However, when my father sat down, Irene told him her pageant experience was so wonderful because people brought babies to her so she could give them benedictions. And people touched her to see if she was real.

That did it for my father. No pageant for Carmen!

Later I learned that Osmel had told Irene to please help him convince my father to allow me to enter the pageant. And he could not believe what she said to my father. It was a very bad approach starting out.

On one occasion, while Osmel was getting ready for the 1983 pageant, I still did not like the idea of competing, but he was still after me to, so I said: "If I compete, it has to be for Zulia."

"That is not possible," he replied.

"See! Then I will never compete."

As I got enamored with the idea and after my father found out Osmel was interested, everybody in the family knew about it. My aunts started telling my dad that he should let me join.

"No! My father will turn in his grave," Dad said.

Tía Norah, his older sister, told him: "Johnny, I really wanted to be the queen at the club and *Papacito* did not let me. Times have changed and the opportunities are many. Let her compete."

Finally, his childhood best friend Filiberto said: "Johnny, do not take away opportunities from your children. You do not know where that opportunity will take her."

I think that finally made my father agree!

The Miss Venezuela pageant for 1984 was on the way before of the end of 1983. Some candidates started to appear in newspapers and magazines. The gossip columns started talking about how the pageant was starting to shape up, including who were the best candidates so far. One columnist mentioned that so far Miss Zulia was not in place and that the state organization was not even talking about the competition. She added it had been said that Osmel was saving that for Laura Álvarez's sister. When I read that, I was in shock because I had not decided to compete and Father had not agreed to let me yet.

But once I had Dad's blessing, I joined the pageant in late January 1984. My father and I went to "*La Quinta*," the official office for the pageant that was a house, a pink house, where my father laid down the law to Osmel Sousa.

"She will not have any changes; she is beautiful as she is. She will be with her mother at all times. If her mother cannot be there or accommodations cannot be made for her to be there, Carmen will not go. And finally, she must finish her studies. This is very important to both her mother and me."

Osmel was again blinking as a way to agree with my father. "Yes, Mr. Montiel. Yes, Mr. Montiel," he answered to every requirement.

"Ah! And one more condition. She has to represent Zulia."

"I told Carmen María that is almost impossible," Osmel said. "But I had my hopes up that she was going to compete this year and I was able to save that slot for her."

In so many conversations with Osmel, I had always said if I entered the pageant it would only be for the Zulia state. And I went further and told him that I knew that "if" my father were to approve my participation, it would only be if I represented Zulia.

He would keep telling me that was impossible because they sent their own representative elected in a competition in Maracaibo.

He said he could not go over the organization in Zulia and select another candidate. Somehow, Osmel managed to put the 1984 Zulia competition on hold waiting to hear from me.

Once I was officially a pageant participant, I used my ever-positive outlook to be sure I became Miss Venezuela. That is the best tool ever. Think as if it is already done!

Just like I did when I went to Italy at fifteen. It was a difficult time for my family. Turning fifteen is very important for us in the Latin culture. My father preferred to give us trips to celebrate the occasion instead of big *quinceañera* parties. I was set to go to Italy where my oldest sister lived at the time.

One day close to the scheduled departure, aunt Marys, Mother's sister, was at our house having breakfast with us. She said: "Well, if God wants it, you will go to Europe."

To which I answered: "God wants me to be happy. That is why I know I am going!"

That January, I started a grueling routine that took months of hard work, dieting, exercise, massages, makeup classes, cocktail parties, photo shoots, rehearsals, etc. I was exhausted!

The competition was brutal, especially because the press had announced a set of three "favorites," always saying the crown was among the three of us. That created some friction with the rest of the girls, plus the fact that my mother was always included as a chaperone. However, I cannot say there was truly ugly behavior, just a few harsh words here and there, definitely not as ugly and dark as the press said it was behind closed doors.

I had decided to brush off the comments, except for one time when a group of the girls called me to a meeting while we were waiting for the bus to take us to rehearsals. They told the officials at the pageant to not interrupt us because we were planning a surprise for Osmel, which was not true! Instead, they talked down to me for being a favorite of the press, like that was my fault.

Even the girl I thought was my best friend was part of that ambush. When they finally opened the door, I went straight to Osmel's office and quit.

"Osmel, I do not need this aggression," I said. "I do not like conflict. It is not who I am. This was very ugly and I do not see how can I see eye to eye with any of the girls after today."

I was crying. My makeup was ruined. All of us had to have professional makeup every day because we were being photographed at all times. Osmel did not know what had happened since he had just arrived at La Quinta. After it was explained and my makeup was repaired, Osmel promised me that he would fix the problem and asked me to please not leave the pageant.

After that, my new friends became Martha Salas, Miss Departamento Vargas, and Mariela Salma, Miss Anzoátegui. Through the rest of the pageant, more of us became really good friends and still are today.

During the last week of the pageant, we were all at the Macuto Sheraton Hotel in La Guaira, the coastal town that is a half hour from Caracas, where we rehearsed every day to be part of *Buenos días, Venezuela*. We had to be up by 6:00 in the morning or earlier, and our days lasted until midnight or later. The upper floor of the hotel was reserved for all of us, and Osmel had the presidential suite, where we spent every night playing games and socializing. Friendships grew among us, along with some unfriendly encounters. We played tricks on each other, but had fun however tired and busy we were.

One night in the presidential suite playing games, I was seated on the floor while Miss Falcón stood in front of me. Suddenly, she looked behind herself and saw me seated there, forcefully stepping on my foot.

"Ouch!!!" I was in pain.

My toes had already turned purple. The doctor was called and said that the toe was broken.

"What? What am I am going to do?" I asked the doctor.

"Wear flats," he said.

"But I have the pageant!" I wailed.

"Hopefully you will be better by then."

Indeed, I wore flats and limped badly for a few days until it came time for the press presentation, which was two days before the final night. We rehearsed for both events, which included international artists.

Rocío Durcal from Spain was the main entertainment for the press presentation, which was shorter and had only two clothing changes: a cocktail dress and a swimsuit. It was beautiful. Held at the round pool of the hotel with a runway in the middle of the pool, the event featured the current Miss Venezuela and Olympic swimmer Paola Ruggeri in the water with synchronized swimmers.

It was not my best day. The press commented that I looked harsh. Of course, I did. I had blood in my hair! I had cut my head open before the event and it was exploding in pain.

At the hotel we have no place to get our makeup or hair done except in our rooms, and there were two of us per room. Julio César, my makeup and hair artist and dear friend, came to my room to get me ready. He did my makeup first and then my hair, which was long, healthy and beautiful. After undoing the rollers and brushing my hair, he told me to stand up and bend over to brush my hair from underneath all the way down. Then he instructed me to stand up and flip over my hair.

We did this all the time at his salon to make my hair look more beautiful and luxurious. Only this time, we had not noticed I was under a ceiling lamp. When I stood up, I hit the lamp hard.

"Ouch!" I screamed and started to cry.

"No, you cannot cry," he said. "The makeup!"

Julio checked my head, but did not say anything. As the saying goes: "The show must go on!" I touched my head and felt a wound. When I pulled back my hand, I saw blood and started to scream: "It is blood. Blood!"

My mother was there. She was mute as they sat me down and brought medicine for the headache. I sat there trying to calm down before I had to join the show. My mother went to her room to get ready, and I would not see her again until later.

When we were assembled in the positions that were assigned to us in the line, my father came with water and more pills for the pain. My mother told him what had happened, and he was so worried.

"*Estoy mejor, Papi. Gracias por las pastillas.* (I am better. Thanks for the pills)."

My head was still exploding, pounding with the pain. But the show must go on! My face was showing the stress I was under from the head injury and from wearing high heels with a broken toe. And of course, the press wrote that I should not be a favorite since I looked horrible that day. The press was so mean. Did they know what had happened to me? I wondered because they managed to know everything. My head was cut open and I was doing my best not to limp. It was not right that the press talked about me without ever mentioning what happened. The truth was not told. I wanted to quit again, and I did.

I went to my parents, who said they would support me in anything I decided to do. So, I packed and went with them to

Osmel and told him that I could not take it anymore. That I was going home.

He calmly talked to us: "Carmen, the press, whether they know the truth or not, are going to write whatever they want. Are you going to let them control your life?"

Wise words! Advice that has been very important during my life. So, I stayed.

The night of the pageant was brutal. We were all in our own worlds, worried about our individual makeup, hair and dresses. Oh! The dress. That was the best part because the dress expressed our taste, personality and elegance. My mother and sister were in charge of the dress. It came from Caracas to the hotel. Julio César was in charge of me. He directed my mother to keep the dress in their room until he sent someone for it. At that time, there were no cellular phones or beepers.

My father waited until he said: "That is it. I am going down. I am not going to miss my daughter's competition."

This man, my father, the one who did not want me to compete, now was competing more than me. And did not want to miss a second of it. That is a true father. As a true Latino, he used to get nervous while I was in the rehearsals because I was skinny with skinny legs, which my father did not consider beautiful. He wanted me to be fuller. So, while watching the rehearsals he was exasperated and used to tell my mother that I was not going to win with those skinny legs.

She would tell him: "Johnny, I think it would be better for you to get out of the theater. She is perfect for this. In the world of fashion and beauty, skinny is in. This is not the '50s or '60s."

Finally, Julio César sent someone to pick up the dress because it had to be back stage before they closed the doors. So, his idea to bring the dress down at the last minute was not going to work.

"But who is going to take care of it?" Mother asked. "Julio César is worried that something will happen to it."

"I will be watching it," Julio César's assistant said.

That way my mother and sister were able to watch the whole thing, though they got down to the theater late. The doors were closed when they got there and could not get in. Finally, someone saw them and said: "Let them in. They are Miss Zulia's family."

Then they waited for another hour because "customs" for the dancers were delayed in traffic due to an accident on the freeway from Caracas to La Guaira.

The pageant finally started. It was a major production that required 300 people and animals on the stage as "The Circus." It was so difficult to direct everything that the pageant producer, Joaquín Riviera, dressed as a clown to coordinate from the floor. Pilín León, Miss World 1981, rode an elephant. And we girls were separated into the different groups making up a circus. I was in the gypsy group.

However long the pageant was, it felt like a dream. It came and went so fast. And finally, I had a crown on my head. I had won!

CHAPTER 10

Overcoming My Fears

WALKING OUT AFTER dropping my son at Sunday school on a beautiful morning in December, I had nothing to do. It was December 8, 2013 to be exact, and Juan Diego was preparing for his first communion next May. I could not even go to the gym because Alejandro had stopped paying for the membership so I could not use it. Neither could the children. Tennis lessons for Juan Diego were over!

Working out had been my way of life. I did spinning, yoga, weights, tennis, snow skiing, everything I could to stay active. Plus, working out made me feel good. I had never smoked a cigarette and only drank socially. I knew that abusing alcohol aged you and deformed the face with bags under and on top of the eyes, just to mention a few side effects. Eating right not only helped keep my figure but also was a way to stay healthy. But now I was going to find out in seconds that I had been accused of alcoholism, drug addiction and, yes, of being crazy.

I got in the car and checked my phone because I got a Facebook Messenger notification from a reporter at *El Diario de Caracas*, who was asking my opinion on information that had gone viral. He attached it.

It read: "Do you want to comment on what is going around Facebook?" It was an article from a small newspaper in Colorado talking about the plane incident and the DUI. The article was completely wrong, exaggerating everything. The story was based on Alejandro's information. No one had ever called me or my lawyers to get our opinions. Plus, this was old news. The plane story was from June, and the Colorado incident was from two years ago. It was obvious Alejandro was behind this. At one point, the story attributed a quote to "Alejandro said" and "a source close to the plane incident" in another part.

This was a small free newspaper. It was the beginning of December, and the town was dead. Not even the people from Venezuela who vacation in Vail would arrive until around after December 15. Who knew this was coming out and put it on Facebook so the Venezuelan people would spread the story? In time, I learned that Alejandro's half and only sister was behind all of this. It turned out to be an orchestrated effort, because Alejandro was in Colorado the week before, during the Thanksgiving break. Funny, they always had a rocky relationship. I was the one trying to keep the family together for my children's sake. Alejandro had always refused to talk to her when I was on the phone with her.

My heart dropped. I could not believe the way this story was told. I was formally accused of "intimidating a flight attendant," but the article accused me of "assaulting the flight attendant." All of it was based on false accusations. At the end it said: "They both filed for divorce."

I do not know how Alejandro pretended not to know that I had filed for divorce not once but twice. How could he have gone this far? He was embarrassing our children.

After the Colorado incident he always said: "If this leaked to the press, Carmen, what would you do?"

"I would have to tell the truth," I used to answer.

"Really? And who would believe you? Nobody has believed you so far."

It was his way of keeping me under his thumb. He knew I had done nothing, and the possibility that this injustice could leak was the worst that could happen to me. I was regarded in Venezuela for what I always had been: a level-headed, hard-working and intelligent student, daughter, mother, and sister! I was loved in Venezuela for that and was an example to be followed. Now this.

That was one of the reasons I could not talk about the situation. I was trapped. How could I get out of this? How? My children would be publicly embarrassed. My innocent kids. I had become his prisoner.

Once I was able to get him out of the house by court order and the divorce started, I started gaining strength. But almost two months after the federal accusation came in, I lost all the progress I had made. I was weak again.

In the meantime, Alejandro was on a spiral with drugs and prostitutes. When I went to court to get my daughter back, everything became public on November 20, 2013. At least it became public record for anyone that wanted to research Harris County court records. Everything was revealed: the drugs, prostitutes, car crashes, everything. What happened to me was not exposed by the press, and it was already old news.

But Alejandro would not forgive me for exposing him in court.

The girls were sleeping at home. As soon as they woke up, they would see the story in Facebook. I do not know how I managed to drive home. I was shaking, crying, destroyed. God, what have I done to deserve this? Why does Alejandro want to hurt me so much? Why does he want to hurt his children? I thanked God that Juan Diego did not have a Facebook account.

When I got home, the girls were still sleeping. I called my lawyers to tell them what had happened, emailing everything to them and informing them it was all over Facebook. I was trending.

They said: "Carmen, you cannot say anything. Everything you say would be used against you. This is Alejandro's way to compromise you since he has not been able to get you on the stand to testify under oath about this before the trial. Even if what you said was used in Venezuela, Alejandro would make sure it got to the prosecution."

Everybody wanted to reach me and get my opinion, but I followed my lawyers' advice and instructed them to contact my legal team. Of course, they never did! I do not think they speak English.

The negligence of the media in Venezuela was apparent by the next day. The false story was repeated and got bigger and worse as it went like a snowball effect. It all started with *El Diario de Caracas*. And just like that, in a split second, I went from being a beloved Miss Venezuela remembered for my charity work, for being a good daughter, wife and mother, and a competent professional with all the accomplishments I had achieved to this new person Alejandro had created. My identity was stolen!

The girls finally got up. Thank God they did not open Facebook right away. They came down to have breakfast and saw me crying.

"*Mami*, what is going on?"

When I started explaining, they went to the story on Facebook and both started to cry. They could not believe how this read.

"*Mami*, we know the truth and this is not it," Kamee said.

"I know, Baby, but this is what people are going to believe for now on."

They both cried with pain and anger. It had been too much for both of them. Their family was gone, we were having money problems, they faced losing their mom, the only responsible adult they have had, and now the embarrassment. They were very positive that I was going to be able to fight and win because they knew it was a lie.

Alexandra said: "*Mami,* you can turn this around. And I know you will."

"Only if I win, Baby. If not, no one will ever know the truth."

We all cried together.

The following week proved to be a nightmare. All of their friends, English and Spanish, were talking about the story. They were embarrassed all the time. Ultimately, someone sent a mass email to all parents and school personnel. I never understood why. Why would they want to hurt my children so badly? I did not go to school. It was the three of them. They were the ones facing this embarrassment.

My mother was back in Orlando when this happened, thank God, because I do not think she could bear anymore. She deteriorated a lot while she was with me, knowing everything. Seeing me suffering so much was devastating for her.

I had never spent such a lonely December. Christmas for me is a time of luncheons, get-togethers and parties. But nobody invited me to any.

It is also the time of my birthday and getting everything ready for the children from Santa. But that year, I had nobody to invite to my birthday and did not have enough money to buy them Christmas presents. I decided to drive to our apartment in Miami for Christmas and New Year's. By court order, I had the children for Christmas, while Alejandro had them for New Year's. They planned to fly from Miami to Houston to Colorado. And I was staying in Miami with friends and family for the new year.

Alejandro kept asking the girls where we were going for the holidays, so he knew we were driving to Miami. On December 19, my birthday, I had packed my car and the children to leave, but something was wrong with one of my tires. I unpacked the car and went to the dealer to have it checked. It turned out to be a defect covered by the warranty from Mercedes Benz and the car had to stay in the shop.

I had planned to spend my birthday on the road to avoid such a lonely day. Nobody called, except my family and friends from Venezuela, Miami and other places. Of all my Houston friends, not one cared about the children or me.

In case Alejandro managed to enter the house while we were gone, I took the most important art pieces to Marisol's house. Marisol had become my new best friend. Who would have thought that someone I just met was going to become my most reliable friend? She had moved from Spain three years before and had come to my birthday party last year, which was the last big party in my house. There she saw my house full of friends, all of them wanting to be recognized as my best friend. Looking back, I realized how shallow it all was.

When Marisol saw me with the art, she wished me happy birthday. Not knowing I was leaving on the day of my birthday, she imagined that I was going to be with great company with as many friends as I had. It was not until months later that she realized I was all alone, except for my children, and I had started driving that day.

"How could they?" she asked. "They were your friends. They all were catering to you on your last birthday."

I could not answer that. There was no answer for it.

Alejandro called the girls to ask if we had gone already. They told him what was going on and that probably we were not going to go. It all depended on how long the dealer needed to keep the car. He offered to buy airplane tickets for all of us to leave that day.

When Alexandra came running to tell me, I was suspicious. This man that is trying to take away everything I have and make sure I do not have a penny or a nice vacation or a nice anything, suddenly wants to buy plane tickets for the four of us today, a

Friday during the high season at Christmas, to go to Miami, a vacation destination.

He wants me out! He always tried to break into the house every time I left. Why would this time be any different? His desperation to get us out confirmed my suspicion.

Luckily, the dealer called to tell me my car would be ready late that afternoon.

I arranged to have the house guarded around the clock while I was gone. Later that evening we started our journey to Miami, stopping in Louisiana one night and at my sister's in Orlando for two days. The children were happy for the first time in a while. We sang and played games on the road. I was happy even though I was weighing less than 110 pounds.

In Orlando, I took Juan Diego, Kamee and my niece to the parks. Juan Diego was so happy. It was like his first time; he was too little when we went before. Alexandra stayed at my sister's because she was sick.

On Monday, December 23, we continued on to Miami. I drove until suddenly feeling sick, and Alexandra took over. When we arrived at our apartment late, I went straight to bed and passed out. Simón, my friend from Venezuela who lives in Miami, had been checking on us through the whole trip. He kept texting and my girls answered, telling him I was sleeping. He told them that if we needed anything, they could call him.

By the next morning, I was not responsive, so they called Simón and my girlfriends Adriana and Zoraida. Simón brought antibiotics. By the time my friends arrived, I could hardly talk. The air conditioning was broken and the apartment was hot.

"No, no, no!" they said. "He is not going to destroy you. You have to get up."

I could not. Finally, all the stress of those months had hit me.

They opened the curtains and windows. They called to have the AC fixed. I was so sick that my poor children had to spend

Christmas locked in the apartment. Here I was trying to give them a normal life! And I was so down I could do nothing for them.

They left on December 28 for Colorado, and my brother David came to stay with me. It was as if I was little again. On January 2, the girls called to tell me that Alejandro had broken his hip skiing and a former employee of Alejandro's had interesting information to share with me.

Back in Houston, with the start of the new year, I hoped that the ugly story would be forgotten, but that was not the case. The trial was supposed to be at the end of January. Alejandro managed to get the story in the *Houston Chronicle* before then. Little did he know that the trial would be postponed every three months for over two years. At this point, everybody in Houston knew about it. Some people called me enraged with Alejandro. Many found out about the divorce and what was happening now through the newspaper story. Some, knowing Alejandro, could tell right away what was true, but others believed it. In any case, they opted to stay away from me. Then the story aired on the television newscasts.

Once again, my lawyers were dead serious about me not saying a word. But my lawyer was interviewed, and he said that I was the "victim of years of abuse in the hands of a serial abuser." Then his lawyer wanted equal time, insisting the day after that what my lawyers said was a lie. It became a "she said, he said."

I started exercising in the house gym. It was not the best but at least I could do the Stair Master and the machine with weights. Little by little I started to build up my strength. I have suffered from asthma since I was nine years old. Even though with time I had overcome exercise limitations, it was still hard for me to finish a 45-minutes class, but I did it.

However, I was never able to run. Running was something I always wished I could do, to be able to just put on running shoes and enjoy the outdoors. I was envious to see people running in the park whenever I drove by, especially when the days were beautiful.

I kept thinking about how I was once. How I was fearless and overcame many obstacles in my life. How I had graduated with *magna cum laude* honors, overcoming my dyslexia. I wanted to be that person again. I had lost her. Where was she? I asked myself so many times.

I was living due to the generosity of many people. I had always taken care of myself and did not want to allow myself to deteriorate. With the help of friends that owned spas, I was able to care for myself. Marynés and Mirta from Purely You Spa took care of my face, while Escarle from Alira Spa cared for my hair color. One day at the spa, I met her trainer Carolina. Both Carolina and Escarle are runners. We started talking and I told them all my excuses for not being able to run.

"I have tried, but get this feeling of sudden death," I said. "This is how people must feel when they are going to die."

Carolina and Escarle laughed.

"Really!" I insisted. "We were not meant to run. Only four-legged animals are made to run."

Yes, I was getting my sense of humor back. I was making fun of it and saying it in the funniest way, but the truth is that was how I felt.

Whenever I tried to run, after a few minutes I felt like I was going to die. It was definitely the asthma, but mostly it was fear. Fear that running was not compatible with my condition and that I could die of an asthma attack. It paralyzed me. Yes! Fear paralyzes you. And it felt like sudden death.

So, I made excuses: "Man is not made to run. We are two-legged animals."

Carolina told me to try little by little: "Carmen, run two minutes and then walk two minutes, and from there build up."

I took her advice, feeling if I could overcome this, it would prove I could overcome the rest. It was a way to rebuild myself. I decided it was time to overcome all of my fears.

Little by little I started running until I built up to a one-mile run. I felt like Rocky that day. If I had been near stairs, I would have gone to the top and screamed like him.

My goal was to be able to make it around Memorial Park, my dream place to run. I built up to it: around my house to a mile and a half, two miles, two and a half, and then to the park for three miles. I did it! Running gave me a new life. It was the best way to get all the stress out. Running at the end of the day saved me after facing whatever the day served me, whether it was in family court or federal court.

Next stop? Overcoming the fear of skiing alone.

I set my mind to it. As good a skier as I am, I had never skied by myself. It was a sport that Alejandro and I shared, so I always went with him or the children, or friends many times. But I was never put in a position where the option was to ski alone. And if I was, I just did not ski.

I thought I was not going to ski for a long while unless I went with my children. In February, I went with all three of the kids to ski in Colorado. I was not alone at all, either being with them or with friends. A lot of people from their school ski were there in February. It has been a tradition for years, and it was the last year for my senior daughter's group to ski together. I had accomplished skiing without Alejandro and now I needed to be able to do it alone.

In April, almost a year after I filed for divorce, I went to Colorado to close the ski season. For the first time, I ventured to ski by myself. As usual, I skied from the house to the first lift, then got on the chair and went up the mountain. Alone! All by myself! It was cold, not as cold as usual because it was spring, but it felt cold because I was scared.

All the way up I wondered what I would do if I could not come down. I checked my phone to make sure I had the number for the ski patrol just in case. Getting off the first chair, I went on to the next, where the easy green runs are. It was getting colder. I checked my boots, making sure they were tight enough, and skied a short way to the start of the easiest run. I stood there and looked at the terrain. It was beautiful. The day was sunny and the sky was blue. I took a deep breath and started down. I skied with ease.

When I finished that run, I felt accomplished. Yes! I did it! But it was a green. I kept on going to the next run, a blue, a little more difficult. As I did before, I stood up and took a big breath. And on I went!

I could feel the snow under my skis and hear the sound on it as I carved. The feeling was even better than before.

Yes!!! Yes!!! I finished my second, more difficult run all by myself.

The final step was the last stretch on a black. This is the most difficult run. I started shaking but took another deep breath and on I went. As the run was more difficult, I was a little tight, but decided to relax and went on. After that, my turns got better, and I was carving better and better at every turn. I cried when I finished. I was afraid no more!

Another accomplishment. I was getting my fearless self back.

CHAPTER 11

The Brother Cover-up

I AM WEARING BLUE jean overalls, so very pregnant. And so very happy to be having my first baby. A girl!

It is a Sunday of March 1996, and I am decorating my daughter's room. Today I need to pick up a rocking chair that I bought and had it stained with the same color wood I am using for her bedroom.

Alejandro has a Jeep Cherokee with space in the back. I am waiting for him to come home from the hospital, hoping he comes with me to pick it up since I am pregnant and should not carry that chair.

But when he got home, he said he was too tired and wanted to watch TV.

I leave disappointed. Not even pregnant could I be 100% woman. I am not used to doing it all. But ever since I got married, I have had to.

Growing up my father had what was called the Boys Department. In our house, some things were left for the boys to do, because we were women and should be taken care of. But none of that has worked in my married life. I have had to do it all.

I was trying to get the rocking chair inside the SUV by myself but there was not enough space. The man helping me at the store suggested folding down the seats in the second row to make more space. First, though, I had to lift the bottom part of the seat. When I did that, I saw a brown bag.

When I looked inside the bag, my world turned upside down. Two boxes of condoms! I almost fainted! The man brought me water. I had to use my inhaler because I could not breathe.

I confronted Alejandro when I got back home. He acted calm, like it was the most natural thing, not nervous or surprised. He said they belonged to his younger brother, who was single at the time.

"So why did he put them under the seat? The seat of your car?" I asked.

"Carmen, he left the bag in the car. I knew this was going to happen if you saw it, so, I put it under the seat."

Alejandro called his brother to convince me that the condoms were his.

"Here, Carmen, he wants to talk to you."

"I don't want to talk to him."

"Carmen, take the phone. Look at you! You are pregnant. Do you want the baby to receive this stress?"

As usual, he was trying to make me feel guilty. As a doctor, he was always talking about how stress in pregnancy was bad for the baby. So, I took the phone.

"Carmen, those are mine," his brother said. "I can assure you. I bought them and left them in his car."

I handed back the phone to Alejandro.

After they hung up, Alejandro looked at me.

"Carmen, I love you. You are giving me a baby. Do you ever think I could hurt you like this?"

Little did I know this would turn out to hurt me even worse down the road.

"You know my brother. He is always desperate to get a girl. He was going out that night and bought them when we had a drink first. Then … Murphy's Law happened. He left them in my car. So, I freaked out and put them under the seat. This was a while ago. We both forgot about it."

Less than a month from giving birth, I was feeling so bad. But I was having a worse time believing this. I went to my bedroom to watch television leaving him alone in the family room to watch TV by himself.

His brother came over later that day, going on and on about the whole story. Now I know Alejandro called him and told him to come convince me of the story.

CHAPTER 12

Houston, Here We Go

ALEJANDRO MET ME almost at the peak of my popularity in Venezuela, when he was a medical student. Already named Miss Venezuela, I was working on Venevisión's *Buenos días, Venezuela* show. I understood it was difficult to be with me with the attention I attracted, especially when I started the morning program *Complicidades*. It supplanted *Buenos días, Venezuela* with a 100% feminine format: a Miss Venezuela, former Miss Venezuela candidate Maite Delgado, and renowned journalist Eva Gutiérrez.

The success I had with Miss Venezuela paled in comparison to the smash hit that *Complicidades* became. Eva, Maite and I became the most important women on television in Venezuela. We set a precedent still remembered in Venezuela today and introduced a format that was copied in the United States in the 1990s by Barbara Walters with *The View*. Definitely, putting several women on a variety program is still the best combination.

Complicidades had the most favorable ratings in the mornings in Venezuela, and we dictated all the fashion guidelines, makeup, hair, everything! Going out on the street at the time was quite an adventure. People looked and others asked for autographs. We did not pay at restaurants. We had a total celebrity status!

Alejandro joked that by marrying me he would be known as Mr. Montiel, not by his last name. I always thought he was comfortable with this situation and admired him because of it. To me, he showed great maturity and self-assurance. But actually, he was carrying out his plan as an abuser by choosing someone who he not only admired but also wanted to be like, and then destroy me.

When we got married, we both went on to live a life of incognito as students in two towns in the United States: Winston Salem, North Carolina, and Johnson City, Tennessee.

It was kind of a break for me. Although I have always been grateful for the popularity that Miss Venezuela and Venezuelan television gave me, it was nice to go out on the streets where nobody knew me. I was able to spend all the time in the world on studying and exercising since Alejandro was so busy with his training in internal medicine.

I was happier in Johnson City, Tennessee, where I devoted myself to studying and being a university town girl. People there were more used to foreigners, which was not the case in Winston Salem. Therefore, life was more pleasant and I felt more productive.

We went to Tennessee because Alejandro got kicked out of the internship program in North Carolina. Why? Actually, I never knew why. It took me years to find out the truth like so much about Alejandro. He said he was leaving because it was better for me.

I had studied Arts at the Central University of Venezuela and was studying Journalism after the Miss Venezuela pageant. When I left for the United States, I spent my first year studying English so I could get into college, and when we left for Tennessee, I started college there to continue my Journalism studies.

However, the university accepted very few of my credits and I thought I would never graduate. I only planned to be there for two years, then we would return to Venezuela. Every time you transfer, you lose credits, so it would be impossible. I went to the language lab to improve my English and the person in charge was Olga, a lovely Cuban lady. I spent the days without seeing Alejandro. Wherever I went no one spoke Spanish, so I stayed talking to Olga for hours. My mind needed the rest of speaking in my own language.

One day I told her my frustration that the credits for all the subjects I had studied in Venezuela to become a journalist—writing, literature, language—were of no use to me in Tennessee for the same career.

She suggested I should talk to her husband, who was the president of the Spanish department at the university.

"¡Niña, él te va a dar la solución! (Girl, he will give you the solution)."

So, I did. I went straight to his office and asked for him. His secretary told me he was in class but could see me when he got back.

I decided to sit outside while I was studying. Time flew by. When I walked into his office, a tall, blond guy was standing there speaking to the secretary in English.

I waited for them to finish. Suddenly, he turns to me and asked in English:

"How may I help you?"

Thinking he was an American teacher, I told him the lady knew what I was coming for.

"She's the student who wants to see you," she said in English.

He had the greenest eyes I had ever seen. I never would have imagined this was Rafael Aguirre! Seeing him, I remembered Joaquín Riviera, white and blond with a nice Cuban accent. I transported myself to the *parrandas* in the halls of Venevisión dancing salsa.

"Good afternoon!" he said with that Cuban accent I had missed so much.

"Ah, good afternoon. My name is Carmen María Montiel."

And I started speaking Spanish:

"¡Mucho gusto!"

Of course, once he started talking, there was no doubt that he was Cuban; he sounded just like Joaquín Riviera. I felt as if I was back in the halls of Venevisión, where the Cuban accent was the rule to which I had become so accustomed.

After I explained to him what I had studied in Venezuela, how the important credits in Spanish Journalism did not transfer here, and that I had to graduate in two years, he told me he had the solution.

"Do a double major in Journalism and Spanish," he suggested. "That way, I can accept all the credits that have to do with Spanish. It's more credits, but it doesn't matter because with the credits they're going to accept from you, you still end up finishing faster."

Assuring me it could be done, he said descriptions of every subject I had taken in Venezuela, no matter what department it was from, had to be translated and certified by the Spanish Department so the university would accept the credits. I felt like I had gotten an angel.

"The best thing is for you to do the translation of each subject and I will certify it," he told me. "Here is the Spanish program with all the subjects we offer, so you compare them with yours. Find the full program of the university and do the same thing with the other subjects."

Then we started talking about a thousand other things. How nice it was to be able to speak Spanish with someone else.

I went to work, not only translating the Spanish subjects, but also journalism and art courses that could be considered by the university. The easiest part was the Spanish Department. But the other stuff was a job because I had to do more than just translate the program. I had to review Department by Department and make appointments with the dean to deliver the translations certified by the Spanish Department. The dean then had to consider it.

After a few weeks, I started getting answers. When it was all over, it was official that I would double major in Spanish-language Television Journalism and take three more courses per semester, graduating just as we had to leave Tennessee. However, in order to take the extra credits, I had to keep a high average. Although English was not my native language and I had just learned it, I managed to get the best grades, thus obtaining the approval of the dean of the university to take the extra credits. In this way I succeeded, thanks to Professor Aguirre, in counting years of study that I saw lost.

Alejandro told me, "The truth is, Carmen, when you get a Cuban, everything goes great for you."

And it was true! He told me that when he was still applauding or admiring me. The narcissist looks for someone he admires or wants to be like, but often hates for the same reason.

My days passed quietly until the university learned that I had been Miss Venezuela. I had a Venezuelan colleague in French who told the teacher, and then the news spread. The university contacted me for an interview in its newspaper, and then I was interviewed by the local newspapers. University pamphlets featured me as one of the "Personalities who have attended this School." My days of anonymity were over. Alejandro told me that everyone at the hospital said they had read my article in the Johnson City newspaper. Once again, I had become a celebrity in my college town.

I graduated and Alejandro finished internal medicine. Instead of returning to Venezuela, we went to Houston, where he started a fellowship in Pulmonology and I took advantage of working to gain experience in the United States before returning to Venezuela.

Graduating with honors from college gave me an advantage: Alejandro had a better way to sell me to his father, who always blamed me for being a beauty queen and working in television. Everyone was impressed with my ability and intelligence, especially since I was able to graduate with honors in a second language. Alejandro's family now left me alone. No more insults and derogatory comments. I showed his father that I was not just a beauty queen.

Alejandro had applied to several programs for his specialty. His two priorities were Iowa and Houston, Texas, where I wanted to go because my family and Spanish-language television stations were there.

On the day of the match's result, Alejandro asked me to call about the results. I was afraid we would end up in Iowa, his first choice. Nine months of cold weather was too much for me to bear coming from the Caribbean. I prayed for it to be Houston, his second choice.

When I called, a warm and pleasant voice told me the result was Houston. I screamed so loud that the man said he could see I was happy.

Alejandro always supported me in my dreams and I loved him even more for it. He wanted me to go wherever I wanted in my career. He wanted me to achieve all my dreams. We became so well connected that we were able to know what the other one was thinking. We could laugh at ourselves. We were great dancers and were admired every time we danced. It was our specialty!

During that time, we bought our first house. It was a new house, and we got to choose everything, from the plans to the floors, bathrooms, paint color, accessories, all of it. I had always wanted to have a house that I somehow designed and this was the closest thing to it, but I thought that was going to happen when we got back to Venezuela.

Alejandro had said: "It is your dream house. Build it as you wish it to be."

Of course, when he moved in, he proclaimed that he had officially moved into Barbie's house. It was all in pink tones. But back then, he was special and in love with me. He wanted me to be happy and have all my dreams. He had faith in what I had accomplished, telling me that I was going to write my own ticket when we got back to Venezuela. I did not know he was already cheating.

In Houston, he was always present, joining me when I was having parties or went out with my co-workers. He was very different from the person he was in Tennessee.

We were in sync the whole time. We were a fun and fun-loving couple. He was never affectionate, but he was like that. People thought we were the perfect couple, so it was a shock to everyone when they found out what was going on in my house.

When he was preparing to finish his specialization, he announced that we would not be returning to Venezuela. The problems with his father never stopped, so he was afraid that entering into a working relationship with him was an uncertain situation. And working for someone else in Venezuela was not possible; his father would never forgive him.

"Carmen, we're going to stay for two years, save money, and then I'll have the financial authority to negotiate with my father. Everything is money for him."

"Alejandro, the J-1 is not a two-year visa. You know we have to go back or to a low-income area for two years. We can only save if you're in private practice and that will take more than two years."

"I'll find a way," he said. "You'll see. I'll be able to do both."

And so we stayed in Houston. I was not happy. I wanted to go back to Venezuela and work there. I was postponing having babies because I wanted to be in Venezuela when I had them, with the support system of my mother, sisters, brothers and family. Also, help was so easy to get in my country.

Time was passing and my biological clock was ticking. I was already 30 and could not wait any longer. So, the decision was made and we got pregnant with my first baby around the time of the trial for OJ Simpson. I was so sick for the first few months that I did not leave the house and saw the whole trial in bed. That was when I learned how trials are acts of theatre. The whole scene of "if the glove does not fit" was staged like a Broadway show.

I wondered to myself why he was not testifying. The faces of the lawyers, their calculated movements, the tones of their voices were incredible. It was the best TV show of the time. Later in the evening, parts would be reproduced with comments on the news. Little did I know that what I saw and learned at that time was going to be part of my life later.

Once we stayed in Houston, we started the process of changing our visas, until we finally got the residency. Every step had a lot of paperwork. But the worst thing was the residency. We had to have lots of documents, including birth certificates with new stamps and dates. I called my cousin, Constanza, who was working at the time for the Communications Secretary in Venezuela. It was easier for her to get birth certificates with all the requirements. Alejandro's brother was also going through the same process. So, I ordered three birth certificates.

Finally, when my cousin had everything, she called us.

"Carmen, they're ready. I'll send them via FedEx."

"Great! You're the best."

"By the way, poor Alejandro, they did not love him," she said laughing.

In my family, we joke all the time. I understood that she was joking and asked her why.

"He wasn't registered until he was almost two."

In Venezuela, the baby's father has to register the newborn in court with witnesses who can testify that the baby is legitimate.

Mario asked me to fill out his papers. When I finally got the documents, I started with ours and checked the birth certificates.

Alejandro and Mario were registered the same day. In that case, I figured the only thing that had changed was their names and birth dates. However, I decided to read Mario's birth certificate to make sure everything was okay. That is when I noticed there were many inconsistencies. His mother's day of birth and age were different, along with many other things.

I thought for a while about what to do, finally deciding I had to fill out every application according to the legal documents and expect the same agent not to review our application.

When Alejandro came home that day, I informed him that everything was ready.

"Alejandro, how strange that both you and Mario were registered in court on the same day with the same witnesses and there's so much difference between the two birth certificates," I told him.

"Like what, Carmen?"

"Like your mother's birthday and other stuff."

At that moment, his face became very serious, then he began to speak. He said his mother and father never married and that, in fact, his father was still married to his first wife when his father registered them. What his father had done was illegal, and that is probably why in the rush of the moment all the mistakes were made.

I quietly looked at him and felt his pain. He was embarrassed by what he was telling me. I said to myself, this is not your fault. I even thought that would never have influenced me if I was going to fall in love with him. I hugged him. And told him that.

But the next day, while we were talking about other things, I said: "Alejandro! Like I told you, your birth is not your fault, but the lie is. I'm not comfortable with the fact that you've been lying to me for so long, and if you can lie to me about something like this, I wonder, what else can you lie about? I have a problem with that."

My life returned to the unknown when I dedicated myself to having children, raising them and working for Alejandro. Having each of my children was my most precious achievement. I wanted to be a mom and have time to dedicate myself to my kids, to be a full-time mom. Yet I was so used to working that continuing to work with Alejandro in his practice made me feel alive.

In 2001, a doctor who worked for him became a partner and either his wife worked in the office or I got out. I decided to leave because I was tired of Alejandro playing the good cop and the bad cop in the office to control employees. He put me in the bad cop role, and I did not like it, so I saw this as an opportunity to end a situation that seemed toxic to me, besides not being who I am.

Now I had extra time on my hands. The girls were in school and I decided to dedicate myself to what I have always liked to do... help out! I joined several charities, the largest being the creation and organization of the patron's support group for the new Latin American Art Department at the Houston Museum of Fine Arts, "The Maecenas." The important thing was that I managed to raise funds for different organizations, which made me one of the most sought-after women in Houston to make donations and raise money for the benefit of others.

I quickly left anonymity again to become a recognized name in Houston and part of what they call the Houston society. I was photographed at every event. Charities wanted me to be part of the board of directors, president of their galas or any charity event they organized.

With this also came recognition from charities that present awards through their fundraising events. In 2008, it was the list of the 25 Most Beautiful People in Houston. The biggest awards in the city came in 2010 and 2011. Being Latin made them even more significant.

In September 2009, it was announced that I was one of the ten deserving "Woman of Distinction" for 2010. This event, the

Winter Ball, takes place in January and recognizes ten women who have an important curriculum in social work. The only way to get the honor is for a former recipient to nominate you. A board then selects the candidates. Selected in secret, the honor is not easy to get.

I knew I had been nominated because Miriam Sera, who nominated me, asked for my resume and more information about my charities. I gave her everything she needed in May, but I did not think I would be selected. I know many that have not been. So I forgot about it.

It was time to entertain the kids for the summer and when we got back there was always a rush with back-to-school uniforms, books and the routine. And for some reason or another, we struggle to connect again with friends.

What brings us up to date are the organizations we work with. Between school and supervising the construction of the new house, I attended the board meetings of the organizations with which I collaborated, when Alejandro suddenly called me. It was about 10:00 in the morning as I was leaving the construction site on my way to a meeting of the Board of Directors. He rarely called me, unless he needed something.

"Hello, *mi cielo*! (my heaven)... What are you doing?"

I told him I was on my way to a meeting at Unicef.

"What are you doing on September 15th?"

"I don't know. Why?"

"Ah well! I'm not good at this. You became a Woman of Distinction and that day you get the surprise."

The announcement of inclusion in the Women of Distinction did not reach you in a letter or a call, but the Crohn's and Colitis Foundation Committee arrives with the person who nominated you to announce it when you least expect it. They bring you a bouquet of flowers with the letter. Miriam had called Alejandro to coordinate the surprise, and he had ruined it.

"So, invite some friends that day to lunch at Tony's. I'm sure there are many. Give me the phone numbers of the friends you want to invite and I'll take care of it."

Good that he was taking care of it, but the surprise was ruined.

As soon as I got back to my charity activities, I started getting recognized. Alejandro showed he was proud of me. I felt that he was pleased to see I was successful in everything I did, again.

On September 15, I was at Tony's with my friends and Alejandro. Had I not known what was about to happen, I would have suspected because I never had lunch with him. In the middle of the meal, foundation members, the president of the Winter Ball, and Miriam arrived with flowers and the letter designating me a "Woman of Distinction," an honor in the city of Houston. Alejandro looked proud and my friends were happy. We took pictures, along with another candidate who was in the same restaurant with her surprise that day.

From there on, a series of events related to this was held. The official announcement was made with cocktails at Saks Fifth Avenue, lunches and get the dress. The dress is always important for these events and we women!

I have been faithful to Venezuelan designers and like to be introduced as wearing Venezuelan talent. So, I went to New York to order my dress from Ángel Sánchez. The dress he designed for me was later added to his collection. And with this I went to New York to enjoy a little more of the city that fascinates me.

It is important for my children to be part of these events. These are moments of pride and union for the family. I bought the girls their dresses and Juan Diego, who was only five years old, got a tuxedo. We stayed at the Sheraton Hotel, where the event was, and I got dressed there. We all went down; we were beautiful. The perfect family! I looked at them and thanked

God for everything I had in life: my children, a husband who supported me and a job that fulfilled me.

At the presentation I was escorted by the CEO of Saks. When they finished reading my biography and presenting me with the award, my son shouted with his little baby voice, "Mommy!" The whole room broke into laughter.

The house was ready, and we moved in October. It was a crazy year. In August, we moved the office to the new building. I started to notice that Alejandro was drifting away. But we had so much to do that I thought it was more of the same.

When we moved in, we did not have gas in the house. I found out about it the day of the move, so there was no way to cancel it. Without gas, we could not cook and there was no hot water. The club was close to the house and became everyone's bathroom. To cook, the maids went daily to the old house.

I was very busy moving around, unpacking and taking everyone to the club for a bath at the end of the day.

One of the office employees leaving for another job had a farewell party at a bar near work. Alejandro told me to go, but it was impossible for all I had going on. He left work and went with his employees. Years later, I learned that Alejandro ended up kissing one of the employees in front of everyone else in a jealous rage, because she said he was not the most attractive man in the office. All this happened while I was in the house organizing the moving mess.

Every December before Christmas Eve, we went to Beaver Creek to spend Christmas and New Year's. Estela, my nanny for 18 years, was already gone, so I did not have the help I always had, especially with my son. We were getting ready to end the year 2010 with a new house and new office. I was finishing a year of success, still busy. I felt that I had accomplished enough, because we had risen from the Stanford disaster.

We had gotten to Colorado, picked up our suitcases, and are now riding in the van from Denver to Beaver Creek when my phone rings.

"Hello! I am looking for Carmen María."

"Yes, this is she."

"This is Cindy, from the *Houston Chronicle*. We've tracked you down because you're one of our selected 'Best Dressed' for next year."

"Really?"

"We just need to know if you're available for certain dates next year, which are important to this event. Give me your email to send you everything."

Alejandro listened to my part of the conversation and saw that I was excited. I signaled him that all was good. He smiled.

When I ended the conversation, I told him what it was about. I explained to him that, along with "Woman of Distinction," these are the two best honors in Houston.

He no longer looked as happy for me as before. It got my attention because he generally was happy about my accomplishments. But we were on our way to Beaver Creek, distracted by bags, kids, snow and the holidays.

Upon returning to Houston, I joined the Best Dressed events: announcements, lunches and the final event, a luncheon in this case, not a gala. Once more, I trusted my elegance to Ángel Sánchez.

"Alejandro, the Best Dressed luncheon is March 30, which falls on Thursday, so it would be easy for you to cancel your office appointments. It is your easy day!"

"Carmen, canceling is always a problem. I'm really not happy about this."

"But I told you from the beginning what the important days were. You're always proud of these events."

"I'm very busy," he said and went.

That day, I dressed my children as princesses and a little prince. I had a hairdresser at home to get the hair of the three women ready.

We were all up getting ready, but Alejandro would not get up. Finally, when I saw the time, I went to wake him up. He was mad.

"Alejandro, you knew we had this and you didn't go to work. Your day was canceled. I talked to Becky to make sure everything was covered."

He was angry for the rest of the morning. We were finished getting ready, and I decided to ignore the situation. He is not a morning person, so I thought he would get over it.

Since I had to be at the venue earlier for pictures, I went on and Alejandro stayed with the kids to go a little later. Good thing I took the car.

After the photos, the guests started arriving and I went out to look for the children and Alejandro. They were already there. I had checked the table where we were sitting and told them where we were. Alejandro was gone. I was uncomfortable since it seemed he did not want to be there. For the first time, I felt he was uncomfortable with my success. For years, I had been anonymous, but not anymore.

The time came for the fashion show. We were accompanied by a gentleman who helped us stand around by the runaway. As we paraded, they read our biography and pointed out all our professional and philanthropic achievements. I could see my kids smiling and clapping, while Alejandro was on the phone distracted. For a minute, he looked up and applauded.

After the show, I sat at the table with Alejandro, the kids and some friends I had invited. Alejandro was angry to the point where I felt sorry for my friends. Once again, I was trying to cover up his actions with my friends. Of course, everyone was taking pictures at the table and you could clearly see from Alejandro's face that he did not want to participate.

There were events after lunch during the whole day. We all went with our husbands. I had already arranged with my friends to take my children back home.

I was telling someone at the table that we were going to a cocktail party at Neiman Marcus, when Alejandro announced he had to leave.

"Why? You know we are engaged for the rest of the afternoon."

"I have to go back to the office."

"Alejandro! The office has been canceled. I talked with Becky."

"There's something I couldn't move. I have to go."

And he got up and left. Not without first asking if there was an ATM. I had seen money on the nightstand. So, why did he need more money? But I was in the mood to avoid arguments and had not asked.

I stayed at the table finishing the event. Then Micheline took my children to the house. It's a good thing I brought my car since Alejandro left.

I went to Neiman Marcus's cocktail party alone where they were all with their husbands. In time, I would learn that Alejandro took money for Cara when he left.

CHAPTER 13

The Game Changers

I WAS SEATED WAITING to be called into Bob's office, thanks to a friend's recommendation. His office was not in downtown, unusual for a criminal lawyer. After a short wait, I entered his small office. There was almost no space for the chairs in front of his desk.

Bob was an affable man, what you would call a good old boy, an older man born and raised in Texas who knows everybody.

We had already had a short conversation over the phone, so he knew what judge was presiding over my case. He told me he had had lunch with her the day before. That sounded good to me.

He proceeded to explain that he was almost retired, but would handle the case behind the scenes. The front-runner would be his young associate, Zack Fertitta. Then he called him into the office. More and more I value first impressions, and Zack seemed nice, pleasant and a very sweet young man. He looked like someone I could trust.

I told them my story and everything that had happened in my case, explaining my husband had an assault case pending in Harris County and there was evidence that a judge saw my bruises, along with a video recording of my house that night.

Zack went to search the system for information on the case and did not have a happy face when he came back.

"The case was dismissed over a month ago," he said.

"What? How could that happen? My attorney never told me that."

This confirmed my suspicion that something was going on between my attorney and Alejandro's lawyer.

"Well, it can be reactivated if we take over your case," Zack explained.

According to my case file, the last motion for a continuance was filed by my own lawyer. He lied to me! He had said it was the government who wanted to postpone.

I do not like people who lie. And my own lawyer, the one who had my life in his hands, was lying to me. This meeting was feeling better and better as it went on.

We talked more about the case and Bob gave me a price for their services. OMG! How and where was I going to come up with this much money? But I had to save myself from this lie.

Everybody had homework when we finished our meeting. Zack was to find out more about Alejandro's assault case and my case, while I had a lot of thinking to do. I was worried about making this decision, but it felt right. After all, I had found out about two lies in that meeting.

Still, I needed to be extremely rational about this decision. I called my sister María Eugenia, a lawyer in Venezuela who understands the legal system better than I do. We talked about everything that bothered me about my lawyer and what the possible new ones brought to the table. I asked her to come to Houston and meet with both of them. She had met my current lawyer at the beginning of the year, but had never sat down with him to go over questions in detail.

María Eugenia agreed! She arranged the airplane tickets, and I scheduled both meetings, first with the prospective lawyers and a day after with my current attorney. We planned to ask all the questions we already had, plus the ones that would come up after the meeting with the lawyers I was considering.

When María Eugenia arrived in town, we had a long talk about every aspect and minuscule possibility. We got ready for our first meeting with the prospective lawyers.

Bob greeted us when we arrived, telling me he was taking my sister with him and I was to meet with Zack. I did not like this separation. It made me uncomfortable. My intention from the beginning was that the two of us would meet with them.

Zack was there with another lawyer, who he introduced as Andino Reynal. A tall handsome man, Andino reminded me of a boyfriend I had when I was 17 years old.

He was a former prosecutor that had dedicated himself exclusively to federal cases, and that was why he had been invited to the meeting. I would find out in time that he and Zack were the greatest friends.

Andino explained he had worked for the judge presiding over my case, which I thought would work well for our case.

In fact, Andino would become very disillusioned later on to see a judge he had admired deeply break so many constitutional rules.

His job as clerk for that judge had brought him to Texas in the first place. Over time, he explained how a New Yorker/ Argentinian became a Texan.

After graduating, he applied for jobs with many different federal judges, and the judge presiding over my case hired him right away. It was such an honor that he had to withdraw all his other applications right away. Later, he became a federal prosecutor, until he decided to join the private sector and be a defense attorney.

It was valuable that he knew the court and spent enough time in that building to get good information on my case. He said that the feeling in the building was none of this would have happened if Alejandro had allowed me to lay my head on his shoulder.

While that was true, there was so much more to the story. And it was so incredible that people could not even imagine.

We went over details and things that could be done. First, he investigated his cases thoroughly and hired certain people for that. This was an extra charge, but I agreed it was necessary.

My sister finally joined us. We conducted our conversations in English at all times. Although Andino's name sounded Spanish, many times people raised in the US do not speak Spanish.

When my sister started to talk and ask questions, Andino said in perfect Spanish with an Argentinian accent: "¿Vos sos abogada? (Are you a lawyer?)"

Then we both go at the same time, "You are Argentinian!" He said yes and we started laughing. Apparently, we were both asking that question in our heads.

We felt comfortable enough with these two young lawyers, but I still did not like Bob separating us and neither did she. Over lunch, she told me that he was all about convincing her this had to be done and kind of scared her. She knew what he had charged me for the first meeting, but raised the amount when he met with her. That was a point we both did not like.

We thought it would be wonderful if only we could hire the younger lawyers. My current lawyer was considered to be the second best criminal attorney in town. But these guys were young and eager to make it. We both felt they would fight for me.

The next day, we met with my current lawyer, who had added a female associate to the team probably because the federal prosecutor had. It looked like they were trying to balance the act and not make it look as if it was men against one woman—my feeling exactly since all of this had started. Everyone involved, except me and the judge, was a man, even my husband.

This female associate was trying to convince me I had done something wrong, which I resented, to the point that I told my attorney that he needed to brief her on my case. Otherwise, we were wasting our time, especially since my sister had come all the way from Florida.

We asked about the black box. He said it was coming.

We asked for the plane's log. He said it was coming.

We asked about the employee manual. He said it was coming.

I reminded him that we had been asking for all of those since everything started.

In response, he went on and on about how the process worked and how time consuming it was, assuring us we would have everything in time for trial.

Finally, I asked: "You mentioned an investigator when this all started. I had some reports from him of two interviews he did. Is he still working on the case? Does he have any new discoveries?"

"Yes, he is still on it. As soon as he has more discoveries, I will send those to you."

Once we felt everything had been covered, we left the meeting and once again sat down to go over every little detail. After a long discussion about the meeting and the fact that Bob had raised their fees, we decided I should stay with my current lawyer because it looked like he was doing the work and was taking care of every aspect of the case so far. Still, I was uncomfortable with his lies and the time he had taken. But you can never question a liar or they will fire you.

My sister left and I faced the possibility of going to trial in late March. By then, everything we had requested and some more investigation in the case should be on the table. I was hoping!

CHAPTER 14

I Saw Evil

My war was a spiritual one, as are most wars we face in the world right now.

I saw my husband transform himself into someone I did not know. When he looked at me, it felt as if the Devil was looking at me. I could not recognize his eyes anymore, and his stare scared me. At what time had Evil come into my house? When had he taken over? Who invited him? What allowed him to get in?

Religion had always kept us apart. I am a practicing Catholic, but he was not a believer. However, he let me raise the children within my faith because he recognized it was important. When he needed something, he asked me to pray for him and called me his intermediary. Even if he was not much of a believer, I felt like he respected God.

The changes started in 2008. By 2011, he was evil. I did not recognize my husband anymore. Every time he looked at me, I saw Evil. It gave me chills; he was someone I did not know. I could not stop thinking that Evil must have those eyes. I asked myself how it happened. Was it the drugs? The prostitutes? How did Evil take over ?

When he moved out, I was weak, spiritually and psychologically. Through prayers, Bible reading and help from my spiritual advisors and other spiritual people, I understood that I could fight this fight only by getting close to God. It was the fight of my life. But having Alejandro gone did not kept Evil away for long.

With the help of doctors and spiritual guidance, I started getting strong and able to fight my wars, all of them. But once I was ready to change lawyers for the airline incident, apparently Evil was not happy.

The week before I had taken the big step to change lawyers, Yorketta, a woman I had not heard from in years called me. We were never friends, just acquaintances. We used to live in the same neighborhood, but never saw each other except at certain charity events.

I was surprised by her call. After the entire town, the whole world, knew about the airline incident portrayed in the newspapers, no one, not even my friends, wanted to talk to me. But she called like nothing had happened.

She was wondering about the dress from Mafud, the Mexican designer we once brought to Houston for a charity event with the Latin Women Initiative. She wanted to buy it or rent it to wear at a wedding in New York. I thought silently: "In reality, I needed the money now."

Mafud bases his designs on Mexican culture, and many of his pieces have paintings of famous Mexican artists. Mine was a simple one-shoulder dress with a painting of Rodolfo Morales. She was there the day I tried it on and I remembered the look on her face. She loved the dress, but I had already decided I was going to buy it.

Finally, I answered: "Whatever you like. To tell you the truth, I am getting a divorce and I need the money."

"Oh My God! I did not know about it. Have you filed for divorce already? You know I am a lawyer and, even though I cannot practice here, I work for some lawyers. Probably I can help you."

"Well, my divorce has been in the making for almost two years," I told her, but I was also thinking about changing divorce lawyers so I was willing to talk to her.

"I can stop by your house next week to try the dress on and talk."

Since that last meeting with my lawyer, I was determined. After more than year and a half, once again he still had not gotten the black box from the airplane, the manual for employees or any other records from the plane. He was preparing to go to trial with nothing but my daughter's and my testimony.

I had never been in this position, but my feelings were telling me this was not right. I felt that I was walking into a disaster. The government had offered me a deal—a deal Alejandro was clearly behind and under which the custody of my children would be jeopardized and I would be guilty of a minor assault against him!

"What? He was the one who attacked me in the plane."

"Carmen, they are not dropping the charge," my lawyer said. "I have never seen them do that. This is a great deal."

He was treating me like an ignorant idiot. He had never seen them do this? That is what the government does! The feds offer a lesser charge but find you guilty anyway.

"No," I told him. "I did nothing on that airplane. I can prove the truth."

"You are so arrogant," he replied.

"I thought you said that my husband is the arrogant one," I retorted.

I thought to myself: "I only had known two really arrogant men, and they both had called *me* arrogant."

At another time in my life, I would have told my lawyer that, but I was still so weak.

I had left that encounter thinking I could prove the truth, but not with that lawyer. I felt as if my husband had bought him. Everything is possible in Alejandro's world. It was Thursday afternoon. I went home and called the lawyer I had met back in October.

When he answered the phone, I asked: "Is this Andino Reynal?"

"Yes, it is."

"This is Carmen María. Remember me?"

"Yes, of course."

"I would like to meet with you because I would really like for you to have my case as long as you feel good about it."

"Carmen, I knew you were an innocent woman when I talked with you."

During the meeting that Friday, I explained to him why I had not hired them a few months back. I told him the truth was very important to me and that was why I was going to be truthful with him. Revealing what I did not like about Bob, I said I did not want him on my case. I said I did not feel good any longer having someone I could not trust handling my business.

He agreed with me and took my case. By the next Friday, we met to finalize the process of transferring lawyers.

I had completely forgotten I was meeting Yorketta that morning. When she called me, I was at my new lawyer's office and asked her if we could meet tomorrow instead. She sounded disappointed, but this was more important. My life and my children's lives depended on it.

Andino had already found out everything about my case and said he was going to inform my now former lawyer on Monday about the transfer. I did not have to bother with it. I gave him my ruby necklace in good faith. I could not wait until I found the money to pay him. I needed to do this fast since the trial was coming up. Before I left, he said he needed to talk with my daughter who had been on the plane. So it was decided I would bring her the next week after school. I felt relief and at peace. I knew it was the right thing to do!

This feeling was confirmed when Yorketta came to my house the next day. I was home alone when she arrived. She looked even thinner than the last time I saw her. She had cancer a few years ago and after that I had not heard from her or seen her until now. It was like she had disappeared.

She was completely taken by the house.

"Carmen, this is beautiful and grand."

"Thanks! I had my dream house, but not my dream life."

We sat down in the study. She had a folder in her hand. I did not know what it was. We started talking about the last few years, her illness and my divorce, when suddenly she said: "I found this in the system and you are in terrible trouble."

Opening the folder, she pulled out information about the airplane case. I could not help but think of course she knew about this before she called me. I was suspicious from then on.

She started talking about the latest motions and that the trial was coming up.

"But you are with the best lawyers for this," she said.

"Well, I am changing lawyers. That is what I was doing yesterday."

"No! You cannot change lawyers."

"Well, it has all been done!"

"I know about these things; you are in the best hands."

"I thought you were going to look up information about the divorce and a possible lawyer for that."

"Yes, but I found this, and this is more important."

"It has already being decided. I changed lawyers yesterday."

"Listen to me, you cannot change lawyers! This was no coincidence. You needed to talk to me so you don't make this mistake."

"Please don't. It is already done," and I stood up.

I could tell she was mad. I said: "Let's go try the dress. Have you decided if you want to buy the gown?"

"No, I cannot buy it."

We went to my bedroom to get to my closet. On the way, she started to talk about her illness, how difficult it was, how much pain she had to endure, and how she was able to overcome it.

My closet was two stories. The second floor of it was the third floor of the house. On the third floor there was only the closet, the attic and a terrace. The place was completely isolated and closed. We entered the closet and went to the third floor, where the gowns were. I took the dress from the hanger and gave it to her, while she was telling me how the pain she suffered was unbearable.

"I felt I was dying," she said.

She stripped down and I could not help thinking that she was sickeningly skinny and her body was full of scars. I said to myself, "The dress is going to be too big for her."

While she was putting on the dress, she said: "One night I dreamed I was in pain, the same pain I had every day. It was terrible, and I kept asking for something that would calm the pain. I was screaming like an animal, and I could see myself becoming that animal. It was a beast."

She was making gestures of how it looked. Her face started to look like a beast. I could not help but be scared. Then she added: "And that was when I talked to the Devil."

At that moment my body went cold.

"He said to me: 'I would take away the pain if you give me your soul.'"

She was looking at me with that animal face. I looked around and realized that no one would listen if I screamed.

I went to the spiral staircase and started to go down, telling her: "The mirror is down here. Come, so you can look at yourself there."

I was scared. I sped down the stairs. Once we were down, I changed the conversation to the dress and how it looked on her. Incredibly, the gown looked perfect on her, and her face was back to normal.

She said she needed some shoes to go with it.

"With all the colors in this gown, you have many choices," I said.

"Do you have something?"

"I do not let anybody use my shoes. People's walks change them. Please change, so we can go down."

I wanted to get out of that closet. I was fearful. After she changed, we went back to the study.

I told her I had an appointment and had to go. I was in such a hurry to get her out of my house. And I did not want her to have my dress. I had the worst feeling about this. She took the dress, her handbag and the folder. She was never going to leave that behind.

While walking her out, I asked when was she coming back from the wedding. She gave me the date, and then I asked when was she giving me back the dress.

"I will be back that following Monday," she said. "You tell me when after that."

"But I need payment now."

"What? I had valuable information about your case. That is my payment."

"I know everything about my case. There is nothing new about it that you brought."

"I told you that you couldn't change lawyers."

"Sorry, that had already been decided and done. Therefore, your information is useless to me."

Suddenly, she threw the gown at me and left. I locked the door and started shaking. Turning on the alarm, I went to my bedroom, got in bed and started to cry with chills.

I started to pray "Our Father…"

I called my friend Lilly, and told her: "Lilly, the Devil just left my house."

CHAPTER 15

Ignoring Me

W E WENT TO Italy and Greece in the summer of 2003. It was a trip with many stops: Rome, Venice, Athens, Crete, and Paris. The girls were seven and four years old. We had a wedding in Rome, and I did not want to go without the girls, who were on summer vacation.

"Carmen, I insist the girls should stay at home," Alejandro said. "It is a lot of work and a problem to travel so far away with them."

"Alejandro, I cannot leave them. They are out of school. It breaks my heart. This will be their summer vacation."

His brother, also a doctor and a year younger than Alejandro, still was single. However, he had been dating a girl for over a year who was 17 years his junior. For the last few years, he had been tagging along on our summer vacations.

Calling to ask what the plan was, he gave me his credit card number to book him exactly like us, except he was not attending the wedding and would meet us in Venice.

When we arrived in Rome, Alejandro gave me a pill to "update my natural clock to European time, so I would not have jet lag," according to him. That night, we had a rehearsal dinner. All of my friends were there for the wedding, and we were expected to go to everything related to the ceremony. Well, Alejandro and I slept all afternoon and got to the dinner when it was ending. And that was to get my clock attuned to Roman time! Now I could not sleep at night.

The girls behaved beautifully, not only at the wedding, but also during the whole trip. They are such troopers and love parties. They were so excited to see the bride and groom.

The ceremony was held at a 500-year-old church in Rome. The bride took a long time to arrive, and Alexandra, who was only seven years old then, said: "If the bride does not show up, I can marry the groom!" I treasure each and every one of those moments when she was a sparkly little girl.

Kamee was attached to me every second.

Alejandro avoided me the whole trip. That is when I started to notice a look from him that felt like dislike toward me. That same look came back around 2011.

He mostly stayed at the hotel, while I was out and about with his brother, the girlfriend and my daughters. I did not realize at the time that he had been cheating all along during our marriage, but now, I wonder if he had a girlfriend back home he would have rather been with and that was why he was hating the whole trip.

In Venice, I was so miserable that I cried while showering. There we were in such a spectacular place and it felt like I was alone. I might as well have been on this trip with my girls only.

We arrived in Greece, where we had a villa we were sharing with his brother for a week. The view was unbelievable.

But he continued with his attitude. I was going to the beach alone with my daughters. One day, walking to the restaurant, I saw him in the gym. He had said he wanted to stay in the room and sleep. I thought we could have gone to the gym together.

I went into the gym and said we had to talk: "Alejandro, we are here in such a spectacular place and you have been avoiding me. Not only that, but you had been verbally abusive to the point where I don't want to be with you. I cannot take this any longer. As soon as we get back to Houston, I am filing for divorce."

I was dead serious and I think he felt it. He went on his knees and started to apologize: "Carmen, I have been so stressed. I promise you I am going to change. What is it that you want?"

He had been sued for malpractice and wrongful death by two different patients' families and went to trial for both cases. One of the trials was postponed after tropical storm Allison.

Though the trial had already started, some of the jurors lost everything due to the flooding. The trial was canceled and then restarted. The plaintiff added new evidence and accusations to the case. These cases took well over two years, and that was what he used as an excuse for his behavior.

I was not able to be present for them. His lawyer's advice was: "Your wife is too beautiful. It is better for her not to attend the trial. The jury can sense she is a trophy wife."

Was I?

Today, sometimes I wonder what really happened with those patients after I learned that one patient died because of malpractice. During the divorce, someone complained to the Medical Board about him and once the Board's investigation started, they found out about all of his arrests. As a doctor, he has to report everything to the Board, but he never did. During the investigation, he had to appear in front of the Board. His malpractice insurance covered his legal defense costs. I came to learn that the Medical Board does not protect patients, just as the Bar does not protect lawyers' clients. They protect their members.

To his question I answered: "I want more time as a family."

"Okay! Fair enough. As of today, you will have it."

Sure enough, for the rest of the trip, which was only three days, he was present. The girls were with us everywhere and went to every restaurant. I was so proud of the way I raised them.

However, with so many stops, I had to pack and unpack constantly for the four of us. I was tired of luggage. For the last stop—Athens and finally Paris—we were staying in Paris for two days. Packing the bags again, I put the clothes for the day trip and Paris on top, along with the last change for travel back to Houston.

To keep them from going through the luggage, forcing me to pack all over again, I went to the living room and said: "Enough! The luggage is ready and your changes are marked per day. I labeled the bags. No one touch the luggage."

"I told you not to bring them, Carmen."

"No. That is not the problem. They have behaved wonderfully. Do not say that. But next time we travel like this, I am going to teach them how to pack for themselves."

And I did.

When we got back home, Alejandro said that he was changing his practice, limiting his hospital work and doing more office work.

In fact, limiting his hospital work was a way to avoid more lawsuits. The lawsuits he had were from the families of hospital patients, those he saw while hospitalized and had never seen before or after at his office.

But that change did not translate to a better life for us. Only for him.

CHAPTER 16

The Stanford Bank Disaster

WAKING UP TO a bluebird day, the sun is bright. It snowed the whole night. The snow is fresh, and we are looking forward to fresh powder skiing.

It is looking to be a great day. The foundation for the new house is being poured today back in Houston. I spent months working on the plans, making sure everything was how we wanted it to be, so no changes would be necessary.

As usual, I take the children to the ski school, coming back for breakfast before heading to the mountain. My cell phone rings!

"Carmen, turn on the TV. The federals have taken over Stanford," a friend from Houston said.

I never imagined "the federals" would become part of my vocabulary later in life. I changed the channel. We always watch the local channel in the morning to check on conditions for skiing.

I scream at Alejandro: "Come, come. The FBI has taken over Stanford Bank!"

He came out of the master bedroom with his winter underwear and one sock on. The other sock is in his hand. He started to shake and went pale.

It was on all the Houston channels, but had not made it to the networks yet. My God! FBI agents were like flies all over that beautiful white building, which was a sign of wealth and opulence. They were going in and out. Civilians, Stanford employees, were coming out with them.

Alejandro told me to call our bank agent in Venezuela, who said they knew what was happening in Houston. Everything had been frozen.

"How about Antigua? Is Antigua open?"

"They are open, just like us. We do not know what is going on exactly."

"Were you able to pull our money out?"

"I put in the order, but it takes ten working days."

For weeks, there had been talks about Stanford facing troubles. In fact, it was the topic of conversation at a party the day before we left for Colorado. Many of our friends had money there and other friends that worked at the bank had been at the party. At the time, it sounded like just gossip.

Stanford employees used to say they were the envy of other banks because Stanford was doing so well. However, we had ordered our investments liquidated.

"I am checking on it, Carmen. As soon as I know something, I will let you know."

Alejandro never dealt with anybody directly. I was secretary, mother, housekeeper, office manager, etc., etc. I was his go between. He did that to reassure me that even though the accounts were under his mother's name, I had some type of control. It would prove to be a lie later.

My stomach was upside down. I had to go to the bathroom and throw up. Every penny we had saved was in Stanford Bank, a decision Alejandro had made to put everything in one basket. And Stanford came into our home through his little brother's reference.

We were counting on that for the children's college education. God, my children! They were out skiing. I did not want them to know or see what we were feeling. I am so worried about their future.

Alejandro served himself tequila. It is only 10 a.m. And he also served me one. He was pale and shaking.

"My best years of work are gone," he said.

His comments never included me, as if I had done nothing for us or never worked.

"Alejandro, we are still young."

"Carmen, I am almost 50 years old."

My cell was unstoppable. All my friends that also had money in Stanford were calling. They wanted to see how we were doing and if we had more news. They were in shock, just as we were. Alejandro suddenly announced he was going to ski.

"I am not going to waste my bluebird day," he said.

"Forget about it!" I told him. "You are not doing well, please look at yourself, and you are drunk. I cannot handle losing it all and probably also becoming a widow."

He looked at his hands shaking and agreed with me. Instead, he said he was going to get drunk. I had never seen him like this. He was a wreck. He looked devastated, desolated and lost.

The bank calls: "Carmen, your money is out."

"The money is saved!" I screamed.

Alejandro came and hugged me. I do not think we had ever embraced in such a way.

"Thank you, God."

God was good sometimes for Alejandro. But other times, he acted better than God or like He did not exist at all. And for Alejandro there was nothing after death. He always said: "The patients that come back after I resuscitated them all say they have seen no light."

I felt great that we saved the money, but felt terrible for the other people that lost their money. Our happiness did not last long. The bank called again to say they had made a mistake, that it had been somebody else's account. I kept thinking we could have saved the money only a month ago.

"That is it. I am getting officially drunk," Alejandro said after the call.

I was scared, too, because he was gone. He looked so lost that I was afraid how this whole thing would play out for him. Suicide ran in his family. His brother killed himself when he was eighteen years old on his father's bed. He had always threatened that he would do that, too. He sat on the sofa, looking so lost.

All of this stress could have been saved!

Early in January I was, as usual, checking real estate. We were in Beaver Creek. I came across an apartment in the building we had always liked, The Saint James, in the village, with a gym and interior pool. The three-story apartment had four bedrooms and a loft. The kids were growing and I was looking to the future when they would start inviting friends to come ski with us.

I called my realtor in Beaver Creek to set up an appointment to see it after skiing. The apartment was spacious with two views, to the village and the mountain. It was a much better property than the one we had in a location we had always wanted. We both liked it, and I told the realtor I would get back to him. We discussed it while we walked to our apartment from The Saint James.

"I really like it. How about you?" I said.

"Me, too. But how are we going to buy it? After all, our apartment is paid for, and we are going to build the house in Houston. We are not going to get another loan."

"We have the money in Stanford!" I said smiling.

"What? What are you saying?"

"Simple. We buy this apartment with the money from Stanford and put ours on the market. Once ours is sold, we put the money back in the bank."

"Should we go that wild?"

"Alejandro what is the money for, if not to use it for things like this?

"Let me think about it."

Of course, he never approved it.

I was on the phone and the computer, checking on more news. Somehow, I felt that if it had not made national news, this could be just a hiccup.

"OMG! The foundation of the house has been poured," I said out loud.

"That has to stop, Carmen. There is no way we can build that house now."

Of course, he gave an order, and I have to be the one dealing with it. I called the builders. They confirmed the foundation had been poured. I was even more scared then. We could not sell the land with the foundation there. The day passed so slowly. We just stayed in the apartment and drank. We slept, too. I spent a lot of time on the phone.

Finally, it was time to get the children from ski school. They were happy! They had a good day and had no idea of what had happened. I was thinking that we needed to be very lean in order to survive, cutting all unnecessary expenses.

After getting the properties and accumulating the savings, we indulged ourselves. I shopped more often and bought more expensive things. Somehow we had become big spenders and a little careless. After all, we had worked so hard for so many years. We had built a practice and a family, and now it was time to enjoy it.

However, my idea of enjoying what we had accomplished was completely different than Alejandro's. I did not know at the time, but he was indulging himself in a different way, and not in a way we could both enjoy.

We finished our trip to Colorado and went back to Houston. Back to reality! We had tickets for the Ballet Ball, one of the biggest and most important fundraisers in Houston. We were sharing a table with good friends. Of course, the tickets went to waste because Alejandro did not want to go. He called me frivolous, saying he needed charity now.

That same night, one of our Stanford friends decided to have a dinner with only Stanford victims so at least we could heal our wounds together. Again, Alejandro did not want to go, but after everybody called, we went.

Once there, Alejandro kept drinking. At one point, he had a panic attack. He was outside smoking with the men, and the women were inside. Suddenly, he entered about to pass out, shaking, white and sweating. He made it to a sofa, fell and started shaking.

We all gathered around him to help, trying to figure out what was wrong.

"He cannot talk. He cannot talk!" I said.

One of our friends, who is a doctor, said: "Let's give him space and time. He has had a panic attack."

Money was so important to this man that losing it was devastation. He felt as if his life was ending and started to drink on a daily basis. Every time he got home, he went straight to the bar and served himself wine or a whiskey. He would drink every night, every day of the week, something he had never done. He was a social drinker.

But alcoholism runs in his family. His grandfather from his mother's side died from it.

Alejandro used to drink alcohol like it was a soda. My father would say: "*Alejandro, los tragos hay que campanearlos para que te duren, así no te emborrachas.* (Alejandro, you have to shake the drinks and play with them so they last; that way you don't get drunk)."

Days passed and we were at a standstill. The house was not moving forward, and he was afraid. We were now paying interest on the first withdrawals for the building loan. This was not financially sound. The builders, who were Syrian partners, proposed to help us withdraw the loan faster even if it was not for the house.

Alejandro got excited: "Yes! I can get money right away." After they left, he told me to start doing that.

"And do what with the money, Alejandro?" I asked.

"Put it in the bank," he said.

"We have to pay interest on that money," I protested.

"Then we have that money in the bank and are paying interest on it, but not building the house. This has so many shades of illegal, forget it. I am not doing that. It's not only illegal, but we would be in a worse financial situation."

After a month passed, Alejandro was still drinking on a daily basis. This new habit would become his way of being, and he was still having panic attacks. I was giving him time to come back, but it was not happening.

One day I decided to tell him that we needed to move forward with the house. After all, we were not building it with the Stanford money. We had a loan for that, and the land was paid in full. We could not sell the land with the foundation on it. Doing nothing was a mistake. We had to move forward.

I told him: "We lived with very little when we first got married and had no money to spare. Now you have a practice that produces good money. What we need to do is live very lean, spending little, and we will recuperate in time. We cannot continue paying interest forever. Life goes on! We need to move forward."

He agreed with me. I think mostly because he just did not want to think. He wanted someone else to think for him. It seemed like I always did that for us. And that is exactly what we did!

Alejandro started working like he did when he first started the practice. He had lowered his workload, but was now on a mission and became a workaholic again. Our income went up to such an extent that by summer I was looking for a piece of land to build our own building for the practice. We had enough money for the down payment. And since Alejandro no longer trusted banks, he agreed with me about building the office. I had been telling him to do so for years.

"You were right, Carmen! Real estate is the way to go. So, let's build our own office."

"Now?"

"Yes."

"Alejandro, we are building the house, and paying a mortgage for the house and interest for the construction. If we built the office, we would have to do the same: pay double. We will be building both a house and office, paying four ways. It is too much. I am scared to do that."

"Let's do it, Carmen. Make it happen! This is what we are going to do, so you do it or I will do it."

Somehow I became this person that had to prove myself to him, because if I did not do what he said, the criticism would never end. So, I became this person that wanted peace and wanted to prove that I was that good or better. After all, I am a Montiel, and we have always been fighters and hard workers who can do anything. I never realized this was abuse. But it was, because it was a way to make me not go against him. He knew how to manipulate me.

I started looking and found a piece of land near the hospital for a great price. My realtor at the time helped me. She wanted to prove herself to be a friend, but time would tell that she was not.

We bought the land. Then, I started looking for a commercial builder. It is so very different to build commercial versus residential. I researched many commercial builders and their references. Finally, I got a very good one for the best price. I have always been good at getting good people for the best price.

Getting ready to build was a new world for me; the requirements in commercial had nothing to do with residential. The state of Texas had to be involved with its regulations. I was so busy building a house and a commercial building at the same time, while managing our expenses and the office to be able to make it happen. And of course, there were the three children with their school responsibilities and extracurricular activities, while making sure my husband was getting better from the Stanford situation. But being a mother always was and still is the most important thing to me.

We were making it happen. We were building the new house while paying the mortgage for the house we were in, just as we were building the new office while paying rent for the office building we were in, plus maintaining our mountain apartment in Colorado. It was quite an accomplishment after all that had happened to us.

We tried to keep life as usual, and around that time I went to an event at Saks Fifth Avenue. I was one of their favorite clients. You can guess why. They raffled a weekend with a Bentley and guess who won it? Me! Wow! I was so happy that life seemed to be smiling at me still. I came home with the ticket and told Alejandro about it. Of course, it was for me to drive because I won it!

I kept the ticket until it was the right weekend to have the car. That turned out to be the weekend we had a gala and another event, but also the weather was sunny and perfect. I went with the girls to get the car. I wanted a convertible, and they helped me choose. Black with cream inside! We drove back together to the house to take Juan Diego for ice cream, all with the top down. The girls sent pictures to their friends while I was driving.

On Saturday, we had a Unicef gala. I let Alejandro drive the car for that. We met some friends and when we picked up the car, Erika saw that we got in it and screamed: "Alejandro, I love you! You are the best."

Alejandro's first panic attack had happened at Erika's house. I think she believed Alejandro bought the car, and that was an accomplishment after his panic attacks. But it also showed how shallow people can be about money.

What she did not know was the car was mine. I had won it. It was my luck, not his.

He had been very mellow since the Stanford financial loss. The way he had put that money away was so wrong that I knew this was a punishment. He also knew that I had had the idea that could save us.

One day in a drunken rage, he finally said: "Tell me! Tell me it is my fault. I know you have been dying to say it to me."

I did not want to antagonize him and did not take the bait for that fight. By organizing our expenses, I knew we could stand up again. But Alejandro was not coming out of it, and drinking was a way for him to forget.

CHAPTER 17

The Guns

I HEARD THE GUNSHOT and did not move. I was so scared. What had happened?

There was a lot of confusion...was he dead? Was I dead? Is this how dead feels? He moved, and I realized we were not dead. I thanked God!

He got on his feet: "See what you make me do," he said. "See where you take me." He kept the gun pointed at me.

As soon as I could stand up, I ran to the door, opened it and left running. I was wearing pajamas and my feet were bare. I locked myself inside the first door I found open. It was a janitor's room.

I was crying and scared. "God, please! Make this be a dream," I said.

What is going to happen? I thought. Someone must have heard the gun shot. The police must be on their way.

Alejandro had purchased that gun a month ago. I had hidden it and all the rest of them. I waited for close to thirty minutes, but nothing happened—neither the police nor Alejandro came looking for me. After all that time with nothing happening, I decided to leave. Going down to the lobby, I got a taxi and told the driver to take me to my brother's house. I had no money and did not know what time it was. When I arrived at my brother's and rang the doorbell, he was surprised to see me at that hour and in that condition. I had been crying for so long that my face was swollen.

"Please pay the cab," I said to my brother.

"Of course, Baby."

In the meantime, my sister-in-law came to the door and hugged me: "What happened, Carmen María?"

I could not stop crying and shaking.

It was Halloween. I have always loved Halloween, dressing up and the costumes. As usual, we all wore costumes and went with the children to our annual party for the kids. Alejandro and I came as Bonnie and Clyde. I wore a short blond wig with a 1920s style mini-skirt dress. Alejandro looked like Al Capone! His initials are AL... I had never thought about that.

When we finished with the children's party, we dropped the children at home and drove to the Hotel ZaZa for Unicef's annual Halloween Fundraiser. I served on the Unicef Board at the time.

The party was full with lots of people, all in costumes. I recognized some right away, but others were disguised really well. It was fun to find out who was who through the night.

Every member of the Board was there, and we were on call for pictures and to introduce people. At times, Alejandro had to stay by himself because I was held up in conversations. At some point Alejandro's look aggravated. I asked him if anything was wrong.

"No, keep on being the life of the party," he said.

"Excuse me?"

"Nothing," he replied and kissed me. Somehow it felt like a Judas kiss.

A while later, the organization's president came over to ask if I was going to be able to attend the next meeting because the gala was approaching. Alejandro ran by us, screaming at me: "We are leaving, Carmen. Now!"

He was furious. I did not understand what had happened. I ran out behind him leaving her standing there. He was gone already. We had decided to stay at the hotel in order not to drive after the party. I got in the other elevator and went up to the room.

"What is wrong, Alejandro? Why in such a hurry that you could not wait for me?"

"Carmen, this is so typical of you. You are a regular butterfly. Just worried about others and not me."

"Alejandro, I am one of the hosts. I am on the Board."

"I want sex now, and you are too busy for that."

"And how am I going to know that?"

He left the room. I figured he was so mad that he was going to cool down, so I undressed and put on pajamas. I was in the bathroom cleaning the makeup off my face when I heard him come back. When I finished, I went into the room and saw him sitting in a chair with a gun inside his mouth. The world fell at my feet.

"Alejandro, please don't do that," I said softly.

"This will end everybody's misery," he replied.

He had pulled the gun out of his mouth but put it back in when he finished speaking.

"Alejandro, what is wrong? What happened?"

I got close to him on my knees. I started pleading with him: "*Mi cielo*, please don't do this. We have three children that are waiting for us at home."

I felt comfortable enough to put my hands in top of his and try to get the gun out of his mouth. I was successful. But then, he turned the gun to my head.

"I am tired of your super star status," he said.

I was dead cold and scared. I asked God for time and calm for him. He started talking nonsense. I put my hand on top of his and started lowering the gun away from my head. But suddenly he started trying to pull it up, and then both of us tried to force it from the other. We ended up on the floor with the gun, and bang!

In 1994, concealed weapons were allowed in Texas with a license. After my first daughter was born, Alejandro invited me to get the license with him. The two-day program on a weekend was a good activity to do together. I had never liked guns, but after the scare at my house—a friend was arriving, and a man with a shotgun robbed her in front of my house—I was worried. More and more scenarios like this were happening in Houston. That is why I had accepted.

Of course, after we got the licenses, Alejandro started buying guns as a hobby. He gave me a small beautiful one to carry in my handbag. However, once Alexandra grew, started to walk and looked in my handbag, I put it in the safe. The hobby became my nightmare. Alejandro knew I did not like guns and that I tried to stay away from them. I refused to clean them because they scared me.

So, he started using the gun every time we had a fight. The first time he put the gun to my head during an argument, I was able to release myself and call the police. Knowing the police were on their way, he got down on his knees and pleaded for me not to say anything, that he could lose his medical licenses and then how could he support me and Alexandra. When the police came, I told them that we had been having a fight, but that everything was okay now.

Later, when Alexandra was already walking around the house, we had another fight in which he cornered me in the closet with a gun in his hand.

"I am so miserable that I want to end all of this now, because I see you are also miserable."

I cried, pleading for him to please release me. I called out for the maid to come help me. He let me go, but I called the police. This time he was mad.

"You are definitely crazy! Calling the police for what? To end everything we have? Is this what you want for our daughter? I am going to open the door and you better stay away from it or you will see what is going to happen to you."

Alejandro opened the door and told the police that Alexandra, our toddler, took the phone and accidentally dialed 911. That everything was okay in the house and I was in the bedroom holding my baby.

After that, I was very distant with him. I was scared and felt trapped. Within a few days, he came and apologized, saying he would never hurt our daughter or me. He claimed being very stressed about the growth of his brand-new practice and the added responsibility of having a daughter and another on the way.

I got peace for a while. For a few years, he did not threaten me with guns again. However, he kept buying them while I hoped he would stop that hobby.

He and Alexandra had a special bond. He was really in love with his daughter, and she loved him back so much. I could relate to that love and was happy she had it, because I always felt the same way with my dad. I felt like he was going to be a father like mine.

Then, my second daughter was born. Although he wanted boys at the beginning, he was very much in love with the girls. I had been worried he would not love Kamee because he was so in love with Alexandra and had wanted a boy, but he was very happy to have another girl. Those were the best years of our lives.

We bought our second home, which we built in Spanish Colonial style. I was pregnant when construction started, but lost that baby.

We moved to the new home in May 1998 and once again I was pregnant. It felt like a lot of newness: new house and new baby on the way.

When Alexandra was born, I wanted to name her after me. After all, it is family tradition. It was the name of my father's mother. However, Alejandro did not want to. He said he did not like my name.

This was one of many things I did not understand about him. He did not like my name.

One of my best friends and the maid of honor at my wedding was Alexandra Muchacho. I always liked her name, plus it was a form of Alejandro's name. He said we should name her Alexandra after himself.

I told him I liked the name, but if we had a boy, he could not be named Alejandro, because everybody in the house could not have the same name. I knew in time that Alexandra's name was going to be shortened to Alex.

He agreed, not very happily, adding: "If we ever have another daughter, we can name her Carmen María."

Like that was ever going to happen.

There we were having our second baby on December 30, 1998, almost on New Year's.

A girl! My dad was in town at the hospital with us when Kamee, as we nicknamed her, was born. So, there was no question she was Carmen María by family tradition. She was taken to neonatal because she was born with meconium and needed to be checked to make sure she did not inhale it. Alejandro went with her; as a physician he could enter behind the doctors. He was worried his baby could be exchanged.

He came back and told me everything was good. She was healthy and beautiful. Alejandro was very excited because this baby had blue eyes. He said: "Her eyes are sky blue, blue as blue can be. She has your father's eyes."

"Alejandro, forget it. They will change just like Alexandra's did."

Alexandra's eyes were blue when she was born, but by the time she was six months old, they had turned green. At one year old, her eyes were hazel.

"No. This is different. This is a blue I have never seen."

At one point, when we were alone in the bedroom, he said: "Do we really have to name her Carmen María?"

"That is it, Alejandro. Go outside and talk that over with my dad. He was very disappointed when we did not name Alexandra after me."

Two beautiful girls in the house, and we were living a blessed life. Alejandro felt spoiled. He had three women who adored him. The girls waited for him every evening to dance with him. They pulled out their little table, just their size. By day, they sat at it to paint, color, play scrabble, etc. In the evening, it became a dance floor for them. On that table they were able to reach up to Daddy's height and dance like little princesses.

It was our daily routine, one Alejandro looked forward to and so did the girls and I. It was happiness like no other. Kamee's birth and the new house gave us peace for a few years, until Alejandro was sued for malpractice, not once but twice within a year. Once again, stress became the excuse for his behavior with two lawsuits and two trials back to back. He was scared and mad at the world. He hardly talked to me, and whatever I did even if he had free time, he refused to do with me. It was one of many forms of his abuse. But

I was busy with the girls and tried to stay away from him. As I had learned when he was stressed out, the best way to handle it was to stay away from him.

The trials took almost four years. One was to start in 2001. It did, but then tropical storm Allison hit Houston, leaving the city devastated. The trial was canceled because some of the jurors lost their homes with the flooding. That gave the plaintiff time to find new ways to prove the case. This case delayed the other.

I was forbidden to go to court. Alejandro learned then that beautiful people do not do well in trial because people tend to dislike them. His lawyer advised him not to let me go to court: "She is too pretty. Instead of helping you; it will hurt you. They will think she is your trophy wife."

Which is what I was! I just did not know it. I was a way for him to show all his former friends and classmates who hated him that he was able to get Miss Venezuela.

After everything was calm again, we had our third and last child, our only son. I thought that adding the boy he longed for would put a final touch of endless happiness in our lives. And yes! It was peaceful for a while, or so I thought. I would learn later that he was cheating up and down, but I did not know at the time. Ignorance was good. I was happy!

Alejandro had stopped buying guns. He said he had them just for protection. Until one day in late 2005, he pulled a gun on me again when a discussion that turned into a fight ended in my closet with a gun inside my mouth. Tears rolled down my cheeks while I prayed to God that he would stop.

"I have to put you and me out of this misery," he said.

It felt like an eternity. He pulled the gun out and I ran. As soon as I got to my bedroom, I started screaming for the maid. She came in, only to be run out by Alejandro screaming at her to leave. My son was a year old. I had a nurse from Venezuela holding my son downstairs away from the incident.

I again ran into my closet and locked myself in. He stayed on the other side asking me to open the door. After a while, he was silent and started to cry. I could hear him. I was too scared to open the door though he begged me to. Time passed and finally I opened the door. He was still crying and apologizing.

"I love you and my family, my beautiful family," he said. "I would not hurt you. But you need to stop, Carmen. You get the worst out of me. You are able to get inside my head in a way that drives me nuts."

It was always my fault. I replayed what had happened. What had I done? I wanted to see what it was that I did that made him act like this. I could not find a reason.

He did not take out the gun again until 2008, on the night before hurricane Ike hit Houston and devastated the city. We were waiting to see if we had to leave town. Everybody was a bit skeptical because previously, in 2005, hurricane Rita went to Louisiana instead of Houston, and the transportation system collapsed when all outbound roads got choked with people leaving at the same time. However, if there was no indication that Ike was changing its route by Friday, we needed to do something. Alejandro came in Thursday night and told me to go with the children to his brother's in College Station just in case, because he was on call that weekend and had to stay.

We had dinner and went up to our room to watch television. Later, when Alejandro went downstairs to get something to drink, his cellular phone vibrated. I checked it in case it was an emergency. Instead, it was an answer to this text message he had sent earlier: "Hey baby! I am planning to stop by tomorrow night."

"Yes, Baby. I can't wait to see you."

As Alejandro came back into the room, I said with the cellular in my hand: "I see you have plans tomorrow."

"What?"

"Alejandro, I read your text messages. And BTW, she said she is waiting for you."

"Give me my phone."

"No, Alejandro, I am keeping this for the divorce. I think I have had enough."

He came over to me trying to get the phone, but I ran out of the room. In the hallway, he caught up with me, forcing me to give him the phone. At some point, he bit my left arm so hard that I felt his teeth penetrating my skin. I screamed, and the kids came. When he saw them, he let me go. I ran back into the room and locked myself in. My arm was bleeding, and he was banging on the door.

"Open the door, Carmen!" he screamed.

"Stay away, Alejandro. You are scaring the children."

"Open it, Carmen, or I will open it myself."

"Alejandro, I am calling the police. I am bleeding."

Two hits and he broke open the door. Then I tried to lock myself in the closet, but he put his arm in so I could not close the door, entering the closet with a gun in his hand and grabbing me.

"You are stupid!" he said. "You want to divorce me for a whore that dances at the Men's Club."

He put the gun inside my mouth.

"Listen to me. You are not getting a divorce. You are not taking my family away. I am not doing anything bad. This is just for fun. Are you listening to me?"

With the gun inside my mouth, I was scared to death.

"You are going to do nothing, Carmen. You are going to be the pretty wife you are and stay put. Do you understand?"

I nodded as well as I could since the gun was still inside my mouth.

"Can I pull the gun out now? Can I trust you not to call the police or do anything stupid?"

I nodded again. He took the gun out and left.

The next day was the day I had to pack and go to College Station, but I spent the day calling divorce lawyers and making appointments for the following week. I landed three meetings. Weather forecasters were not completely certain that the hurricane was going to hit Houston. Many of my friends decided to stay because of the uncertainty. It had already happened with Rita, when we all left and nothing happened.

I had too much on my mind and decided to stay. Little did I know that my worst nights would not come from natural disasters. I was not talking to Alejandro, and he was in the guest room.

However, we had to face the hurricane together because of our three children. It was early September, school had just started, and we had just come back from our summer vacation. My oldest daughter had gone to a camp in Venezuela and brought back a souvenir, lice! I had done all types of treatments, but they had failed. I was down to an olive oil treatment as a last resort. By then my second daughter had lice also. It was spreading, and now this.

In the midst of this mess, my daughter ended up in my bed on my pillow throughout the night. I did not know until later that the "aliens" were already on my head.

The electricity had gone out at around 9 p.m. We lit candles. Through the night, when the hurricane hit, Alejandro and I had run around the house securing all the doors. It felt like the wind was going to open them—seven doors downstairs and three upstairs—so we put chairs under the doorknobs to "lock" them.

When water started coming in, we put down towels, rolled up the Persian rugs, and took them to the second floor. It was a lot of work, and we did not sleep through the night. I had spent what was left of the night with the children in the guest bathroom that was in the middle of the house, the most secure place in this case. Alejandro went to our room with Alexandra on my pillow.

The next morning was devastating, with trees on the ground, all types of debris around, and my entire tile roof destroyed. The ground around the house was all red. I understood then that the bomb like noise we heard in the middle of the night was the tiles hitting the ground. Everything in town was closed: the hospitals, stores, grocery stores, gas stations, everything. Even the airport was closed. There was no electricity. That meant no air conditioning. Of course, the heat was worse than ever, especially with the humidity that the hurricane left.

It was Saturday with nothing to do and nowhere to go. I sat on the patio by the pool doing the lice treatment for the girls when Alejandro came out and announced that he was meeting his brother midway to pick up a generator, which he no longer needed since the hurricane had not hit there. He acted as if nothing had happened between us the night before. The generator was only big enough to run the refrigerator, but we were still without air conditioning.

Later that day, Alejandro told me the hospital had been damaged and would be closed until further notice, which could affect our October vacation. A trip to Egypt had been planned to celebrate our 20th anniversary with a cruise on the Nile and side trips to Petra, in Jordan, and Israel. I was chairing a big gala for the Institute of Hispanic Culture in October, and we were leaving after that. But in the back of my head, I was wondering how this trip could happen after the incident last night.

I did not focus on it, however. At that moment, we were in survival mode due to the hurricane. My immediate worry was that we would not have enough food to feed the children. We still did not know how long the recovery would take.

The solution to have the refrigerator working was a nightmare. The generator was very noisy and emitted a lot of gas, which gave the girls and me asthma.

By Sunday, we could not take it anymore and decided to drive to our apartment in Colorado. During this survival state, what had happened the night of the hurricane lost importance, especially when Alejandro told me: "Look at me! I am here with you and the children, taking care of my family. You are the most important thing in my life. I am sorry if I wanted to go see a woman dance. That is meaningless compared to this."

We stayed in Colorado for two weeks until Houston was back to normal. I hid the gun when we returned, another gun joining the others in a hidden cabinet with a very difficult access. I thought, "no gun, no problem."

My gala was a total success, and we left on our trip. We had to shorten it by a week, after spending two weeks without working. We had a great time. It was the honeymoon we never had. I felt we were at peace. But something was wrong. Something I did not know. Alejandro had a double life that I had no knowledge of. This was when it started developing little by little.

CHAPTER 18

The God Syndrome

OUR NEW FAMILY ROOM was grandiose, a contemporary two-story space with concrete floors. Massive pocket doors disappeared inside the walls and the room opened to a club size pool. On the other side were the formal living and dining areas, and access to the wine cellar that I had designed so the bottles looked like they were suspended in the air. An open bar stood on one side of the room ready to party and to indulge his growing alcohol habit. On the other was a beautiful modern fire place with colors that could be changed, and that gave way to the breakfast area and kitchen.

Alejandro stood in the middle of the family room looking around. You could tell that he could not take it all in. This was the first night in the new house. He looked more than proud; he looked like he felt invincible!

I had built the house of my dreams, the house I had been dreaming about since I was a little girl. It had everything you could imagine, even a two-story closet. Every little girl's dream!

But to him, it was proof that he was GOD. A year after losing all our savings in Stanford Bank, he now had the commercial building and this.

Alejandro and I always have had very different approaches to managing money.

Before we became a couple, one day he pulled a big roll of bills out of his pocket. I could not help myself and had to ask what he was doing with all that money.

"I got paid today," he said.

He worked for his dad while he was attending med school.

"Don't you get paid with a check?"

"No, my dad gives me cash."

"Put it in the bank."

"I don't have a bank account."

"What do you mean? You work, and you don't have bank accounts? You are 24 years old."

I was very disappointed. At age 20, I had checking and savings accounts. I was very organized with my salary. He was 24 years old and did not even have a checkbook.

"So, what do you do with the rest of the money?" I asked.

He looked at me for a long time but never answered.

"You spendd it all? All of it? Don't you save?"

I felt like I was talking to a little kid. He spent all of his money every month, which was why he put it in his pocket. It was also a power trick for him to be able to pull that much money from his pocket in front of people. But he was so young that anyone seeing him probably thought he was in drugs or something like that. Med students typically do not have that type of money on them.

We had just met, and I looked at him like a friend. I was not attracted to him. After all, we had agreed that I was going to be his godmother for his baptism. He had never been baptized.

I explained the importance of being mindful with his money and told him that I could not be with a man who was so disorganized, immature and irresponsible with money. At the time, I never thought he had other intentions toward me other than friendship. That was why I went on lecturing him.

I can only imagine how he had felt because the next time I saw him, he had a checkbook with him. I smiled and said: "Welcome to the world of adults."

With the checkbook came credit cards in his name. The one he had been using was his father's.

At 20, I was a world ahead of him. At the time, I had thought he was immature about money probably because he was spoiled and had never thought he needed anything beyond what his father could provide for him. But this behavior set a precedent for what the rest of our life was going to be.

Once we got married, I was in charge of all the finances for us. He always said I was better and more responsible. However, he always made the big financial decisions about investments while I was in charge of all deposits in our checkbook and bill payments. Why?

As students we did not make much. His salary had been minimal during his internship, and I had used my great savings for my years of school.

Once I graduated and we moved to Houston, I started working for Telemundo as a reporter and anchorwoman. During this time, his salary as a fellow was a little better. Both salaries were deposited in our checking account. I managed all the money, making sure all payments went out in a timely manner. We were able to earn an incredible credit score over 700. However, we were living on a tight budget. We had bought our first house, had two new cars and the normal expenses of day-by-day living with not much money to spare. However little we had left, we saved.

I had been looking forward to getting back to Venezuela once Alejandro finished his training. Now, after graduating in the US with honors (*magna cum laude*), speaking English, and working in the US television business, I could write my own ticket back home, like Alejandro had said.

But no! Alejandro did not want to go back. The relationship with his father had always been a very difficult one. As a doctor, he could not go to work for another doctor; he had to work with his father. But working for him created a very uncertain situation because his father had a tendency to fire his own children if he woke up with a bad temper that day. We could not go back and start a family under those conditions.

Alejandro had to have stable working conditions; it was important for his reputation. So, we stayed in the US. I was miserable. The idea was that it would be for two years in order to save enough money for him to be able to negotiate with his father. But who he was lying to?

Visa changes affected me greatly. I could not work. Alejandro started his own medical practice, but did not want me to get involved in it. How the money came, whether in cash or credit cards, and how much was paid out in insurance and other expenses were mysteries for me. Once we filed our first year of business taxes, it was reality check time! Nearly ten thousand dollars was missing.

I had no way to account for it because I was not working at his office. Our CPA explained to him that he had not had time to take care of those details. The medical business is very demanding. Time spent in office work was time wasted not seeing patients. And that is how I became his office manager.

There was never again a penny missing! I was able to keep overhead down, which enabled us to start saving money. Within a year, we were saving good money. For some reason, Alejandro did not trust American banks, so we put the savings in the Tiger Funds of Asia.

He started making friends at the hospital. The problem was that whenever he made friends, he thought those people hung the moon. They were never normal relationships. He fell in love with these people.

For example, he became close friends with a Colombian doctor who had a nephew doing a development in Colombia. This doctor was helping him get investors from his physician friends. Alejandro became very excited about this deal and of course had to give this young fellow some money. After all, we were going to become rich with this!

"Do you know, Carmen, how many patients I have to see in order to be able to make decent money?"

"Alejandro, I do not like this. Some venture in Colombia. Colombia is such a dangerous place, corrupted and full of crime. How are you going to secure our money?"

Back in 1994-1995, Colombia was at its worst. But Alejandro said: "You know nothing! All you are is pretty, and all you do is stand in front of a camera. And even that is over for you. What do you know about this? Leave the men to it. I have already committed $100,000."

What I knew about it was that it never made me feel well. I did not trust that doctor or his nephew. After about a year, the money had become $135,000. I realized that we had made money, not lost it, and I wanted to pull out. But no! Now, if we invested all of it, the earnings would be even better. The infamous nephew was in town, doing the investor rounds to convince everybody to stay in.

"Carmen, I am the one giving the least amount," Alejandro said. "I will look like a fool if I pull it out now. The doctor is putting his money where his mouth is and has money committed, too. That proves his nephew is not a thief."

And there we went. There was no way I could take the money out. At this time, we had sold our first home and built a new Spanish Colonial home. I would much rather put money in properties. That money I can see and touch. Paper money never made me feel comfortable, especially since all of it was under his mother's name.

Now, we had our first daughter and were expecting our second child. We went to dinner with the "nephew," and I was feeling so bad. Always hungry, but it was not hunger; it was an unpleasant feeling in my stomach.

Even though I was pregnant, Alejandro would not let me eat my food. He had this custom—terrible manners, according to my mother's teaching—of eating from someone else's plate. He had always eaten my food. I ordered spaghetti with mussels, which was very hot when it was served. I was waiting for it to cool down when he rolled up half of my spaghetti with one fork.

"Alejandro, please don't. I am very hungry."

"Then eat."

"It is too hot. I am waiting for it to cool."

After a while, without caring, he took the rest of my spaghetti, leaving almost none for me. By then, he had finished his entree. He eats very fast. I put my plate on top of his. That was my life.

Another year passed, and our money was GONE! All of it, all…gone! As was every penny in the Tiger Funds. The Colombian nephew was nowhere to be found, and the doctor was avoiding everybody. He said that he was not talking to his nephew!

More and more I became convinced that properties were the way to go. I had come up with the idea to build his office space and stop paying rent. But he refused, saying he needed to be at the hospital.

We skied a lot also, four to six times a year, always at the same place, Beaver Creek, Colorado. I started telling him that we were paying someone else's mortgage and if we kept going at that pace, we could be able to pay our own.

"What is it with women and real estate?" Alejandro said.

Instead, he became partners with his partner in crime, who worked for his father-in-law and felt used, abused and underappreciated. He had told Alejandro he was the one who had the knowledge and worked the hardest. The rest of the children were lazy.

Wanting to go off on his own and start a freight forwarding/contractual oil company, he did not have the money. He was just a little employee at his father-in-law's company. Of course, once his father-in-law found out about him going solo, he stopped at nothing to make him feel bad.

Alejandro had to help his friend, the one who was able to get more girls for Alejandro later on. After all, that was the way he entertained his oil clients. So we put up all the money for him to start his business. We became his partners but under Alejandro's mother's name.

"Carmen, this is the safest way to protect our money from lawsuits," he said. "Remember, as a doctor I am always running the risk of getting sued."

I never liked the fact that everything was put under his mother's name. How could I claim any of it as ours in an emergency? Seventeen years passed, and Alejandro's friend never gave us one penny of dividends. Not only that, but also Alejandro went out and incurred a loan of over $700,000 to help him with an investment in cargo ships that went belly up. And us? We still had to pay for the loan.

Our investment advisor ended up paying the loan with our savings without our authorization. Another one of Alejandro's genius investments!

We still had managed to save important money. Our investment agent was a friend of ours that Alejandro managed to alienate. We needed to move our money, and here came his brother, the only brother that was not a doctor and always needed money.

He had a friend who had just started to work for Stanford Bank and was pressuring Alejandro to invest the money with his friend because they could piggyback off each other and earn more interest. Stanford was offering a CD (certificate of deposit) at 8% interest. Nothing is more secure than a CD, and once we were all in Stanford Bank, they would treat us as a family account and the interest would go up.

We had lost a lot of money in the dotcom crash. We were tired of Wall Street, but at the same time I had never trusted his brother. He used to call Alejandro with investment advice, taking 10% right away. We always ended up losing the money, and he never gave us our 10% back. In fact, I found out years later that his brother was supposedly getting inside information that he sold to Alejandro. I was glad we never made a penny, especially if that was true.

Alejandro transferred all of our money from three different accounts to Stanford. We were making good money, but I think the maximum was 10% when the group account reached $5 million. His brother was getting a free ride with this.

Nothing made Alejandro happier than to see the monthly statements from Stanford at the end of the month. I was able to buy the apartment in Colorado, which was a great investment since we used it a lot. But still I could not convince Alejandro to build an office. I searched for build or buy options, but he was apprehensive. He would rather have the money in the bank.

I had to put an end to our family bank after we lost more money with another of his new friends. It looked like people befriended him to get money. His friend Roberto still owed us over $700,000!

I had been successfully buying and selling land, including the property that would become our dream home. My dream, totally paid for! But disaster was headed toward us. We had lost money during those years, but never enough to devastate us.

However, with the Stanford Bank disaster, we would lose all of our cash money.

We had always been able to survive. But this? Recovering from this loss within a year would become something Alejandro could not handle well. By helping us, our family, I helped him become a monster.

CHAPTER 19

My Life

W E WERE PADDLING IN THE RIVER on a beautiful day during summer vacation. My mother, aunts and their friends always came up with ideas to keep us entertained during vacation break. El Parque del Este was one of those perfect places for children in Caracas, Venezuela.

At the park, we walked, played games and had a picnic made by our mothers. Later in the day, we rented boats, one for the boys and another for the girls. Once when we were all the way on the other side of the river, in an area difficult to see from the shore, a boat full of boys from the bad neighborhoods rushed and got close to us. They started yelling bad words and threatened to kidnap us. They said we had to kiss them. The four of us in the girls' boat told them to go away. I was only 12 years old. My sister was 14, my cousin 10 and a friend 16. The boys, our cousins, could see us, but were mostly going in circles. They started screaming at the strangers to stay away from us, but they just laughed at them swirling around.

They got ahead of us and grasped the front cord of our boat, starting to drag us with them. We pleaded with them to let our boat go. My cousins were screaming and crying in frustration that they could not come close to us.

Suddenly, one of the boys began coming over to our boat. We all started screaming. I looked around to see what could I do. Suddenly it came upon me. I stood up, grabbed the paddle, raised it and said, "If you come over here, I will hit you now." I was determined; my eyes were fearless, staring straight at him. He started backing down and let the cord go. His friends started paddling away from us fast. We started yelling, and the rest of the girls hugged me.

After that, my mother used to say: "*A ti no se te muere el muchacho en la barriga* (The baby will never die in your belly)."

After years under Alejandro's hands, that girl stopped existing. I was strong back then. It took my husband years to break me down.

I do not know when the abuse started. It is difficult to understand when you are submerged in it. The emotional and mental abuse comes first, even though I did not know what it was then. I thought he was just rude at times and disrespectful. He did not "do" respect. I rejected it and thought it could not affect me. I never imagined that it was a form of abuse. After all, that does not happen in our social environment. We are educated people, highly educated people.

But once he decided to get rid of me, that was when things got dangerous and I did not have an idea that was what was happening. I thought his insults and put-downs were a way for him to express his frustration and they had nothing to do with me. I tried to understand his situation, telling myself it must be difficult to be with a woman as successful as me. See, I started making excuses for him even back then! That is what abused women do!

Life happens, and we get busy. I was busy at twenty years old with a successful television show. I was the spokeswoman for many products, while working on my broadcasting degree at the university and running a nonprofit organization that helped pediatric hospitals in Venezuela, Peru and Ecuador. My days were long and full.

Probably, the abuse all started when we were dating. But I was able to stand my ground then. Now, I realize I probably ignored the signs because I had not understood them, recognized them or had the time to analyze the situation. In such a full life, his innuendoes were minor or unimportant to me. Never a confrontational person, I was not raised in a family where manipulation was the rule.

One night on the way back home from the foundation's office, traffic in Caracas was (and still is) unbearable, causing my car motor to overheat. I had to stop at a gas station to cool down the car. He was waiting for me at home, and I was late! When I got there, he was beside himself, acting like a mad man screaming at me. Accusing me of being with another man, he called me a liar. I tried to explain, telling him the car had overheated. He screamed, "If the car is overheated, the hood should still be hot!"

He put the palm of his hand on the hood and burned himself. After that, he apologized. I was upset. I told him I did not like to be called a liar or accused of being a cheater.

Well, to catch a thief you need a thief. Now I understand! I should have realized then that this was his pattern of behavior. For the rest of our lives, he would accuse me of his acts. At one point, I ended our relationship, after he insisted that I not go to Maracaibo for a job engagement. He had chicken pox as an adult at 25. I was working on my *Complicidades* television show, the morning's top rated, and attending college at night.

Because he was sick, we had not seen each other for days. On Thursday, he called and said he could not come over to visit me. It was the 1980s, and we were so formal then. He visited my house every night as a boyfriend.

"Carmen, I cannot go over tonight. I will see you tomorrow."

"But I am leaving tomorrow after the show for Maracaibo," I replied.

"Well! You are not going."

"What do you mean? I am part of the Miss Zulia pageant. For weeks they have announced on television that I am attending."

"If you go, this is the end of it."

That was the end of the conversation. It was my work and my career. I went to Maracaibo anyway, and our relationship was over. He did not call and of course I did not call him. My mother taught me to "never" call a man. Three months passed. I was moving on.

It was a busy time for us at Venevisión as we got ready to celebrate our 25th anniversary with a major production. Every show in those 25 years of programming was part of a two-hour show and musicals. Working with Venevisión at that time was a dream come true. And it was a time when Venezuela was at its best economically, what I called the Golden Years.

After the *Complicidades* morning show, we had just enough time to work on our dresses for the next day's program before heading straight to the Municipal Theater for rehearsals the rest of the day for the anniversary production. Working with Joaquín Riviera, who was directing the production, was like being in the military but it was also magnificent. I had a super full day with no time to think about Alejandro.

Antonio Adolfo was responsible for all the programming involving the promotion of Venevisión and its values. One day, we had given him a ride. Just Eva Gutiérrez, Maite Delgado and I were in the car with Antonio.

"Girls, what are you up to?"

"Rehearsal, just like you," we answered together.

"But you have three hours."

"We all have to try on our dresses. So, we are stopping at each designer." It was always like that because we were always together.

"How about lunch? Are you having lunch?"

"No! No time," we all said.

We rushed during those three hours and got to rehearsal late, just a little. We sat down in the back, hoping Joaquín Riviera had not noticed we were late. Suddenly, we saw Antonio walking to our aisle of the theater with two bags. He sat down and handed them to us.

"Lunch girls," he said, then stood up and walked back to sit with Martha Rodríguez Miranda, his partner in the Department.

The girls teased me about him: "Come on, Carmen. He is not bringing us lunch. This is for you!"

In fact, he used to put roses or donuts on my studio chair most mornings.

Once the anniversary show was a thing of the past in October, we started working on the pre-sale for the next year's Venevisión budget. This was a production that was done every year to secure the network's budget for the following year. It involved taping the presentation, then showing them to clients every day throughout November. In December, we started recording the Christmas salute. And finally, the year wrapped up with a big Christmas party for Venevisión and all its sister companies. Once vacation started, I went to Houston to work on an English immersion course.

I came back in January busy and happy. Another great year had started. As usual, we had lunch with the star we had interviewed that day, Spanish singer Paloma San Basilio. That evening, while driving back home, a red traffic light got Alejandro and I back together when we stopped our cars next to each other.

He fooled me! He said he would never again impose anything on me. Even his jealousy disappeared, it seemed. People learn from their mistakes, and I thought he did.

It was a stressful time for Alejandro. He was studying to pass the test that would enable him to apply to practice his medical specialties in the US. His father was a bully, abusing him verbally, emotionally and financially.

During our courtship, his father made life very difficult for Alejandro because I was a former beauty queen and television personality. At 24, Alejandro was still dependent on his father. He was a full-time student in the School of Medicine and worked a few hours at his father's medical practice. Then his father cancelled his credit cards and cut him off. That was the way he used to control his children. Alejandro was left drifting from his mother's house to his cousins' houses.

Some people said his father was crazy. As a doctor, he was known for not practicing traditional medicine, giving his own pills to patients and not letting them know what they were taking. That was why people called him *"El Loco."* His excuse was that he was a researcher and a genius.

Also, there was a streak of rebellion in him that Alejandro inherited. They felt they were above the law or that the law knew nothing. Once his father complained about why he had to stop at a red light in the US when no cars were coming. He believed a law like that was ridiculous.

"Well, if you don't stop, you will get a ticket of $200," I said.

"Oh! Now there is a reason. I will stop then."

For them everything was about money, not rules, respect and civility.

At first, my father did not like Alejandro because he had been told that his father was a wife beater.

"Carmen María, people said that his father was a wife beater," he told me one day.

"Are you sure it is true?"

I was young and did not know much about his family then. In reality, not many people did. They were immigrants from Lebanon, working people. His uncle had a place where tires were redone, and Alejandro's dad was the only one in his family that went to college. As a doctor, he was able to mingle with the best of the best in Venezuela.

Too young and innocent, I thought at first that domestic violence was an accident and not inherited, that children should not pay for their parents' mistakes or be labeled because of them.

A few months into our marriage, Alejandro hit me for the first time in front of one of his brothers, who was visiting us. His brother did nothing. Had he seen a scene similar to this before? Did he think this was normal?

Looking back, I realized Alejandro thought he had acquired power over me because I had left everything to get married. I was living in a foreign country and did not speak the language. I had left my successful TV career and was completely dependent on him. However, after this incident, I left the apartment. I did not know what to do or where to go. I debated going back to Venezuela. But for what? Go back as a failure? Returning after just a few months not even able to speak English? I had lost my placement at the Universidad Central de Venezuela. What was I going to do? For sure, I was not even getting my job back.

I went back to the apartment in the morning and told Alejandro I would not ever tolerate that again. That if it did happen again, I was going to call the police. At that time, he was on the verge of being kicked out of his internship at Bowman Gray School of Medicine at Wake Forest University. This was the last thing he needed. It was so bad that he wanted to quit. I did not know exactly what was going on. But when he said he wanted to quit, I said: "You are not a quitter. You are going to stay here and make it work. We will make it work, whatever is happening."

And we stayed! However, he ended up getting kicked out of the program. I never knew why.

All abusers and bullies are cowards. He saw the risk he faced so he backed down, at least for a while. However, the verbal abuse never stopped. Back then, I thought he was trying to make me mad. But in reality, he was destroying me little by little. There were always diminishing comments or outright insults toward my family and everything I did, whether it was good or bad. There were sarcastic comments or comments to create fear. But I was stronger then. I had answers for his comments or just laughed them off. For example, he started saying I had wrinkles when I was 25 years old. I started taking care of my skin at 15, cleaning and moisturizing my face every day. I never went to bed with makeup and always cleaned my skin before sleeping, even if I did not have on any makeup. As I started working and making my own money, I invested in better creams.

When we got married and moved to the United States, we had the life of students living on a tight budget. However, I had savings in dollars from my work and kept buying creams, my only indulgence.

"Carmen, why are you spending money on those creams when you are so young?" Alejandro asked.

"It is preventive medicine, Alejandro. Why would I want the creams once I am wrinkled?"

He has always been worried about getting bald, as it runs on his father's side, constantly checking himself in mirrors to see his head in different light. But one day out of the blue, he came close to me and said: "Look, you have wrinkles around your eyes."

I was surprised! I checked myself in the mirror and nothing was there. But to him it became the way he said hello, goodbye, and I love you, etc.: "How are the wrinkles today?"

One day I heard him talking to one of his brothers on the phone, telling him laughing how he had me checking mirrors. "I told Carmen she has wrinkles around her eyes and now she goes from mirror to mirror."

Yes, I was starting to believe it, starting to see wrinkles around my eyes. But after I overheard that conversation, I realized he was up to no good. One day, when he asked me how the wrinkles were today, I said: "Very well, thanks! I am not worried about wrinkles. After all, there is a solution for this. But look at *Star Trek: the Next Generation*. It is the year 2400 and they still have not found the cure for baldness. The captain is completely bald."

He looked at me surprised. He never expected that from me. And that was the end of that!!!

I had comebacks. I knew how to stand up for myself. But that ability started to disappear once his abuse wore me down more and more. I started to be slow with my comebacks until little by little, they stopped.

Part of our Venezuelan culture was to be funny. People were expected to be fast and come up with smart answers. Plus, my pageant training made me even faster. I had to be ready to answer many questions in interviews. So, it has long been part of who I am.

My mother always said that out of her children, Pedro and I were the funny ones. One day, when she visited me at home in Houston, she said, "*Carmen María, este país te ha puesto tonta. Ya no tienes la chispa de antes.* (Carmen María, this country has affected you. You are not the funny girl you used to be.)"

Is it this country or my husband? His mental abuse toward me was already taking a toll. I did not know those innuendoes could do so much damage. Without realizing, I was careful of what I said or did, because I was avoiding his criticism. He also withheld sex from me as another form of punishment during the first years of our marriage. It became another way to fight. He would not talk about it beyond blaming being stressed on all the problems he had in his program. There I was, a new bride and not having sex. I never understood and felt there was no purpose in being married. In the meantime, all of my girlfriends and cousins were getting married. I thought: "Welcome to misery."

When we had to leave North Carolina, after Bowman Gray kicked Alejandro out, he negotiated moving to a lesser program. This came back to haunt him later, when he started private practice in Houston and got privileges at the hospitals. Bowman Gray gave him a bad reference.

Alejandro always had trouble in any program he went into. His explanation was that everybody was jealous of him! That used to be his line. Just like he had problems with every friend he had. It was never his fault. It was always someone else's fault.

We went to Tennessee, and he concocted the cover story that he had to sacrifice his wonderful education at Wake Forest University in order for me to study Broadcasting at the university in Tennessee. I hated it when he told this lie, painting him as the perfect loving husband, because I could have attended the university at Greensboro in North Carolina. This was when he started using me as his cover-up. I was even his cover-up when I called the police to report his attacks or every time I called the police.

Once we moved to Tennessee and I started college there, I was Carmen María again. In Tennessee, I became a star again! I was on the Dean's List every semester, graduating *magna cum laude* with a 3.94 GPA. Once the school found out I was a former Miss Venezuela and second runner up at the Miss Universe pageant, I was featured in the school newspaper and recruiting pamphlet. They even ran my story in the local newspapers.

In two years at the college, no one had ever met Alejandro. He never attended the parties and events at the school. Toward the end, people started teasing me: "This whole story that you are married is a lie. You made that up to keep boys at bay."

It took a year and a half to get back to Venezuela. We spent Christmas with his father in Europe, so it was only fair that we spent New Year's with my family. My parents also invited his mother to spend New Year's with us. But Alejandro had to spend it with his father because he was afraid his financial assistance would stop. I never understood that.

We were to spend New Year's at my aunt's house and Alejandro was dropping my father, mother and I there. He was verbally rude to me all the way there. As usual, I did not understand why. Trying to keep the peace, I hoped my parents were not noticing his behavior toward me. How naïve.

At one point my father said: "Alejandro, if you keep talking to Carmen María like this, I will get out of the car."

Alejandro did not expect this reaction from my father and he stopped.

He applied for a fellowship in lung medicine and entered the Baylor College of Medicine in Houston. I was thrilled because my brother and his family were in Houston. I would finally be close to at least one member of my family, which I missed a lot. We were family type people. My family was so big that I missed the mess. There were never only a few of us. There were always a lot. And friends! Friends became our family and just added to the mess. Yes, we were Latin and loud. But we loved each other and had fun.

But Alejandro hated it.

Once I moved to Houston, I was always in touch with my brother, visiting him and his family or having them over. Alejandro started criticizing my brother and his family for anything. There were always critical comments. Many times, he just did not want to see them, to the point where we started seeing each other less and less.

At the same time, Alejandro started criticizing my mother and father all the time. We were living thousands of miles apart, they in Venezuela and us in the US. However, he constantly commented about them, like he had just been with them the weekend before. It became his new motto.

Until one day I said: "What is it with you? Suddenly you have had it with my parents with complaints you never had before. You never said those things about them. What is wrong?"

"My mother knows it very well!" he answered. "She is at your parents' all the time and has very little good things to say about them!"

His mother, a woman that never got married and whose father died of alcoholism when she was a child, who had no experience with people in a relationship or as couples, suddenly was an expert in marriage and relationships. And she was criticizing my parents about the way they treated each other, talked to each other and cared for each other. Or was she making things up?

"Your mother is a manipulative bitch that has your father under her little finger," Alejandro continued. "And I am not going to allow that to happen to me. My mother is warning me about all of your techniques that you have learned from your mother."

OMG! My parents had opened their doors to his mother. They added her to our family and took care of her mother (Alejandro's grandmother) whenever she had to travel. Just like family does. This is what family is all about. And in exchange, his mother was a character destroying my parents!

My father is an old-fashioned Latin man. Ever the gentlemen with a good strong character that we all respected. Added to that, he is from Maracaibo, where people are very strong, and my mother is controlling my father?

My parents were married for 40 years until my father died. There was a lot of love between them. My mother was a wonderful mother, always putting us first and working to support us when need be. She loved my father and was a wonderful wife, taking care of him and cooking everything he loved. She still is such a strong woman, putting up with my dad, who was a spoiled but wonderful man. Nothing is perfect, and as a couple they had their problems, but he was a loving husband and a great dad. He loved us deeply.

In my house, it was yours, mine and ours, yet he treated and loved us the same. It was all about family in our house. So, when I married Alejandro, my parents accepted his mother as part of us. It was not possible to do the same with his father, because he hardly talked with anybody; he felt he was above everyone else.

They invited Alejandro's mother over often to eat. And she was included in every event, get together, dinner, lunch, barbecue, etc., that my parents had at their house. My father became her protector.

She always asked him for advice. On two occasions he saved her from losing her savings to her brother, who was stealing from her.

But his mother abused that love and trust, using those visits to destroy my parents' character in front of Alejandro. She had never had a family environment and, in fact, had a terrible relationship with her brother and hated her brother's wife and children. As a matter of fact, Alejandro and his brothers did not like their cousins and did not have relationships with them.

I thought it was strange that his mother had no relationships with anybody on either side of her family, because I have relationships with my first cousins, second cousins and so on. When I asked him where he was getting this, he said: "Nobody knows better than my mom because she is always at your parents' house."

I replied that she was until today! I called my mother to tell her what his mother was saying about them. After that, she was never invited to my house again. But that did not solve the problem because his mother's poison was inside Alejandro and he repeated the same things about my parents whenever he could.

When I got to Houston, I put myself to work. I wanted to get back to television, but was ready to try new things after graduating from college, so I decided to get into news. I went around and dropped off my resume at the two Spanish television stations in Houston, then called them and met the people there. I was trying every possible way to get in. By December, I had a job at Telemundo as a reporter; within months, I was promoted to anchorwoman.

I was thrilled. It was an opportunity to work in news. No more entertainment, beauty advice, or horoscopes. Now I was going to join a serious newscast and become a journalist. I started my new job and was ready to be the best. Of course, this came with sacrifices. Telemundo only had newscasts at 5 p.m. and 10 p.m. I finished at night after 10:30 and was home by 11. By that time, I was exhausted. Plus, I had to spend Christmas and New Year's Eve working. But it did not matter; I was learning and working in what I loved.

During the holidays, Alejandro and I met after work and celebrated together. He was happy I was feeling fulfilled. And I was happy he was doing what he loved also. Alejandro watched the newscast every night, just to see my piece. Every night when I came back from work, he would tell me: "It is incredible that the female news anchor is so bad. She does not know how to speak Spanish. They need to seat you in that chair."

And that was my goal! To get promoted as news anchor. After all, I had the experience of conducting a four-hour live television show in Venezuela.

When Alejandro was proud about me, he was really proud. He talked to others as if I hung the moon. Life was simple and we were happy.

It was not easy to get the news anchor job. I was the only communications major college graduate in the News Department, yet the news director did not want to give me the position, because I was too white, educated and came from an upper-class background. Therefore, our audience could not empathize with me, or so he said.

Alejandro was infuriated. "Why are they not giving you the seat? There is nobody better than you."

It came as an order from the network to give me the position, after I introduced myself to a network executive that was visiting Houston one morning before my boss arrived at the office. As a reporter, I had to arrive at 9 a.m., while my boss came later. So I walked by the office the executive was using, stopped, introduced myself and gave him my resume. The network had been conducting a national search for the position when the perfect person was already in house.

In punishment, my boss had me doing two jobs, reporter and anchorwoman, for months. I was working over twelve hours a day under a salary, not an hourly rate. They had told me the station could not find a reporter, so I found her myself. She was a young girl, Oralia Galván, whom I had interviewed about an explosion in Guadalajara. I had come across her on the street while asking people if they were from Guadalajara. After the interview, she said she would love to work in television so I helped her. To this day we are friends!

However, my first job in the US would prove to be my first experience with this macho society. I was paid less just because I was a woman. Being a college graduate with honors did not mean a thing. It got even worse when the anchorman was replaced at the station by a reporter who was a former furniture salesman with no college education, and he still made more money than me.

Why? Just because he was a man.

Still, I loved my job! I had always liked being a broadcaster, and doing the news was a new and incredible experience. I worked hard, writing every story I read.

Alejandro was doing his training as a fellow for pulmonary disease. He said he was working late and on call. Many years later, I found out that he was having affairs back then, and we were just married.

My work would prove to interfere with our lives. After I was given the chair as anchorwoman, I had to cancel a trip to Buenos Aires, Argentina, because I was scheduled to cover the Republican National Convention in Houston in 1992. Alejandro did not mind because he knew how important it was for my career to be part of a political convention. I joined him in Venezuela once the convention was over. He was so proud of me then and who I was. Once I arrived, he had all kinds of questions about my experience and was happy to hear everything.

"Alejandro, I met Peter Jennings and Dan Rather, prime-time news anchors for the major US television networks."

"So proud of you, *mi cielo*. You were in the big leagues."

"Yes, I was! It felt so good, so real. If only my accent was better, I could work in English stations."

"And you will. I have no doubt you will," he said.

Once I was back to being who I was, the career woman, successful and once again supporting him monetarily, he was not abusive to me for the time being. However, he was still cheating. I did not know this until we were in therapy in 2011, when he confessed little by little all of his indiscretions, even the night before our wedding. Every session was heartbreaking. I had lived a lie for so many years.

He never touched me again until 1995, when I started working for him. He had finished all his schooling and started his practice. I was managing everything. He was working so hard 24/7, always on call with long hours. I was helping him. One morning, he got a call while we were still in bed early in the morning. He talked and then I heard a woman at the other end say "I love you."

He hung up. I told him I had heard what the woman said. He denied it, and I insisted she said that.

Then he got on top of me and started punching me while saying, "You have a problem. You see ghosts."

Then he stood up, took a shower and went to work. Later around 11 a.m. he came back, which was rare. With his long hours, he had never come home in the middle of the day before. He apologized and said again that the woman never said that. Instead, it was a nurse giving him an update about a patient.

"Carmen, I will never ever cheat on you," he said. "I know you would leave me if I did, and I would not risk that."

Alejandro spent the whole day with me. That was a treat then, because of his long hours. He was working seven days a week and on call all the time.

CHAPTER 20

The Burglary

O N   A   T H U R S D A Y   afternoon in late fall in Johnson City, Tennessee, it had already started to get dark early. I was done for the day, having finished classes, homework and studying for a test. Now I was cooking dinner for the two of us, while waiting for Alejandro to come back from the hospital, when suddenly the door opens and slams shut hard.

"Turn off all the lights," Alejandro screamed, starting to turn them off.

"What? Why?"

"Carmen, turn off all the lights and shut up. Don't say a word." He was closing the blinds also.

"What happened?"

"Shhhhhhhh…" he signaled while looking through the peep hole.

I went upstairs to look from the window of the study. I saw a car parked in the middle of the common parking lot in our section of the townhome complex where we lived. Two young men are walking around Alejandro's car and looking around, trying to figure out where he went. Of course, Alejandro did not park close to our unit.

They walked back and forth toward the doors, trying to determine which unit he was in.

"That son of a bitch," I heard one saying.

"Yeah, all brave making us almost crash, and now he hides," the other replied.

I remembered that I had something on the stove and went downstairs to turn it off. Alejandro signaled me to be quiet. We sat in the dark for a while listening to them talk outside. I was hungry! "How much longer is this going to last?" I thought.

I went upstairs and looked through the blinds again. They were getting inside their car. After a while, they left. I came down and told Alejandro they left.

"Shhhhhh," he signaled again. "They can come back."

"How much longer this is going to take?"

"Shut up, Carmen!"

I went to the kitchen to continue cooking. After a while, when Alejandro realized they were gone for sure, he turned on the television.

"Can you explain what was that about?" I asked.

"These men where messing around in the road, so I cut them off. After that, they started to follow me."

"How weird, Alejandro."

"Yes, Carmen, people are crazy."

In time I came to learn that Alejandro had frequent road rages. For no apparent reason, he got mad and started to follow cars at high speeds and/or cut off other people. After he had guns, he would pull them out and show them to the other person as a threat. I would be inside the car scared to death, screaming at him.

This behavior made my brother never want to drive with him again, after an incident in Colorado on I-70.

"Carmen María, he could have killed us, or those people could have pulled a gun and killed us," my brother told me the night I went to his house on Halloween. He had never mentioned it to me before.

"*Todo malo es cobarde!* (All bad people are cowards.)"

My cell phone started ringing and it was dark, still night. The time on my phone said it was 4 a.m. in California. Who could be calling at this time?

"*Señora, robaron la casa* (Ma'am, the house was burglarized)."

I could not make sense of what she said to me.

"What?" I asked.

Alicia was on the other end. She was one of my maids. I had two; she was the live in.

"I just got here and the door that goes to the front on the side is wide open. I can tell a few things are not here, but I do not want to go in further."

"Alejandro, Alejandro, wake up! The house was burglarized!"

"Ah… okay."

And he turned over and continued sleeping.

"You're going to keep on sleeping?"

"What can I do now?" he answered.

It was like I told him it was raining outside.

I called 911. Silly me, Carmel Police answered. That was confirmation that I was not in Houston. I think and called my friend Amanda, who was my realtor. It was 6 a.m. in Houston. She must not be awake. After all, her children are in college.

"Amanda, my house was burglarized."

She was impressed.

"What? When?"

"I don't know. Alicia just called and told me. I am in Carmel, California. I cannot call the Houston police from here. Please, call the police and if you can, go over. Alicia is scared."

Amanda became a realtor not long ago, and I was her first client. I was working with another agent, looking for a lot to build my next house. I wanted to be close to the children's school and to back up to the bayou. I wanted to feel like I was on a ranch without neighbors in the back.

Amanda pleaded with me to give her a chance. So, I did. I had instructed my realtor to look in River Oaks and Memorial. But

Amanda got to work and found me a beautiful lot in Tanglewood, where I did not particularly want to be. I decided to go take a look. It was a brand-new gated community, and I liked it. We put in an offer.

Before closing on the loan, I went to talk with the developer to tell him about the plan for my house, a contemporary style. He explained to me that there were deed restrictions, but since he was on the Board, he was going to make sure my plans passed. What he did not tell me was that as soon as my lot was sold, it was the last one and he would be off the Board. My plans never passed, so I decided to sell the lot for $300,000 more than what I originally paid for it. Amanda protested.

"Amanda, God has a plan as to why I bought this land. If I sell it for this much, I will understand."

She did not put her name on the sale sign because she was so embarrassed—or she did not have it since she was so new. But with the sale, I was able to purchase my next land with cash. No more loans.

Amanda became my best friend. She started feeling like my success in buying and selling land was all her doing, when in fact it was my luck, my eye on location and prices. With her, I bought and sold many lots. I introduced her to all of my friends. At the time, she had a very limited scope of friends. But I opened up a new world for her that brought a lot of business.

However, when the house was on the market for the divorce, Alejandro opposed having her as the agent. I had to get some-one else. She was out of town when that happened, and I was waiting for her to come back to tell her. She found out before I was able to explain and never talked to me again!

That made me realize that our friendship had a price! But more than that, what she really wanted was to move into my life. Once I was out of the social circle, she moved in, as she was now friends with all of my former friends. Just like Alejandro's sister-in-law started being part of some of the charities that I was working with. They were taking my place, stealing my identity.

But at the time of the burglary, she was the best person to get to help. She had interests in all of my properties and had made a lot of money with me. That was my thought while I was pacing the bedroom, while everybody else slept. I was waiting on a call from Houston for a better report of what was stolen in my house.

Carmel, California, is such a beautiful place. The weather is incredible, especially in August, compared to other places. We had never been here before. It was breathtaking, especially for me. Everything next to the water I love. It is the Caribbean girl within me.

We loved to see the Garcías in Carmel. They were both doctors and our children were close in age, so they had fun, too, when we were together. Somehow Alejandro had managed to keep this friendship. His friends never last.

They lived a quiet life. Everything revolved around their hospital work and the children. I adored Jennifer, such a strong woman who finished her medical training while having her children. And at the same time, she managed to be a great mother. I admired that in her. When they invited us over, she was such a graceful hostess. Worried about us, making sure we were comfortable and having a good time.

Alexandra was not with us because she was off doing her *quinceañera* tour in Europe.

Jennifer's specialty was ear, nose and throat. She took care of me when I had a severe ear infection while breastfeeding my second daughter, Kamee. I swore I was going to give equal time breastfeeding to each of my children. Since I had breastfed Alexandra for six months, I had to do the same for all of my children. I started having ear pain with Kamee. It was not bad and I was so busy with the baby and my two-and-a half-year-old that it was secondary, until I started to have fever.

I called Jennifer, whose second baby was a little older than mine. She came to my house and checked me.

"Carmen, you have an infection. You need antibiotics."

"I cannot, Jennifer, I am breastfeeding."

"If you do not take the medicine, we will need to cut open the membrane and empty the ear. It does not hurt, but is bothersome."

"I would rather do that. I cannot stop breastfeeding Kamee."

On Sunday, I went to her office, where she cut open my ear, drained it and put topical antibiotic drops inside.

"This should do it," she said. "You are going to feel weird for a couple of days, but that will be it. Let's hope on that."

Yes, I felt like I was inside a box. I decided to stay home while it healed, because all noise bothered me. The fever persisted. I called Jennifer again, learning the only alternatives were another cut and clean or forgetting about breastfeeding and taking the medicine.

"I cannot do that to my baby. I feel I am stealing something from her. Let's try one more time."

While in the office, Jennifer said: "Carmen, you are so strong. What you have must hurt so badly, I cannot believe you put up with it. At this point, I would have just stopped the breastfeeding."

It hurt but I thought I could handle it, until I got the fever. This strength will be my savior later in my life.

In the third and last house I built during our marriage, I paid attention to every little detail. Everything I had learned in the previous two houses I had built and the other two I had lived in, I perfected and added everything you can imagine. Not only was it a big house, it had it all, even a hidden closet (that I called my Martha Stewart closet) for gift wrapping and to hide every ugly thing that did not look good out in the study, like printers and file cabinets. I hid them behind built-in bookshelves. Very few people knew about this space that was also designed to serve as a hiding place in case of emergency.

Of course, as the girl with lots of dreams since I was little, I designed myself a two-story closet. Within that closet, I built a cedar fur closet with temperature control and zero humidity. I was finally able to see everything I have since now I could spread out my clothes and not be crowded like my old closet.

On the second level, I arranged all my gowns with evening shoes and handbags, including my pageant gowns and even my collection of hats. That was where the fur closet was with a mink stole my mother gave me that my dad had given her many years ago and a rabbit stole that my sisters and I used as little girls. Since my girls were closer in age, I had a duplicate made so both of them had matching stoles.

My closet was every little girl's dream. It was the most visited place in the house. My daughters took all of their girlfriends there. And of course, the closet became the center of Alejandro's attacks as soon as we moved into the house.

"You have a fortune there. How much?"

He was always making those remarks.

In reality, I did not have much more than I had had before. The furs I used to put in storage at Saks Fifth Avenue as soon as the winter ended. The only difference now was that you could see my clothes. They were no longer all packed in a little closet to the point where I could not see what I had.

Also, my mother, father and family gave me many of the things in my closet.

"How much money would it be if you sold it?" he used to ask.

My closet was years in the making. It had a lifetime of memories.

We moved to the house in October 2010. We had lost all of our savings in Stanford Bank in February 2009. He was desperate to make the money back again. And we were able to recover thanks to my ability to go lean after the loss.

After the Stanford default, we finished the house and built the commercial building, where he had his practice. We also sold our previous home and were able to cover the theft against our life insurance, putting away money for the children's college funds. But that did not put much more money in the bank for us.

Alejandro loves money in the bank. He loves to look at statements growing. But the thing about having all the money in banks is that it can disappear like wrapping paper, just like it did with Stanford.

That is why I think my closet became an obsession for him! He even convinced the girls…look at your mother's closet. Like many things about me with him, the closet became a way to belittle me, like practicing my religion or wanting to spend time with my family. It was not like the closet was all mine. He kept his clothes there, too.

Ten months after we moved into the new house, the burglary happened. What happened with the alarm? How about the cameras? How did they enter the house? It is a massive house with massive doors.

Finally, Amanda called.

"I am here and so are the police. They took a lot, many things from your closet. I do not know in detail what else. You need to see it. I am so sorry."

I started to cry. I am talking to God and saying, "I know it is material and should be thankful we were not there and that we are safe." But I had so many things that were dear to me and had a sentimental value.

Alejandro finally wakes up and asked, "Did they take any of the art?"

"No," I answered.

He turned and fell asleep again. My God!!! How can he?

"Alejandro, I need to go home today. I cannot stay here after this."

He was set to leave that day and I was going to stay a few days with the children. When the Garcías woke up, we explained what had happened. They felt so sorry. We went to the airport and tried to get on the plane. It was a small plane and they informed me there was no chance. But I could wait and see if I got lucky.

While we were trying to get on the plane, Alejandro was mad, mad that I wanted to go. At some point, there were spaces for him and the children. One adult had to go with them. He said, "Okay, I am going with them. You can stay."

"Alejandro, I cannot stay. I have to see what happened."

He was mad. It was as if he did not want me to go that day. Finally, we got lucky and all of us were able to get on the same flight. On the plane, Alejandro was cool as ever, listening to his audio books and ignoring me. I went to his seat and told him I felt a lot of anxiety.

"Why, Carmen? It is okay. Sit down."

"I don't understand you. You are acting like this is an every-day issue. I feel violated. People, strangers touching my stuff."

"Come on, Carmen. Sit down."

Before I got on the plane, I had called Amanda and told her what time I would be home, asking her to be there. I did not know how I was going to feel when I saw my house. I had lost too much in my life lately: Stanford Bank, realizing Alejandro had been cheating, and now this.

We arrived in Houston to the longest drive ever from the airport to the house. It felt eternal. When we arrived, Amanda was there. Downstairs did not look like much had been disrupted, but upstairs was a disaster. Guess what? The main target, we could even say the only target, was my closet! 98 percent of the items stolen were from my closet. The thieves took my shoes, handbags, jewelry, furs and few pieces of clothing. After all, not many people can fit into a size 4.

Oh! And Alejandro's exercise t-shirts, just to say something of his was taken. I could only imagine it was to make it look like something of his was taken. We found this out days later. My underwear was thrown all over the closet floor. Strangers touched my underwear! I could never wear any of that again.

After examining the house, Alejandro went downstairs and opened a bottle of wine saying, "Let's toast what was not taken."

He was happy! The man who wanted to quit his internship because he was failing. The man who was always negative. The same man who hid from the two young men. The man who had panic attacks when we lost the money in Stanford was now acting like he could see the positive side of things and being more positive than anybody else. I could not understand this reaction.

By the next morning, he was making sure I got in touch with the insurance company.

The burglary happened between Saturday and Sunday. The maids had left on Friday afternoon, even though Alicia was supposed to stay until Saturday at 2 p.m. Why she left early I did not know. The other maid, the one who did not sleep in the house, did not come back on Monday nor did she answer any of my calls. It was obvious she had something to do with this.

I called to get back-up copies of all the videos from the securities cameras, so we could see who and when the house was broken in. I already had the police report, but was told it could take weeks until an investigator was assigned.

"Carmen, I do not understand you," Alejandro said. "What do I have you for? You are friends with the Harris County Sherriff. Use it. Call Adrian and find a way he can help us put our case on top."

I never thought like that. I never liked to bother my friends or friends in power to my advantage. Alejandro insisted by saying that we had donated to his campaign and therefore he had to help us.

Well, it did the trick. However, by the time an investigator was assigned, it was over a week after the burglary. Whoever stole my stuff was probably far away in Mexico already.

The insurance company requested an itemized list of everything that was stolen. That was a full-time job! I had to remember everything I had that now was gone. It took me months, because every day I remembered something else.

In the meantime, the investigator started his job. Thanks to the cameras we found out the burglary started at 2:00 p.m. on Saturday. The burglar was a young Hispanic male around 20 years of age wearing a cap, dark sunglasses and surgical gloves. He came in with a key that he managed to put where we keep all keys. How did he know that?

He went to the room where the security system was, then left, apparently to get tools to disable the security system, which is what happened when he came back at 2:30 p.m. There is a Home Depot very close to my house.

The alarm was not on. In the video from the day before, the other maid is standing in front of the pad, probably just to make us believe she turned on the alarm because she knew we checked the cameras with the iPad, which Alejandro did on Saturday. I remember when he looked at the iPad, something was black. I asked him what he was looking at. He said nothing and turned off the iPad.

If he saw black, he should have been alerted, but he did not mention it. However, when the news of the burglary came and he was fully awake, he said: "Yeah, no wonder it was black when I checked the cameras."

Not only that, but he got an email alerting him the cameras were disabled. He did nothing in response. All of this would start making sense when I realized who he really was years later.

The neighbor's maid said she saw a moving truck in the garage but did not think anything of it. The Houston Police Department investigator found out that the other maid moved out of her apartment on Sunday, the day after the burglary. He also interrogated our other maid and noticed she was very nervous. He said she must have known something. She said things in the house that also caught my attention. The lie detector test they had her take was inconclusive. The investigator's advice was not to trust her. I wanted to fire her, but Alejandro advised against it.

"Carmen, you have to keep your enemies close."

"Alejandro, this woman confessed to the police she stole from us, then returned a lot of the things she took."

"No, Carmen, listen to me. I am always right."

She was his employee, not mine. This woman did everything for him. Even cover up when he brought women to the house while I was gone. She ended up in court ready to testify against me for the divorce.

Alejandro kept asking how much we were going to get back from the insurance policy.

"I don't know, Alejandro. All I know is that the loss is over a million dollars. What the insurance is going to pay, I have no idea!"

"I want to know."

"You do understand that 90 percent of what was stolen was mine?"

"I am sorry, Carmen. Poor little you. Little girl that has it all in life now lost a bunch!"

"Alejandro, my parents gave me many of those things. They had a sentimental value."

"Carmen, that is stuff, now MONEY! That is valuable."

I could not believe he said that money is more valuable than something that reminds me of my father, or that my mother gave me with all her love. Or every piece of jewelry he gave me for my children's births.

The other maid was no place to be found. She either moved to another state or went back to Mexico with a truck full of merchandise. The insurance company started to pay and Alejandro told me to open a separate account since this amount would not be taxed and we should not comingle it with the rest of the money. And I did. I went to the bank and brought the papers for him to sign.

After a while, when all had been paid, he said to transfer it to my cousin's bank outside the US and I did. This was the only money I had access to after I filed my divorce. With this, I paid the criminal lawyers, and the rest Hoffman took. However, Alejandro accused me of fraud and stealing the money. But I had every penny accounted for.

The burglary was like we opened the door for them to come in. It was my maid, and she knew where everything was. It was clean, no mess, just my closet.

Alejandro was happy, like life was giving him back what he lost in Stanford, but from my property. God only knows if he got paid by these people. After we were separated, I learned he was having an affair with the maid, and that she was not the only maid he had affairs with.

When I found out about the affair was when the burglary made sense to me. It was an inside job like I had always said, but I did not know until then how much "inside" it was. Was Alejandro part of it?

After 2013, I mentioned my suspicion to a couple of my friends, and they said: "Of course it was him. We all knew it, Carmen!"

CHAPTER 21

My Mother, the Entrepreneur

I ALWAYS THOUGHT THE world was an omelet and I could eat it at any moment—as long as you had good intentions, did well to others, did not hurt anyone, worked hard and always told the truth.

Those were the principles under which we were raised. They were how I was able to accomplish everything and be positive about everything I did. That and the "truth" were the most important aspects for us. My father told us that as long as we told the truth —it did not matter how ugly it was—he would be easier on us. But if we lied, expect the worse.

My mother thought, in fact, that Dad was soft because of it. But not at all; it showed us the importance and value of the truth.

Out of all the examples I have from him about the truth, the best one was when I was in the eighth grade. A group of us decided to skip school, while our friend wrote our names as absent on the school record book. That book was untouchable, much like the Bible. Because of the poor job our friend did trying to make us look like we were absent from the first period, we were all caught. Therefore, both teams were in trouble.

We were starting a long weekend and the school summoned all parents with students to a meeting with the principal on the first day of the break.

How could I tell my dad? But I remembered, as long as I told the truth, it was going to be okay.

Once at home, we were all packing for the break. Our whole family was going to the ranch of one of my dad's friends. We were leaving early in the morning as it was a long drive. I took a deep breath and informed my dad: "*Papi*, we have to stop at the school first."

"Why? What have you done?"

"*Papi*, you see, some skipped school and some fixed the attendance book, so all of us have to meet with the principal tomorrow morning along with our parents."

I did not know how my dad would take any of the violations. It was as bad to skip school as to change school property. But definitely I thought skipping had to be the worst.

"Which team were you part of?" he asked me.

Like he said, the truth will set me free. That became my motto over 30 years later.

"The ones that skipped school, Dad."

"Where did you go? What did you do? And who with?"

I named each one of my accomplices and added that we went to the beach.

"Did you have fun?"

I could see from my mother's expression that she could not believe my father's line of questioning and the way he was handling this.

"Yes, *Papi*, we did have fun."

"Would you do it again?"

"No, never again."

"Okay. What time do we have to be at school?"

"7:30 a.m., *Papi*."

"Okay. We will stop at the school and from there we will hit the road."

"I cannot believe you are letting this go this easy," my mother told him. "You are too soft with them, her especially."

"First of all, if she is telling the truth, you know this is the deal I have with them. Second, I did what she did when I was her age. It is about being young."

Sure enough, next morning we are at the school with all parents and students involved in this terrible incident. It was not only the biggest group that had ever skipped school, but also the largest violation to school property. We were dressed ready to go on our ranch adventure with boots and hats. The car was packed with food. We were all set.

The principal started with the kids that altered the attendance book and went on and on, never getting to the skippers. I could see my father's face; he felt as if I had lied to him. Until finally Dad said: "Wait a minute. In which group is my daughter?"

"The ones who skipped school. I will address that after this."

"Okay, where can I sign so we can go?"

The principal looked at him puzzled.

"I have a deal with them that if they tell the truth, they would not be in trouble, and she did."

My dad, being a *maracucho*, was a very conservative man. His family namesake is an icon in Maracaibo. In fact, when you say Montiel it is automatically known that we are from Maracaibo.

However, my mother is from Altamira de Cáceres, Barinas, a town at the foot of the Andes. A coffee growing town that was the first settlement in the Barinas state, this historical town had been declared Patrimonial Heritage of the Nation. However historic the town was, it still was a small place.

It was said by many that my mother was so beautiful that she stopped traffic! I used to joke with those who said it: "Well, but how many cars were there?"

The truth is my mother was very beautiful; they said her skin had a smoothness and shine like no other. She had big almond shape eyes. They used to be big and full of expressions. Her brothers had blue and green eyes, but the girls got brown eyes. However, her eyes were full of life. When we were misbehaving, she used to open them so big that we knew what was coming. That was all we needed to stop. But that respect for mothers and authority was something we had lost.

My parents' love story is a story of how doing something different can change your life and what has become one of my mottos: "If you stay home, nothing happens. Get out."

My mother accepted an invitation from a friend to accompany her to Maracaibo for a wedding and there, just by coincidence, she met my dad. Dad ran his family's company, then became an independent business owner, until one of those turns in the economy played a trick on him and his company went belly up. That brought about many changes in our life style. School was one, and I started working early on in my life. In fact, all of us did. My mother, to the surprise of us all, started working to support us and went on to show that she was quite an entrepreneur.

She was a good businesswoman and went on to have different companies, but always in the house. That way she could be the mother she wanted to be. She had a flower shop and a catering business. And all of us had to help her. We were her workers; even my father helped.

We managed studying and work time. I grew up admiring her tenacity, ability to work, and how everything she did was great. We all learned to organize our schedules depending on Mother's orders and needs. The worst times were the last two months of the year, when she sold *hallacas* and made

$1,000 a week. It became a tradition that I spent my birthday making *hallacas*.

Second worst was when my mother had big orders for funerals. We had to make what is called *coronas*, which are flower arrangements made only for funerals where leaves from a rubber tree were set with wire hooks—sometimes making my fingers bleed. That is when I learned that finishing my education was ever so important and keeping my career was a must as a woman. However, life and wanting to dedicate myself to my family made me forget all of that. And the fact that I felt I never stopped working because I worked for my husband made me feel like I did not abandon the work force, when, in fact, I did.

My mother never complained during that time or appeared to be stressed out. She handled her new life with grace, showing us how hard work is always appreciated and valuable in life. As she did again years later, when she had to put in ten years of work in the United States to earn all the benefits of a US citizen.

I learned from her how to be strong in bad times by keeping a good face and my head up. She always said: "No one has to know if anything wrong is happening; that is for you to know." I owe my strength to her.

CHAPTER 22

Trying to Institutionalize Me

Women are at the highest risk in an abusive relationship when they try to get out.

Abuse occurs in different ways: Physical, emotional, psychological, financial and sexual. At the hands of the abuser, the victim can even be accused of or forced to commit crimes. The manipulative mind of an abuser can destroy the victim. I never imagined he would organize a series of setups to get me institutionalized, put in prison, and/or forced into a position where I had to stay quiet and allow him to do whatever he pleased without divorcing him, which was the objective because he did not want to split the estate.

Why do women stay? Fear!

The abuser uses fear to paralyze the victim. Children are the most important aspect in this equation because we try to find a way to get out as safely as possible for the children and for us. But that is a very difficult, sometimes impossible thing to do.

Many women end up dead, incarcerated or institutionalized before they get out. These abusers are tyrants that exist at all levels! They want to suppress, manipulate and have absolute power over the victim.

He knew he had lost me and I was leaving him the day I found explicit texts with a prostitute from Treasures. Treasures is a bar where erotic dancers entertain clients. The VIP rooms at those places are often where the real action takes place, as my husband confessed later in couples therapy. Many of these women become involved with the clients as the Treasures dancer did with Alejandro.

Alejandro watched *Mad Men* in hiding. I never understood why. Maybe he saw some resemblance to his own life. Once I discovered what he was watching, I asked him why it was a secret. So we started watching it together.

It was late in the month of May, after we had already had our twenty-third anniversary a few days before. He kept going to the restroom then, while we were at the restaurant. Little did I know that he was texting with someone. However, on our anniversary he had been smiling and telling everybody how good he was that we had lasted so long, while texting another woman or women at the same time.

On May 31, we were watching *Mad Men* at home together and he kept on going to the bathroom. I asked him if he was sick and he replied with a lie: "Yes, I have diarrhea."

After a while, I had to go to the bathroom, too. As soon as I walked in, I could feel the cabinet above the toilet vibrating. I opened it, but did not see anything. When it vibrated again, I started moving things around, until I found a Blackberry I had never seen before. As I sat on the toilet searching this phone and voilà—another text, "Yeah, Baby, I want some sex again."

I started reading all the texts of sexual innuendoes and appointments for rendezvouses. Alejandro started knocking on the door.

"Carmen, I need you please! I spilt wine in the bar."

"Clean it."

"I need for you to do it."

"Get the maid to clean it."

He kept on knocking. It was disturbing as I tried to read as much as I could while going to the bathroom at the same time. I finished in the bathroom, but wanted to read more. It was impossible to do then and there because he was breaking down the door. I opened the door with the Blackberry in my hand.

As soon as he saw what I had, he tried to take it away. I had nowhere to run since the space in that bathroom was so small. I tried to hold on to the cell phone. He hit me trying to get the phone, while I defended myself as best I could. Finally, a punch in my stomach forced me to let go of the Blackberry.

I stayed on the floor waiting for the pain to pass.

"This is mine!" he screamed. "You understand that?"

I could not talk because I was in so much pain. The children were upstairs and did not know what was happening since the house is so big. When he went to the study, I was able to get up and follow him trying to get the phone. That was when the children showed up. Alejandro sent them to their bedrooms and walked out to the garage.

"Alejandro, I read enough. There is no way now that you can say I am imagining things."

"Yes, you are. You are as crazy as they come, Carmen."

And he proceeded to break the Blackberry with his bare hands. I never thought that was possible. Then he threw it next door into the empty lot.

I was paralyzed with what happened; I never expected that. He followed me into the house. Once inside, he said, "Don't ever touch my things."

"Really? And when did you get that phone? How am I supposed to know it is yours if it is hidden in the bathroom?"

Oh no! I should never have answered him. He started punching me while I tried to defend myself, but he was much stronger than me. The girls came out and started screaming. At that point, he stopped and said: "Look! Just look what your mother is doing."

I could not believe he could twist things around like that. How could he? After punching me, breaking the phone and cheating on me, he says I did it! I went upstairs to my bedroom and closed the door.

"Carmen, open the door."

"No, Alejandro. Are you going to keep punching me, then telling the kids it was my fault? Go away. Leave me alone. As a matter of fact, leave the house with your whores. That is what you want. I can see it."

"I am not going anywhere. This is my house, and my children are here. Plus, what you saw is not what you think."

"I have had enough, Alejandro. After what I read, I do not believe any more of your lies. I know what I saw, even if you broke the phone."

"What do you want, Carmen?"

"A divorce."

"Really?"

"Yes! It is over."

"Well, Carmen, be ready to be penniless. I will give you nothing."

I could hear him walking away. I cried in pain. But the pain had many meanings. It was the pain from being beaten and the pain of finally seeing proof of his infidelity, which I had suspected for years but never had proof. It was true! He had been cheating on me, and every time I had suspected, he had hit me.

The next day, I woke up early, took the children to school, and then went to the gym. I did not want to see him. He was getting ready to go on a trip to be part of an event for a pharmaceutical company, something he did a month ago but had never done before. Suddenly, I realized he was going to leave with that woman. At the beginning of May, he went on a trip and when he returned, I threw a party for his 50th birthday and the new house. He had come back very tired, so as the good wife, I gave him the space to sleep in order to be rested for the party. And now, he was leaving again on June 1.

By the time I came back to the house, he was gone, but had sent me an email: "I have never cheated on you physically or mentally."

Then he called.

"Alejandro, I know you are leaving with that woman. You have never gone off on trips; you are a doctor."

"Carmen, they are paying me."

"Really? Where is the money then?"

"You will see it soon."

"Alejandro, and now this. Is it going to be once a month? Do not bother to come back, Alejandro. I do not want you here."

"This is my house, Carmen, and my family. You cannot stop me from going there."

He came back that evening after work and informed me he was not going anywhere.

"Fine! But you still have to leave. Alejandro, it is over. Let's do this in a way that is peaceful for the children."

He started screaming. You could hear him all over the house.

"You want a divorce? You want a divorce? With what? You are getting nothing."

"We have a lot and I am entitled to half or more."

"Really? Only from the house. The rest is in my mother's name. You get nothing."

"It is all ours."

"Prove it!"

At that moment, it dawned on me that all of those years putting things in his mother's name to protect us from liability from his patients was not about that. It was about protecting things from me!

The world came crashing down. What can I do? How about my children? I knew that just like his father did, he will manipulate the children with money to turn them against me.

The kids heard this. How could they not? He was screaming at the top of his lungs. God, please help me. How can I get out of this without hurting my children?

On Thursday, once again I left early. When I exercise I think. I had to make appointments with lawyers, but also needed to find a way to protect the children and myself from him taking what was ours in his mother's name. I decided I needed time to come up with a solution.

I never imagined this was giving him time to put the wheels in motion to get rid of me, diminish my credibility, or even worse, get me thrown in prison or jail. In the end, his purpose was to keep all of our estate and not have to divide it with me. His God is money.

For the last twenty years, I had worked with him, managing his practice and running our personal business, investments, real estate holdings, etc. I knew that once the divorce was filed, he would fire me.

I had not worked in my field of journalism for almost 20 years and now, of course, I was older. Very depressed, I came to realize that I had to break up my family. Though I had been suspicious for years, I never had evidence. It all made sense to me now. Every time he had hit me before, it was not about being stressed. It was because I was getting close to discovering his secret! He had been cheating on me since the beginning of our marriage.

He started to medicate me again.

"Carmen, I will prove to you that you are the love of my live and no one matters more to me. I recognize I have a problem, so I am going to start therapy to heal myself. I want to be healed for you and my family."

And he did start therapy with a doctor recommended by his best friend and partner in crime . That was why I thought he was behaving, or at least was worried and following his doctor's advice, putting the brakes on everything. But we fought a lot. He was unhappy and so was I.

The month of June 2011 passed very slowly. I canceled all vacations for the summer, except for my daughter's trip to Europe with a group of girls from Venezuela who were turning fifteen. One day, late in June, while searching our office phone bill to see why it was so high, I found out Alejandro had gotten the cellular phone through the company that services the office. Looking at the extra charges, I spotted a number I had never seen before. The detail on the bill showed numerous texts to another number, along with other phone numbers. I called and women answered. Alejandro had kept on texting and calling other women, one in particular, until the end of the billing cycle, even after he broke the phone. Obviously, he had replaced it right away. He had never stopped.

When he got home, I showed him the bill I had printed. He went straight to the bar and made drinks for both of us, then came back to the study and handed me a glass.

"Carmen, you need to relax. It is not what you think. Look around. We have it all."

"Alejandro, you have in your head that all this material stuff is more important to me."

"Yes!" he said laughing at me.

"This is who you are, Carmen. This is what is important to you."

"No, Alejandro. What is important to me is my family and to be happy. I am not right now."

He started screaming: "What do you want then? You are crazy. You want to destroy everything."

"No! You did that already."

"I told you, Carmen, you will get nothing. Be prepared to face me in court. I will make your life a living hell, because you are not getting the children."

"How? I have been nothing but a good wife and mother. How can you make my life a living hell?"

He looked at me kind of laughing: "You will see. There is nothing you can do, Carmen."

"Alejandro, we have been married for many years. Surely, I cannot be unprotected?"

"What can you do, Carmen? "

All these years I had never confided to my family about the times he had hit me. Only my brother, Pedro, knew when the Hotel ZaZa incident happened.

I needed a male point of view, so I called a friend and we met to talk. We talked and I cried all night long. He could tell I was not doing well, as I was under the effects of medication and God knows what else Alejandro had put in my drink.

When I got back home, Alejandro was furious!

"Whore! That is what you are, a whore."

"Excuse me?"

"You complain of me, but look at you. Where were you?"

"I met Anthony. I needed a male opinion."

Alejandro laughed and said: "Carmen, I have told you. Men and women are not friends. He just fucked you."

The insults kept coming, and every word was worse than the other. That night, I ended up in the hospital for the first time because I wanted to end it all. Feeling trapped, I thought about committing suicide.

Alejandro made sure everybody knew, but it was his version of the story. He called our lawyer and told him I was crazy. He was establishing the groundwork for everybody to believe I was crazy. The problem for him was that I was diagnosed with severe depression caused by my marital problems, not mental illness. He could not prove I was crazy.

I did not know at the time that he was drugging me. But he told the doctors he was medicating me and what was I taking. It suited him well.

I left the hospital after a week, not just four days as the doctors planned originally. His irrational behavior delayed the process, probably because he was partying while I was in the hospital. The doctors released me into the hands of my husband knowing I wanted a divorce. However, they had told me it was not the time to make major decisions and that I should wait. But they did advise me not to let my husband medicate me ever again. Instead, these new doctors should do it for the time being.

They also recommended couples and individual therapy for us. In time, I realized he must have told them something to make them believe I was in good hands with him. Since the doctors had ordered therapy, I thought that at least we could try to fix our marriage, if it was fixable.

However, while in the hospital I had searched for family lawyers and visited a few of them the day following my release. After I told them everything that had happened, they all agreed that being in the hospital was not going to look good in a divorce and advised me to stay with Alejandro at least a year before filing. That way I could prove that the hospital stay was a one-time incident. What they did not know was that gave Alejandro another year to further his plan. As he did!

In July, I left for Venezuela so my daughter could start her trip from there with the whole group. I stayed with the other two children for two weeks to take them to the beach. As soon as I came back, we both started therapy. It was pointless, because he was lying to our therapist. I imagined if he was lying to him in front of me, then he must have been lying to his individual therapist, too. That was why the sessions were so terrible. We were always fighting because I was trying to make things clear, while he intended to change reality. He wanted me to agree with lies. It was an impossible task.

How could he heal himself like he said he so desperately wanted to do if he was lying?

One day, he left the session because I would not agree with his altered reality. He always presented himself to our therapist as the calm doctor in control; I was the crazy one. I think they believed him, but that day I asked the therapist: "If he is so calm and controlled as he says he is, how come the hospital sent him to anger management classes?"

He got furious, never thinking it would come out. He had hoped that I would never mention it. He stormed out of the office and got in his car. Looking at the therapist, I said: "See, this is who he really is."

The therapist recommended that I wait to leave. In a few minutes, we heard voices outside. We both went to the door. Alejandro was insulting a driver. He parked the car and got out.

"I have a gun," Alejandro said. "Do you want me to use it?"

We both were looking at him. For me, this is his normal behavior, but the therapist was learning about Alejandro.

The driver did not say a word.

"I am not going to let you through," Alejandro said.

When he turned around and saw us standing at the door, he got in the car and left. More and more I realized there was nothing to save in our marriage and he must have realized that was what I felt. As a way to rebuild my trust in him, the therapist recommended that I have total access to his emails, Facebook account, etc.

The day he was to move out, he came home in a happy mood and wanted to celebrate. He poured drinks for us both, always the gentleman.

We went together to therapy, where I was told he was leaving to make things better. I never understood if that was a good idea. After all, Alejandro ended up having the best of both worlds.

Alejandro moved out of the house. After always saying he would never move out, he finally did. Was it the therapist's idea?

However, the recommendation was for him to move and us to see each other only in therapy. This was like vacation to him. He stayed at the Four Seasons Hotel, where he had the time of his life. Still, he stopped by the house every day to make sure I was not going out. Later, it will prove to be misery for me!

I came back home alone. We talked over the phone and he invited me to the hotel, but once I was there, he refused to let me in and told the hotel to get rid of me at all costs.

Alejandro came back home in January 2012 and stay there until he received the kick out order from the court in July 2013.

Marriage can be the safest relationship, but it can also be the most dangerous.

CHAPTER 23

The Pageant II

Alejandro used to be proud of the fact that I was Miss Venezuela. He always told everybody about it. I never did. I thought it was pretentions to put that title next to my name. Not him. His father, however, always criticized the pageant or being part of it. It was very uncomfortable because it was insulting, and Alejandro never stopped him.

Also, when Alejandro was mad, he used it against me. It was strange how it was good when it served his purpose, then negative on other occasions.

Toward the end of our marriage when he went on endless monologues insulting my family and me, he would say things like: "You are who you are because you showed your butt. Yes, Carmen, that is who you are! There is no difference between you and prostitutes!" It ended up making me feel ashamed of the pageant, something I was so proud of.

For my first interview as Miss Venezuela, I was taken to a room next to the theater with César González, a host for Venevisión, along with my mother, father and siblings. Little did I know they were testing me to make sure they could allow the press to talk to me. When we finished, I heard César say: "*Suéltenla. Es piquito de oro* (You can allow her to be interviewed by the press. She has lips of gold)." And that was how they baptized me.

After the Miss Venezuela pageant, it was all about getting ready to go to the Miss South America and Miss Universe pageants. But first, I had to judge the Miss Mexico pageant. Despite the pressure, I was happy and loved my new job.

Maracaibo had a huge welcome for me as one of theirs, for accomplishing the most coveted honor in our country for the second time. I could only love my family more and more as they were all there supporting and helping me. My brother, David, signed autographs when people asked; he also became famous. But my dad only cared about protecting me. He was the best combination of Super Hero!

At the Basilica of Virgin of Chichinquirá or "La Chinita," as we called her, we were scared when the mass of people did not allow me to get out of the car. The Governor of the State of Zulia had to be called to send police officers to give us protection. The people just wanted to get close to see their new Miss Venezuela, but the crowded mass was able to move the car. I started to feel suffocated.

Sábado Sensacional , Saturday's marathon show, was held live as usual, but from Maracaibo—with the welcoming event they had for me. I had two changes of clothes and three appearances. The first was a pink gown. Later, I had to change into a *guajira* gown, the typical dress of our indigenous population, but there was a miscommunication at some point. I was wearing the *guajira* gown in the second appearance and when we were about to go to commercial, the producer said: "When we come back, Carmen María Montiel will be wearing a *guajira* costume!"

My face changed because I was wearing the *guajira* costume already. And I did not have another one. Now what?

During the commercial, we all tried to figure out what to do. People were saying, "Cut this or do that…" until my father suggested: "Let's just add the hair veil and pom poms to her shoes." I did not know my father could be a dress designer!

I left for Peru and the Miss South America pageant against all odds. My predecessor, Paola Ruggieri, had won that crown also and Osmel thought a back-to-back win was impossible. They sent me by myself with only my mother as companion, no makeup artist, no other at all.

The night of the pageant, the Cisneros Companies were holding their annual convention and Osmel told Dad to call me to find out the result, but added: "Remember, she is not going to win. It is impossible."

We were in the hotel's restaurant having our celebration after the coronation when a hotel employee came to tell me I had a phone call.

"Honey, how are you doing?" he asked with a sweet somber voice. He was trying to be supportive.

"¡Papi, gané! ¡Gané! (I won, Daddy! I won!!!") I screamed.

"What? You won? She won!" he screamed to my siblings.

I could hear them all screaming and celebrating in the background.

"I am going to call Osmel right now. They are waiting to hear from me."

Later, I was told that when they got the news, Joaquín Riviera, the producer of the pageant and all major Venevisión events cried, "She did it by herself!"

Just like I will go on and face the biggest challenge of my life later on, by myself and against all odds, but always with my family by my side.

Venevisión flew me to Caracas. I was supposed to fly to Miami for the Miss Universe pageant with the rest of the girls, but Venevisión wanted me at the annual convention to show what I had accomplished: The first back-to-back victory for

Venezuela in the pageant world. In two years, it became a quadruple consecutive win, which is why Osmel expects to do the same in the Miss Universe pageant one of these days.

The day after the convention, I went to Miami. My mother stayed behind because the national costume needed to be refreshed and she had to take the blue dress with her. I traveled full of luggage. My South American sister had arrived the day before. To my surprise, everyone had high expectations for me to take the title, even the other candidates. Eighty-two girls from around the world in one place, one hotel, one competition, and I was one of them.

Venezuela had had two Miss Universe winners in the last five years, so many felt it would be difficult to win again this time. But once I arrived, I was one of the favorites. Venevisión started to get mobilized, with the top people from the company showing up in Miami. My mother arrived with all the other dresses, and I saw her almost daily at rehearsals. Finally, my father arrived.

Miriam Leiderman, one of my toughest competitors in Venezuela, came to the Miss Universe pageant and gave me chocolate after the last rehearsal. Boy did I appreciate that! Today we are the best of friends.

I came close in the Miss Universe pageant, second runner up. However, the public thought I was going to win. During commercials, the majority of the public picked Miss Venezuela first and Miss Colombia second. I lost the Miss Universe pageant because I had a moment of doubt. That was the moment I lost. It was a big lesson. Never doubt.

When I saw my parents after the Miss Universe pageant, my mother hugged me and said: "Venezuela needs you more."

By that time, I had already started to develop the Las Misses Foundation to help pediatric hospitals. My country and nationality are very important to me. To this day I feel connected and have a responsibility to the country of my birth.

The popularity I had acquired in the pageant followed me while I stayed in the United States after the event. One day, I was shopping at Dadeland Mall when suddenly I heard over the speakers that they were welcoming Miss Venezuela, who was shopping there at the time. Of course, my shopping experience ended right then when people started to recognizing me and came over.

When I flew to Los Angeles to be with my sister, Laura, the flight attendant on the plane asked me if I was Miss Venezuela. After answering yes, he escorted me to first class.

Back home, I was busy and traveling a lot with engagements as Miss Venezuela and Miss South America. At the same time, I was participating in many shows for Venevisión Network. When they discovered I was a natural with the microphone, they included me more and more in different shows, until I became a regular on *Buenos días, Venezuela* and covered for Gilberto Correa in "Close Up." That is when my life really changed; I fell in love with this art form.

I had accomplished a lot and became a public figure not only for being Miss Venezuela, but also because of my work as a television personality and later a journalist.

That celebrity status is what Alejandro used to get the attention of the media when he decided to destroy me. In order to discredit me, he had to discredit everything I was part of. He learned as did I that, contrary of what his father thought or said, people in the United States admired pageant women. It took sacrifice and became a platform for positive things in life.

Being Miss Venezuela was even more admired. The women representing our country and our success in international pageants had earned us appreciation and admiration. Therefore, in order to destroy me, he also had to destroy the pageant. That was his intention. He had to prove his father right.

The year of 1984 went by so fast that I did not realize preparations for the next Miss Venezuela pageant had started.

For one of my engagements as Miss Venezuela, I had to go to Barinas, where I met a man who was accompanying the new Miss Barinas. He talked too much. Never trust somebody that talks so much. One morning during breakfast, he asked: "Montiel, do you have a boyfriend?"

"No, I don't."

"Then I have the perfect man for you."

"Really? How do you know? You do not know me."

"I will take him to your house after Easter."

I thought to myself: Good luck, you do not even know where I live.

Easter in Venezuela is a week-long vacation. I had gone to Margarita Island, but he found me there. The phone rang in my hotel room: "Hello! I talked with your new boyfriend, and next Tuesday we are going to your house."

I hung up puzzled. What had just happened? How did this man find me? I do not even like him.

Tuesday, after everybody came back from vacation, this fellow was at my house with the one he called the perfect man for me. I was late for engagements for the upcoming Miss Venezuela pageant, and there they were seated in an armchair in my living room.

Alejandro always described how I was wearing an olive-green leather set with matching shoes that made my eyes look ever so green. My father always called my eyes *"ojos color del tiempo"* (eyes color of the weather) because they change depending upon the color of the clothes I wear or the weather.

They were the first to arrive that evening. My house was known as the "Montiel Club" because it was an open house from Monday to Monday. Everybody stopped by our house, and it became a big get together, because my father liked it like that. He preferred for us to be home, not out, and he was so special with all our friends that everyone loved to go to our house.

We were always serenaded and were the last stop because, as they said: "*Ese viejo sí nos abre la puerta* (That is the only father that opens the door for us)." It was as if the serenades were for him. My dad was a happy man who loved us so much and did everything to make us happy.

My parents and sister were sitting and talking with them, so I sat down and joined the conversation. All the while, I was watching and analyzing this supposedly perfect man for me.

I disliked him. I thought he was arrogant and pretentious. Not even with my title was I ever like that.

Always follow your first instinct. I did not!

CHAPTER 24

The Game Changers II

As TIME WENT on, I felt more and more confident that I had made the right decision in hiring new attorneys—Andino Reynal and Zack Fertitta. If Evil was trying so hard for me not to change lawyers, that meant I had escaped the darkness.

I started my week with a new look at life. Andino called me at the beginning of the week to let me know that my former lawyers had been fired from the case. My new attorneys had requested a continuance, so they would have time to investigate the case since they had just taken over. He also said that they had already hired a former FBI agent to investigate my case and another investigating company to do other jobs. It all felt as if finally the wheels were in motion.

After they had picked up my file at my former attorney's office, I got a call from Andino.

"Carmen, you are going to love this!" he said.

"What? I am all ears."

"I got the flight log from the plane that night. And guess what? The plane more than likely came back due to a combination of bad weather and fuel. It shows in the log there was bad weather in Bogota. We are going to talk with an expert about it and confirm this is it."

I was elated! Finally, the sky was starting to clear. I now know the truth would come out. We can now prove that I had done nothing. I could not help but think that almost two years into this battle, the requested black boxes, manuals and flight logs were never provided. And within one week, my new lawyers were already starting to get what we needed to prove my innocence.

At the same time, I was about to change a player on my divorce team, which would prove to be the answer to all my problems in the family law arena.

I had already had three lawyers in my divorce case. The current one was the best of the three, but he was a liberal and a friend told me apparently that plays a role in the successful outcome of a case, depending upon how the judge is inclined. That could explain many things. In case it was true, I preferred to play it safe.

Bobby Newman, the "bulldog" of family law, accidentally came across my case and was interested in it. I was only willing to change because my divorce started within his firm. After a meeting in which I went further into my case and explained the difficulties involved, he said that it should not play a role in court. I hired him. In one month, I had changed all of my lawyers.

Andino and Zack were happy when they found out that I had retained Bobby and were ready to start a good battle.

As the days went by, it kept getting better and better. Every call was great news. And I was feeling more and more confident in my case. The new investigators spoke with the copilot, who said they had never heard any noise in the cockpit. The only noise they had heard was once I was arrested, but nothing before. He added that the plane assigned for that trip was too small, and it was the first time it had flown this particular route. Also, there was a weather issue, which proved to be a risk since Bogota is between mountains. In fact, when the plane flew back to Bogota later that day, it returned to Houston due to weather.

This information added to the fact that there were many reasons for the plane's return that had nothing to do with me, but I was blamed for it.

In the midst of all of this good news, Andino called to tell me that the government had decided to add a charge to my case.

"What? What is it?"

"The misdemeanor you refused."

"After nearly two years, they have decided to accuse me of assaulting Alejandro?"

"Yes. But they are just mad that you did not take the deal, then changed lawyers and are making them work harder. Do not allow this to bother you."

"Andino, I have the picture with the bruise caused by his assault of me."

"They don't know about that. I am saving it for later."

"I just wonder what part Alejandro has here."

"Well, they are interrogating him soon."

"What? Why?"

"They don't like him. They see him as a risky witness, but he has insisted on being part of the case."

I cried like there was no tomorrow. Why was all of this happening? But I regained my strength and decided to fight it, just like I had done so far.

At the same time, I learned why my oldest daughter came back from New York to Houston. Since he was sure I was going to prison, my husband's plan was to have my daughter move back into the house and help him with the other children.

As I was getting better and stronger, actually knowing this made me feel like: Really? Is that what you are planning? Well, it is not going to happen because the truth will shine.

Alejandro willingly went to meet the government attorneys. In fact, his lawyer worked hard to get that meeting for him. I always wondered where he got the nerve to get that close to them knowing that he had so much to hide. Somehow, he stayed under the radar—like when he went through extensive motions in family court to get his illegal passport. At first, he asked for it with his lawyers. He did not want to leave a paper trail, but then and even after the divorce he did not care to leave all evidence about that passport. I think his lawyers informed him that family court is known as "Perjury Castle."

He went to Venezuela and acquired a second passport with another identity with the help of Roberto, who has connections over there. This second identity came with a separate and different identification card number and last name. In Venezuela, he already faced five counts of criminal charges. Once he filed a motion in family court requesting the passport, it became public evidence, but people had to request the information. The judge heard their lies; it is legal in Venezuela to have two identities or more. After the hearing, the judge ruled that the passport was to stay at the court as criminal evidence.

Alejandro also had an issue with an employee, who was ordering over 800 codeine tablets a month using his DEA number. The director of the Sleep Lab reported this to Alejandro, but he did not fire her or report her to the authorities. There was also the dead patient with the change of records. And that is only what I know about. I had always wondered what else there was. Did he have something to do with the Scooter Medicare Fraud? What else was there that I did not know?

The report from that interrogation was incredible. Even my lawyers laughed when they started reading it because of how out of this world it was. How could a man trash the mother of his children this way?

But on the day of the hearing for the continuance, the new female prosecutor on the case handed the interrogation report to Andino with a look of victory. Like it was a success. Obviously, they used this to scare me, but when it did not work, they dropped it.

Another report said that the other crew members on the airplane thought they were all going to get fired for this incident. They agreed that it never should have happened. And that in fact this flight attendant caused a crisis once he had arrested me, making the plane go into lock down, because the pilot could not communicate with anybody in the back since they were all attending to the flight attendant's needs.

In spring 2015, my lawyers decided to do shock therapy where we reenacted what happened on the plane. The two of them, the therapist and I played the most important roles of that night. I was only myself, while they sometimes played more than one role at times. The therapist was also a lawyer and coincidentally was not only from Venezuela but also from Maracaibo and divorced from a man that abused her also.

We met on a Saturday morning when we all wore informal clothes. It is always nice to see your lawyers as regular people, which I would see more as they prepared for trial and we had more of those weekend meetings. After introductions and saying a few things about ourselves, we started to work.

Once we finished reenacting the whole incident, she asked: "And where is the crime here?"

"Exactly!' I said.

Andino and Zack agreed.

"I don't understand how this happened," she said. "What are they accusing you of? How are they bringing this charge up?"

"That is the problem with this case," Andino added.

"Well, I feel good about it," she said. "You did nothing. So many times, after I do a session like this, we wonder how we are going to defend the person when they are obviously guilty. But here it is clear you broke no law."

She was so taken by my case that when she left, she told Andino she would not charge me.

I left for California before the trial to take my son for his only summer vacation. The life of these poor children had changed dramatically since 2011. While I was there, a month before the trial started, Andino called me again.

"Carmen, they are offering a new deal."

"What is it now?"

"Any misdemeanor of your choice."

"I can choose?"

"Yes!"

"Okay, let me think about it and I will call you back. What is your take on this offer?"

"I can tell you many things, but I don't want to get your hopes up. However, I can tell you they do not want to take this case to trial."

"Then why don't they drop the charges?"

"They don't want to do that either."

"Give me some time to think about it and I will call you back."

I told my sister, Laura, about the call since I was with her. We meditated over it. I also talked with María Eugenia and researched what misdemeanor I could possibly live with. Then, I made a decision and called Andino.

"Andino, I researched all possible misdemeanor charges, and the only one I could live with is gambling."

"Gambling?" Andino asked kind of laughing.

"Yes! See that is my only fault in life. I have never smoked and I am not an alcoholic like my husband claims. In fact, I never drank when I was young. But I like gambling. I love poker. So, that is it. I am a gambler."

I could hear him laughing on the other end.

"No, Carmen, it has to be a charge that somehow relates to what happened."

"Like what?"

"Probably like disorderly conduct."

"No, I cannot do that. I could lose my children and that would be admitting I did something wrong on that plane. I did not."

"I know, Carmen. But it is my responsibility as your lawyer to inform you of any offers the government makes. You never know what a jury would do. I know you are an innocent woman."

"I know, but I am not taking this offer. You have done a good job and have found out a lot of information about this case. I trust in you and in God that the truth will come out. I will go to trial. My father used to say: '*El que no arriesga ni gana ni pierde* (If you do not take a risk you neither win nor lose)."

"Ok, then. When you come back, we will have a lot of work to do."

Less than two percent of people win cases against the US government. I was taking the biggest risk of my life, but I trusted in God that the truth was going to come out in the trial, that we would be able to prove everybody on Alejandro's side was lying, and that we would catch them lying on the stand, as we indeed did.

Lies have short legs!

CHAPTER 25

I Probably Laughed Too Hard

I PROBABLY LAUGHED TOO hard at life when I had my son. His birth made me feel like I could have it all and more, that there was nothing in this world I could not accomplish.

After having two beautiful daughters, I was only missing a son. All of the men in my husband's family had girls, so the odds were against us. But I did it!

Alexandra was right. When she was around five years old, after her bath one day, while I was drying her with the towel, she suddenly said: "*Mami*, you are so lucky!"

"Really, Baby? Why?"

"See you have this castle with your prince and the two of us. And you also have some money!"

I cracked up with laughter. It was sweet, beautiful and true. I only needed a boy for everything to be perfect.

My boy was born on the same day as my father, who I miss dearly. My son was the most beautiful of my three babies when he was born.

My father passed away on October 30, 1999. It was one of the most devastating times in my life. I never imagined that it was possible to feel actual heart pain from sadness. But it is. I knew it was going to happen someday, but not that soon. My father was two days short of turning 71.

I was just coming back from the gym on a Friday morning facing a typical work day for me filled with a lot of paperwork: payments, payroll, and a wire transfer for Alejandro's father so he could buy a medical office for his use in Venezuela.

I was at my desk when my mother called: "Carmen María, we are at the hospital. Your father had a heart attack. It is not looking good. I think you need to come."

I jumped up from my seat and started to cry. It could not be possible. My positive self was hoping that it was just another scare. The truth of the matter was that my father had been in Houston three weeks before and was so weak. I had taken him to a cardiologist who found that his pacemaker was wrongfully programmed. Once they adjusted it, my dad was himself again.

What could have happened? I was hoping he was going to do better.

Alejandro and I were going to France and Spain. My dad kept asking when we were leaving and when we would be back. As if he had known that he was leaving soon.

I called Alejandro. "*Mi cielo*, my dad is in the hospital. He had a heart attack. Can you please call and get more information?"

When Alejandro called me back, he said things were not good and I had better go to him.

My world stopped. My brother, who lived 40 minutes from me, called from his office: "Carmen, I am leaving the office for the house. I will get some clothes and come to pick you up. Get the airplane tickets. This way we are more productive."

My desk was full of papers. I called Continental Airlines, which later merged with United Airlines, as it was the only airline that had nonstop flights from Houston virtually anywhere in the US. Since it was Friday and Halloween weekend, getting tickets to a vacation destination like Orlando, Florida, was impossible and very expensive. If found, a coach ticket could cost around $1,500 to $2,000.

I was on the phone with Continental crying. The lady on the other end asked if there was anything wrong.

"My dad is not doing well. He is very sick and at the hospital. He had a heart attack."

"In that case, if you can give me the name of the hospital he is in, I can sell you the tickets for $500 and put you on standby. I think we can get you on the 10 p.m. flight."

That was the last flight to Orlando out of Houston. I got two tickets for my brother and me. We headed to the airport hoping to get on an earlier flight. Checking in at the counter, we explained what was going on. They had the hospital information for my dad, but said that the only chance we had was the last flight. Because of the situation, we were bumped to the first place on the waiting list.

After spending hours at the airport, we finally got on the plane. I broke down and cried. My brother hugged me. We arrived in Orlando at midnight and hurried as fast as we could to get to the hospital.

The last time we had spoken with my sister, Dad was in the emergency room, but by the time we arrived, he was in the Intensive Care Unit. When we got there, we joined my mother, sister and dad. My dad looks happy to see as, but can hardly talk. He tried and tried.

I called Alejandro and had him talk to the doctor.

"Carmen, it is only a matter of time," he told me.

"Nooooo! God, please don't let it happen!"

My mother looked disoriented. When I talked to her, it was as if I was speaking in another language. The nurse said he was stable and there was nothing we could do now but wait. My sister suggested that we go home and come back tomorrow.

"No, I will not move from here," I insisted.

"There is no place to sleep here but in those chairs," she said. "It has been a long day for Mom. Let's take her to a comfortable bed so she can rest."

We went to my mother's apartment and it seemed like the phone rang as soon as we fell asleep. It was María Eugenia.

"The hospital called. We need to go now. I will meet you there."

"What happened?"

"We need to go."

My mother heard the phone and was in the bathroom. "Mom, we need to go now."

It was as if I was talking to the wall.

"Mom, now."

"No, I cannot go."

"Mom, please, we need to go."

We hurried and met María Eugenia in the waiting room outside the Intensive Care Unit. Finally, a young doctor came out. He looked exhausted and was all sweaty, as if he had run for miles.

"We tried for over half an hour," he said. "He came back, but it took too long and he is…"

"What?"

"He is brain dead."

My mother broke down. So did I. I was hoping this was a dream. That was it: I was dreaming. After all, I had just gone to bed.

"You have to decide what you want to do now."

"What do you mean?"

"Do you want him to stay like that or to disconnect him?"

At the time, I remembered so many times when my dad said, "I do not want to be a vegetable. If I get to be like that, do not let me live."

"He did not want that. He did not want to be a vegetable."

The doctor looked at us. We looked at my mom. And finally, she said: "He did not want that."

So, we decided to disconnect him, but asked to come say our goodbyes while he was still alive. We were crying nonstop.

I was a little girl walking between his legs. That was my favorite thing to do. I do not know how he managed to walk, but it was my way to say do not go! Stay with me; do not go to work.

Suddenly, I heard: "You can enter now."

My mother, brother, sister and I went into the small ICU cubicle. He looked like he was sleeping, so peaceful. We can hear the machine beeping with his heart as we all hugged and kissed him. We took turns, then were all around him.

"I love you, Daddy."

The beep goes faster.

The nurse said: "He feels you. He can feel you are here."

Suddenly, I heard a steady beep. I looked at the machine and saw a flat line.

The nurse now said: "He is gone!"

In the midst of all this pain, it felt like he decided to die with us around him. That gave me some peace. It was a beautiful way to leave.

When I walked out of the Intensive Care Unit, I felt as if I left half of myself there. My love! My first love left me. I was not planning on this, at least not now. I was only 34 years old and did not have a dad. I never imagined this would happen so soon. I had expected my father to be an old grandfather to my children.

Who would I call now? I called Dad every time I had to make a decision, every time I had doubts or any general question or wanted to hear his voice.

It was around 6 a.m., 5 a.m. in Houston. I called Alejandro crying and said: "Alejandro, he is gone."

He sounded sleepy. In a soft voice he said: "I am sorry, *mi cielo.*" That was it. That was all he said.

I called my friend María Luisa. As soon as she answered, she said: "He is gone?"

"Yes!" I started to cry.

"I will do everything I can to try to get there."

My girlfriend offered to come. Alejandro did not. I still think it must have been because he was half asleep. But was not the news and the reason for my call a reason to wake up? I thought he would call me later to tell me he was coming.

We started the ordeal of getting my father buried. My parents had moved to Orlando from Venezuela two years ago. We did not know Orlando, so we went through the phone book to look for funeral homes near my mother's house.

After dropping Mother at her house, where some friends had come over so she was not alone, my brother, sister and I went to get this done. We did not want Mother to have to deal with this.

I never imagined we would have to go shopping for Dad's funeral. It was a bizarre situation. I felt like they were asking us how much we loved our dad.

Once we had decided on the funeral home and everything that needed to get done by then, we moved to find a cemetery. It was already afternoon. We had not slept, but this needed to get done. Once again, there were so many options.

It was so much to deal with, especially when I felt the pain of his passing. I still could not believe my father was gone! We also decided to get a space in the cemetery for my mother now. It comes at a better price when you buy the two plots.

Alejandro called: "*Hola, mi cielo.*"

"*Hola,*" I said crying.

"How are you doing?"

"We are getting the cemetery plot. We got a place that is so beautiful. Just how he would like it."

"I will be checking on you."

"Aren't you coming?"

"I cannot."

"What? Why? This is my father."

"I am on call."

"But the other doctor can cover for you. That is why we have him."

"No, I cannot come."

I stayed quiet for a long time. I could not believe this. After my father, Alejandro is the person who mattered to me the most. How was he not going to be with me when I felt so devastated?

But I had to focus on finishing in the cemetery. Finally, we got done after 6 p.m. and went to my mother's. The Gutiérrez, my father's childhood friends, were there with her. Thank God she had good company.

The phone would not stop ringing. Everybody in Venezuela had been informed about my father's death. I cried myself to sleep, not only for the biggest loss of my life, but also because I could not understand why Alejandro was not coming.

The viewing was on Sunday, October 31, 1999, Halloween night. Sergio, María Eugenia's husband who was in Venezuela for his mother's burial, came back sooner to be at my father's burial. But not Alejandro!

On Sunday, I went to get a black dress or suit because I had not packed for this. I had been in denial, feeling that if I put anything black in my suitcase, it would predict something negative. It is the worst time to shop, especially for something you did not want to wear—something I would trash since having it in my closet would remind me of the worst time in my life.

When we got to the funeral home and I entered the room where he was, I almost fell to my knees as soon as I saw Daddy's lifeless body in the coffin. I ran to him crying with so much pain. He was my love, my protector, my defender, and my life. How could I let him go?

After I composed myself, I saw that something was not right. It did not feel like him. It did not even look like him. Ever since I was a little girl, I remember my father with glasses. That was it. He needed his glasses.

I asked my mom if it was okay to bring his glasses tomorrow and put them on him. She said, "*Claro* (Of course)."

He was so spoiled by all of us and he was such a trooper. He would let us experiment on him, which always made us happy. I remember one day I asked him if I could put my high-heel sandals on his feet to see how would they look if I had his feet. He had the most beautiful feet.

His sister, my aunt Tachi, flew to Orlando from Canada and so did his brother, Francisco, who came from Miami. My cousins and aunt, the wife of another of his brothers, who lived in Orlando, came, and of course Rey and Gladys Gutiérrez. Those three went to school together. My mother's sister, Marys, and her family also came from Miami.

It was not until we entered the funeral home on Monday morning that I realized my father was being buried on his birthday, November 1.

Then, the moment we had all dreaded was there, when my father's coffin was lowered. We did not want to be there for that. Uncle Francisco said he would stay.

I missed my girls. Losing Dad gave me this need to go hug them. I arranged for my mother to come to Houston as soon as she could, then I headed back home.

My brother and I went to the ticket counter together. I can only imagine what our faces looked like as we gave our names to the ticket agent, who said we had been upgraded to first class courtesy of Continental. I looked at my brother and my eyes filled with tears again. That was a different airline back before the merger.

Back in Houston after a turbulent flight, Perucho dropped me at home. Alejandro opened the doors and thanked my brother. This was the first time I noticed how cold he could be. He did not invite my brother in or look sympathetic.

Inside he hugged me and I cried.

"You did not come."

"Carmen, he was already dead. What could I do?"

"It was not about him. It was about me, Alejandro."

I went upstairs to my girls' bedroom and hugged them. I cried with them. Kamee, only ten months, was too little to understand what had happened. She took her first steps on Halloween night, while I was gone. But Alejandro had told Alexandra that *Abuelito* Johnny had gone to heaven.

Alexandra caressed my cheek and kissed me.

"I will miss *Abuelito, Mami*, even if he wanted to put me in the refrigerator."

That made me smile. My dad had joked with her about that, only three weeks ago. More than ever, I felt that his last visit to Houston was a farewell. Worried about our trip to Europe, he kept asking when we were leaving and coming back.

Later that week, Alejandro's step-mother called me with condolence for my dad.

"Zaid says that is how he wants to die, while he is sleeping."

I was thinking: not exactly like that; he was in a hospital bed. I asked her to please send the wire instructions again since it was so crazy that day.

After I hung up. I thought: "How dare his father to have his wife call me. She is not even my mother-in-law. He does not even care to call me."

My friends organized a Mass for the next Saturday. All of my friends and people I knew were there. At the end of the service, most of the people stayed outside the church talking. I saw Alejandro talking with his younger brother and he was agitated. When we get in the car, I asked him what was wrong.

"My dad asked Mario to give him the money for the medical office. And he is mad because you did not send the money."

"Mad? They must know that the day they sent the wire instructions was the day my father was dying. Dad died, Alejandro. My daddy."

"Well, my father is mad at you. He does not want to talk to me and I lost this investment opportunity."

How cold can a person be? That was one of many times in which Alejandro and his dad did not talk to each other. Those situations could last for years.

We had a trip scheduled to Europe, but I did not want to go now. I was spending my days on the couch crying. I could not eat and lost so much weight.

Alejandro told me: "Carmen, it is better if we go. It can help get your mind off this."

I shortened the trip. We were to go to Paris, then the south of France, and from there drive to Spain. I eliminated the driving part and just kept Paris and Madrid.

"I" had to do it. That was the way my marriage worked: "I" had to do it all.

During the trip, tears flowed from my eyes at any given time. It was uncontrollable. Alejandro would ignore it!

My mother had come to Houston just before we left to stay with the girls, which kept her mind off my father's passing. Once we got back home, my mother and I went to Venezuela to finish all the paperwork needed to process my father's death. What was supposed to be a two-week effort became four.

My mother flew back to Houston to be with the girls, while I stayed to wait for signatures and seals.

I came back to Houston two days before the worst natural disaster in Venezuela, "El deslave." Rain caused the mountain to fall on top of the city of La Guaira, which isolated the country since that was where the main international airport was located.

I still had heart pain, to the point where thought I was having a heart attack. It was the pain of sadness. It is true your heart can hurt physically out of sadness. Until one day I thought that only the love of a son could give me back the lost love of my father.

I told Alejandro I wanted another baby, a boy.

"Forget it, Carmen. We only make girls."

He was referring to the fact that so far, he and his brothers had only had girls.

"This one is going to be a boy."

"Forget it."

My pain became a hole in my heart. More and more I felt that I had to have my boy.

I felt I knew him. He was a blond, blue eyed boy, just like my father. I could even smell him. I felt my life was not complete without him.

Alejandro's resistance sent us to our first couples therapy. Little did I know how much we needed it. We ended up talking about everything but the baby.

After two months of therapy, Alejandro declared it a waste of time. He said the therapist was on my side and he was not going back again, that if we had to have the baby in order not to go to therapy, so be it.

I wanted a boy so badly that I started researching how to have a baby boy. I knew some doctors in Venezuela specialized in getting you the sex of the baby you wanted. I went to Venezuela and interviewed one of them, but most of my research was over the Internet and in books. I even bought a Physiology book. I became an expert!

I had a Chinese lunar calendar made especially for me to be as accurate as possible, only trying to conceive in those months the Chinese calendar said were favorable for boys.

I tried the diet, changed Alejandro's underwear, had him stop using steam in the bathroom. He had to drink coffee and avoid wine, etc. We tried it all. I knew I was pregnant in less than 24 hours after the fact. I was sick from the beginning. It was incredible.

In February 2004, we were skiing in Beaver Creek, Colorado, as always when I fell getting off the chair. Conditions were very icy, and it felt like I hit concrete. I knew I was pregnant because my morning sickness lasted for the whole day, but I was waiting for nature to let me know.

After the fall, I stopped skiing for the day. I went down the mountain, got in the car and went to town for an early pregnancy test. Everybody was skiing, the girls in ski school and Alejandro by himself. I went to the apartment and into the bathroom. Sure enough! I was pregnant.

I did not ski for the rest of the vacation and took it easy when I went back to Houston. The doctor gave me a due date of October 30. That could not be, I thought. Not that day! That was the day my father passed away. Ever since he died, I had decided to forget that day, celebrating his life and his birth, but not his death.

Somehow, I knew that this baby, my son, would be born on November 1, just like my dad. And he would be named "Juan" for him. I was 39 years old by then, and for the first time, I had to get an amniocentesis. Also, for the first time ever, Alejandro accompanied me to the doctor's appointment. He never had before, using the excuse that he was very busy as a doctor. I never wanted to be the annoying wife who requested more time for me. So, I understood.

I did not want to know the sex of the baby. I felt if it was a girl, I would be depressed for the rest of the pregnancy and that would not be good for the baby. During the exam, the doctor first did a new ultrasound. The new equipment was incredible; we could even see the baby almost alive, his skin, his eyes… so incredible. At one point, the doctor asked if we wanted to know the sex of the baby.

"No! I don't," I said.

"Yes, I do," Alejandro answered.

We started going back and forth with yes and no, until I told the doctor it was okay to make peace and stop the exchange. When he said it was a boy, I broke down in tears. Alejandro was speechless.

Then the doctor said: "I can assure you with the ultrasound that the baby is 99% healthy. Do you still want the amniocentesis?"

I declined after knowing it was a boy. My dream boy. I did not want to run any risks. Amniocentesis has some degree of risk to the baby.

But Alejandro said he wanted to be 100% certain the baby was healthy. I felt terrible when they inserted the needle. With the ultrasound, we could see how the baby moved his feet away; he felt what was happening.

When we got in the car, Alejandro said he could not believe it: "It worked. Everything you did worked. Against all medical odds, you did it, Carmen."

October 30 came and went. And as I predicted, my baby decided to be born on November 1, just like my father. When they put Juan Diego in my arms, I could not believe it. He was a blond, blue-eyed baby just like my dad had been. He had no hair on his head or eyebrows.

"I am going to call you *Clorito* (Clorox)," Alejandro told me. "You washed out all the Lebanese from my children."

That day I felt complete! My son was my gift from above and beyond. I had gotten everything I had wanted in life and more.

CHAPTER 26

The Silence

I WAS SO MAD at him after the Colorado incident, at the end of 2011. But I was trapped. I just needed to get over it. He was more loving than ever. Somehow, that accomplishment made him feel great—or he knew he had to cover up for what he had done and act like the most loving husband ever.

I kept going with my routine, taking care of the children, the office, and looking for another property to buy. This time, an investment in Miami, where prices were down but always recovered. It was the right time to invest there. Plus, Alejandro approved the purchase in an effort to show he "loved" me. He knew I liked Miami because of the many friends and family members I had there, but also because my mother was in Orlando and that would give me a place close to her.

When discussing the purchase, he told me to get the apartment in Miami, that it would be a gift for me. That never happened!

In February 2012, the Simons called us to meet them for dinner. I was in a casual blue dress because all I had done that day was drive the children around and do office work at home.

I needed to change because we were going to Uchi, the new sushi restaurant in town that was so hot it was nearly impossible to get a table.

"You are fine as you are," Alejandro said. "If you go get changed it would take forever. I am hungry. Let's finally eat at Uchi."

He was already drinking wine as usual. So, we left to join the Simons, who did not know about anything. I covered my bruises when need be. And the rest? How could I talk about it? He was a respectable doctor. I was not going to destroy his reputation, the reputation of the father of my children, the bread-winner of the house.

The Simons were already seated. They did not drink. As soon as we sat down, Alejandro ordered a bottle of white wine. He served me, and I looked at him, saying "You know."

Nobody but Alejandro knew the outcome in Colorado was that I could not drink.

"Come on, Carmen, join me. Have fun! You are so boring!"

He sounded so happy, like the party boy he wanted people to see him as. We were two couples having fun talking, eating and drinking. I mentioned that good Japanese restaurants are where they have the best sake and it had to be drunk cold. Alejandro called the waitress and told her bring him their best sake.

After we went home, we had sex. We did not make "love" anymore. I was so detached from him. And suddenly he called me Cara! Cara was the name of the woman I had finally uncovered as cheating partner. As soon as I heard that, I started pushing away.

"¿Qué, Carmen? (What, Carmen?)"

"You called me Cara … Stop!" And I kept pushing away.

Suddenly, I felt a bite right on my boob. He was biting so hard that it felt like he wanted to take off my nipple. The pain was unbearable. I was not able to push anymore. I could not get my hands between the two of us. He was not letting up and his teeth started penetrating my skin. I was screaming: "Stop. Please, stop!"

Finally, it occurred to me to pull his hair. He cared so much for his hair and certainly did not want to lose it, especially his hair plugs. I put my hands on his head, grabbed his hair as hard as I could and started to pull. That did it! He released my breast, but it was not enough to let me go because as soon as I released his hair, he bit me between my left arm and my chest. Again, I could feel his teeth penetrating my skin. Not able to move that arm, I kept trying to grab his hair with my right hand, but he was pulling that side so I could not reach it.

Finally, we fell off the bed. We were battling, but he was overpowering me. I could not move and was crying out in pain. I kept moving my right hand trying to reach him, when quickly he let go of my left armpit and bit my right hand on the palm. Unable to move my left arm, I was in so much pain, and now the beast had my hand and was biting it at the base of the thumb. He would probably take a piece, but I could not fight anymore or move. The pain was so intense that it did not hurt any longer. I just gave up.

Finally, he let go! I was on the floor consumed with so much pain that it felt like I had just confronted a beast. All the bites on me felt like burns. I was bleeding. I could not move.

He stood up and screamed at me: "You are crazy. See what you made me do!"

"What? You called me Cara. I did not want you on top of me any longer."

"See, you are crazy. I did not call you Cara. You imagined things. Cara, Carmen. They are almost the same."

Like that was the perfect excuse. I was crying from the pain on the floor. He got up and got dressed.

"I am calling the police," he said.

"And tell them what? That you attacked me like a beast?"

"Carmen, you are walking on thin ice. You will see!"

While I was on the floor, it sounded like he did call the police. I got up and took a shower. I wanted to wash my wounds because I was bleeding all over. The water felt good on my wounded skin. Time passed. I thought he was fooling me, and the police were not coming. So, I put on my pajamas and went to bed. When suddenly I heard a knock on our door.

I said to myself that if it was the police, I was in my bed and had wounds to show. After he opened the door, I could hear voices, then steps and knocks on my bedroom door. It was locked because I did not want Alejandro to sleep with me.

When I opened the door, four police officers were standing there. Explaining what happened, I proceeded to show my wounds, which were open and bleeding still. They looked at each other as if they could not understand what was going on. It was obvious that Alejandro's story was different from mine. One of them went back downstairs and talked to Alejandro, then came back up and conferred with one of the officers.

"Ma'am, we are taking you in."

"Excuse me? Can you see my wounds, sir?"

"Well, your husband said you hit him."

"But can you see my wounds?"

"We are taking him in, too."

"Can I put some clothes on?"

They sent a female officer with me to the closet.

Both Alejandro and I were taken in. I could not believe this. How could this happen? Once I was there, I asked to see a doctor to have my wounds looked at. I was in so much pain, and hours had passed as we were processed. The wound on my hand was not looking good.

It took forever to see the doctor, who checked all three wounds and said the one on my hand was infected. He asked me why I was there. When I had explained, he said I should have been taken to a hospital with those wounds.

I called home and my oldest daughter answered: "*Hola, Mami*. How are you? Are you okay?"

"*Sí, mi amor* (Yes, my love). How is everybody?"

"They are sleeping. But are you well?"

"Yes."

"*Papi* called. What took you so long?"

"I was trying to go to the doctor, Baby. I have wounds. It took forever, but they saw me. My hand is infected."

"*Mami, Papi* said that if you don't press charges and he doesn't either, you are both out and all of this can be cleaned from both of your records. That is what you have to do, *Mami*."

It was obvious he had been talking with someone and the only way to communicate with me was to leave a message at home. I had no way out. If I pressed charges, he would, too. I thought about my children and realized I had no other way out. So that is what I did, and we got out. He had his secretary pick us up. I did not talk to him. He talked all the way home, accusing me of everything. There was no point in responding. I knew I was trapped. I had become a prisoner in my own home, of my own life. I was my husband's prisoner!

Once we were home, he told me all I had to do the next day was to make sure this was all erased from our records, especially his.

"Do you understand, Carmen? Do you?"

I just nodded. There was no point in talking. I went up to my bedroom to take a shower, but he got in the bathroom to do the same.

"Alejandro, please don't. Do not get in the shower. I need my space."

He got in the shower anyway, saying: "You know I paid for all of this, and you are not going to tell me what I can or cannot do."

I got out as soon as I could and put a clean pajama. When he got out of the shower, I told him the wound on my hand was infected and asked if I should go to a doctor.

"Ha ha! You are hilarious. What would you say?"

Opening his cabinet in the bathroom, he said: "Here! Take this antibiotic every twelve hours."

The next morning, the attorney called and said everything was taken care of except for our signatures.

"I can drop the papers at your house," she said. "I understand you are not doing well."

"Yes, I am here. Come over whenever you can."

After I hung up, I wondered how much she charged for this house service.

When I heard the doorbell, I knew it was the lawyer and opened the door myself. A tall, thin woman stood there. I showed her to the study, my temple!

There was a poster size picture of all of us, including my family, the children, Alejandro and me. It was a present from *Mi Familia Magazine* the month we were on their cover. She looked at it, then looked at me. Pointing to my daughter, Kamee, in the picture, she said: "I know her. She does horseback riding at the Polo Club."

"Yes, she does," I said.

"I have seen you there. In fact, I saw you two days ago. Were you wearing a blue dress?"

Oh no! The blue dress. That was the day everything had happened. I had gone to pick up Kamee at her class earlier that afternoon.

"Yes! That was me."

"When I saw you, I thought, 'what a beautiful woman.'"

"Thanks."

"Here are the papers."

When I took them, she saw my hand.

"What is that?" she asked.

I could tell her. She was the only one I could tell. After all, she was cleaning up the mess.

"This is why you brought those papers here."

I signed mine. Somehow, Alejandro had already signed his.

"This is a beautiful home."

"Thanks. I designed it." A golden cage, I thought to myself. She stared at me.

"Well, I have to go."

"I understand. Thanks for the personalized service."

I walked her out. As she was leaving, already outside the house, she turned to me and said: "Get out of this marriage. I have seen many women like you who have had their lives destroyed because of men like him."

Then, she turned around and left.

I went on with my life but was very depressed and not able to do much. As the days passed by, there was little I could accomplish. Getting out of the house and explaining my wounds were difficult. The other two were covered, but it was impossible to hide the one on my hand. I told people I burned myself while cooking.

I was so embarrassed. How could I tell anybody what was going on? How could I tell them that I had allowed it to happen? But how could I have ever stopped it? Should I further embarrass my children by letting people know who their father really was?

And how could I leave with this mess on my records? He had me trapped. I knew it, and he definitely knew it. From then on, he treated me more and more like his slave.

CHAPTER 27

Divorce

A YEAR HAD PASSED since the burglary and we were back at California, this time at Disneyland during the 2012 summer.

Finally, Alejandro had agreed to go on a vacation at a theme park with the children. We invited the Garzas to meet us in Los Angeles. As soon as they arrived, we all went out for dinner. The children loved seeing each other. The weather was perfect, so we decided to sit outside at two tables, one for the kids and the other for the adults. This was a treat for us since in Houston there are very few days when the weather was that nice.

After the children ate, they left to go play in our hotel room. There were six of them. Richard, Jennifer, Alejandro and I stayed at the table talking and finishing our meal. As usual, Alejandro was drinking too much.

We talked about the burglary and marriage, a hot topic for us at the moment and apparently for the Garzas also. The conversation degenerated in front of the Garzas when Alejandro started insulting my family. I was used to this, but it had never happened in front of other people. I started to reply to his insults with negative comments about his family. He looked at me with fury. That was not acceptable to him; he and his family were untouchable. He proceeded to insult my father, and I insulted his. Now, he was making things up about my father, but I had told the truth about his and that went way beyond the line for him. Nobody could know the truth about his father or his family.

Richard left for the bathroom while Alejandro and I continued to replay the same arguments but about our fathers. Jennifer was quiet. I was offended. Finally, Alejandro stood up. I thought he was leaving to find Richard and put an end to the conversation, but he came over to me and in a seemingly loving way, grabbed my face and came very close. I thought he was going to kiss me.

Jennifer did, too.

"That's good! Don't fight anymore," she said.

But once his lips were on my cheek, he bit me!

"Ouch!!!" I screamed. And he left.

"He bit me, Jennifer!"

"I saw that!"

"Oh my God, he bit me!"

Jennifer took a napkin and started to clean my face, calling the waitress to get clean water.

"It hurts so badly."

The waitress came with the water and wet another end of the napkin to clean my face. Alejandro and Richard came back.

"What happened?" Richard asked.

"Nothing," Jennifer said.

But I thought Richard should know what his friend, a doctor like him, was capable of doing.

"Alejandro bit me!" I said and left.

Little by little Alejandro had lost his shame and was starting to show his true colors in front of other people.

I had to fire my second attorney when she insisted on going to trial in October without any discovery from Alejandro. I felt I needed a more aggressive lawyer. Also, the judge assigned to our case was retiring and a new judge would be sworn in on January 1, 2015. By November 2014, we would know who was it going to be. Regardless of who it was, any other new judge would be better than the one we had at the moment. Assuming they were compromised, or at least the associate judge was, it was better to postpone the trial. In any case, Alejandro had no complaints about postponing it.

Countless times in court Alejandro was a no show. Even his lawyers did not care enough to show up. By law, he should have been incarcerated, but there was no way we could get the judge or associate judge to issue an order for his arrest. Of course, this empowered him more to keep abusing the system and more importantly me—now that he could no longer get close to me.

What was I thinking! How could I think Alejandro was going to obey the law and pay me my share easily? After all, he had not paid many people that he had parted ways with. Why was he going to be different with me?

When the billing vendor left us, Alejandro refused to pay them the money we still owed. The same thing happened when he partnered with a businesswoman in Dallas on the sleep studies. Alejandro was going there once a week to read the studies with her, and we did the billing in our office. One day, she decided to terminate the association, and in retaliation Alejandro refused to pay her what remained. She sued, but later withdrew it. Why?

My new lawyer had tried his best, but nothing was happening. He gave me a lot of good legal answers, but we were not moving forward. When a new judge took over our court on January 1, 2015, he inherited a mess. Before he came on board, it had been like a third world country court. The backlog was so large that the courtroom was always full. I recognized people coming back many times and saw their cases not moving forward. So, the new judge was overwhelmed.

On January 22, 2015, he presided over my case for the first time. It took him a while to grasp my case. By that time, I was already with Bobby Newman. By coincidence I had met Bobby's wife at a social gathering, and she had said: "It is going to become very bad, but then you will see how everything gets better and better."

Sure enough, my case was a mess. It took Bobby a while to file the motions in court that would get things moving. When Alejandro learned I changed lawyers and found out who I had hired, he was desperate. So, he went lawyer shopping, too, hiring one of the most corrupt abusers of the system, who used his status as the former chair the Republican Party in Harris County to pressure Republican judges. At least that made Jacob Woods feel he had the upper hand in a situation, and Alejandro believed it. But Alejandro did not know that Woods was persona non-grata at the Party because of his corruption and for almost bankrupting the Party. Still, in two years he was going to be able to manipulate the judges before election.

Finally, Bobby got a motion filed for contempt for not following court orders and one to change the temporary orders, making Alejandro give me more money so I could pay my bills since he was not doing it.

As Alejandro's new lawyer followed the same tactics of the previous one, it took us a couple of trips to court—when they objected and/or filed competing motions as a distraction, until everything was cleared and we were finally heard.

The hearing took two days over time. Everybody thought it would be a one-day deal, but they took forever in court that day and we did not finish. We came back after a month to complete the hearing. The judge ruled in my favor and allowed some needed monetary release.

I almost fainted when I heard the ruling. It was so incredible to me that finally, finally the family court saw what the children and I had been going through. Alejandro's lawyers kept asking the judge questions in an attempt to make him change the ruling. But it did not happen. The judge had just stood there looking unhappy with Woods' attempts.

My lawyer eyed me when we walked out. Inside one of the little rooms that are outside the courtroom, I hugged Bobby while saying thank you over and over.

"You just changed the game."

This poor American man was not used to physical expressions of gratitude—something that is so normal for us Latinas. I felt that what had just happened was very uncomfortable for him. When I let him go, I could see on his face that he was taken completely by surprise. I laughed and said: "You better get used to this. It is the Venezuelan expressing machine."

After two years of often not being able to buy everything on my grocery list, having my electricity turned off, along with the gas, cable and every other service you could imagine, I was finally going to be able to make my payments. The house had been damaged for lack of maintenance to the point where the realtor had decided not to show it anymore. Now, he had been ordered to repair it. Even the children had been on the verge of getting kicked out of school for lack of payment. Now, I was going to be in charge of my financials again—something I had always done until it was taken away from me.

My expression of gratitude had not been nearly enough to tell my new lawyer how deeply grateful I was after what I had been through.

My credit, however, was not going to be easy to restore. The credit cards had all been closed for lack of payment, and the card issuers wanted all of the payment or no more credit. The judge had only granted me enough to pay my needs on a monthly basis. The credit cards had to wait until the end of the divorce. By then, the damage to my credit would be even worse.

After the hearing, Alejandro knew he was facing a different situation. Whatever he had been able to do with the previous judge was no longer valid in this court. And even this Republican lawyer with the new Republican judge had no power. This judge wanted to apply the law and be regarded as a fair, honest judge. So, for the next two years of his four-year tenure, that is exactly what he did.

Later, when he was facing re-election, the judge changed. But by then my case was already won. However, he allowed my settlement not to be transferred for over two years and that not only cost me money, it hurt me as I was trying to make a living and restart my life.

CHAPTER 28

Get Back on the Horse

"Get back on the horse!" I heard from afar. The voice was clear, but I could not see who said it. I was lying in the dirt. All I could see was the horse running around the ring. She looked bigger than normal, or was it because I was so afraid that she looked like that.

She was feisty and decided to do as she pleased, running fast and sending me flying through the air, until I finally fell off on my butt after first scratching my back and hitting my head against the fence.

My back hurt!

The pain was unbearable; it felt like all my ribs had broken. I was lying on my bathroom floor all alone.

"Get up! Stop the show!" a voice said.

He had just come back to the bathroom and started screaming at me.

"I can't. I can't move." I was whispering because I could hardly talk.

"Come on, Carmen. You asked for it and then you acted like a little girl. Get up! I don't want the children coming in here and seeing you on the floor being theatrical."

"Leave me alone. Leave, please."

"Yes, I am leaving now and going out. I cannot have fun with you. I need to go look for fun somewhere else, so I am going to get me a whore. You asked why I cheated on Miss Venezuela. You will never get over that!"

He wanted to leave and he was looking for an excuse to do so. I do not know what prompted this incident in February 2013, but he hit me so hard this time and my ribs hurt so much that I thought they were broken.

And I went to Italy just as I said! God always finds a way when good things have to happen. My older sister was living in Rome with her husband. That was how the trip came to be when I was fifteen, my time to travel to celebrate the milestone.

I flew first class on Alitalia, Caracas-Milan-Rome. It was the first time in my life that I was traveling without my parents. You can imagine my dear father giving all types of instructions to the airline when they dropped me at the airport. The poor thing wanted to fly with me—afraid I might get lost or something. He was always my protector.

As usual on most transatlantic trips, the plane left in the evening and was to arrive in the morning. I was so excited that I hardly slept. We had to deplane when we landed in Milan. And that was the biggest test so far of my ability to understand and learn other languages.

I was waiting with most of the people that were in my plane to board the next one. Since the plane came from Venezuela, they were speaking in both Italian and Spanish when suddenly I heard my name called. I went to the counter, and they started talking to me in Italian. Since obviously I did not understand much of what they had said, they told me to follow them. We walked and walked, finally ending up in a storage type area with a lot of luggage.

After more Italian, they pointed to a bag, pulled the nametag and asked if it belonged to me. The name was Montero, not Montiel. Apparently, the bag was left unclaimed and they presumed it was mine.

It was another era, another time. That would have caused the biggest red alarm at the airport today. Once they figured out that the luggage was not mine, they told me to run, again in Italian, because my plane was leaving. I did not know how I understood that, but I did and started running back to the gate.

Once in Rome, Laura and Harry were waiting for me. I was happy and so were they. When they took me around to show me Rome, my eyes could not believe what beautiful and magnificent things I saw: all that history in those buildings, the Coliseum, old Rome, the Vatican, the old city wall, Sant'Angelo.

I wanted to pinch myself. Was I really seeing this?

Their apartment had a magnificent view of Rome. And they had a butler with white gloves. It was a long day. After I arrived, I stayed awake throughout the day until nighttime. When I finally slept, I did not wake up for 17 hours. It was Sunday.

Harry, her husband, was a polo player and belonged to the Polo Club in Rome. Laura took me there, introducing me to an Argentinian girl who lived in Rome and whose stepfather was also a polo player. My sister's idea was to introduce me to the rest of the young people at the club, so I would have more fun. And indeed, that was what happened.

Within days I had befriended everybody at the club, including a big crowd of youngsters who took me in as one of their own. It was lots of fun. They even took it upon themselves to help me learn Italian. Necessity to communicate is the best way to learn another language. In no time, I was speaking Italian and communicating with everybody, but not without having some fun first. They had bought a book and told me that the first thing you need to learn in any language was to know when you have been insulted or how to insult someone else. So, this book had insults and bad words in five languages. The group had more fun with that book than I did.

Able to ride Harry's horses every day, I took classes and had even started training to learn how to play polo, until I realized the danger I was getting myself into.

One Sunday afternoon, we were at a polo game. By then, I knew pretty much everybody there. I had even met many of the players since they trained every day while I rode horses there also. The club was playing against a British team, and we were winning.

At lunchtime, Francesco, one of the players, was joking around. He talked with nearly everybody. He had a great personality and was loved by all.

When the game started again after lunch, we were all sitting and paying close attention to the game. Suddenly, Francesco fell off his horse. He did not move at all once on the ground. But he was a big joker and everybody knew it. We all thought it was just Francesco being Francesco, that he would get up in a moment... and we would all laugh.

But nothing happened! No movement.

Some of the players walked away from him with faces covered, crying. We were all motionless, waiting to know more. Suddenly, people began running and screaming, "Call an ambulance!" Club employees started clearing the area and getting everybody out.

Francesco had died immediately of a skull fracture.

Alejandro was strangling me. I was trying to get away, but he took me by the hair, smacked my face against the wall, and rubbed it in. I started bleeding, powerless to fight him off, and fell to the floor. Then, he started kicking my legs, arms and even my thoracic area. I prayed to God to please make him stop.

Finally, he went away and left me there on the floor. I was in so much pain that I could not get up. I think I passed out.

All I could hear was, "Get back on the horse." I got off the horse and left my life a while ago. I was not the person I used to be. All my strength had gone. He was running my life, making decisions for me. The little energy I had was spent on caring for my children.

I lost track of time. Then I heard him come back: "Come on, Carmen, stop the show and get up before the children see you."

I gathered my strength and looked up to see he had bathed and changed, ready to go out. In the shower, the water soothed the pain, but my ribs hurt so badly that I could hardly breathe. I could not cough. For days, I covered the bruises with long sleeves and always wore pants. No dresses for me for a while. Nearly every inch of my arms and legs had been bruised and I had a big bruise with scratches on my forehead.

Carota was his nickname. It means carrot in Italian. He was the caregiver for Harry's horses and my equestrian trainer. The sweetest Italian man, he was an expert in horses.

He was called *Carota* because his hair was the color of a carrot. To me, however, it sounded more like *caraota*, which means black beans to Venezuelans. So, I used to tease him.

Every morning when I met him, he would have my horse ready, having decided which one I was to ride that day. They were all polo horses, big and so beautiful. They were all very good, except one female that was very moody. I did not like to ride her, but *Carota* always said: "It is you who control them. Not the other way around. You need to learn to ride horses of all types and temperaments."

The pain in my thoracic area was not going away. Finally, I told Alejandro I needed to be checked.

"Come on, Carmen, stop complaining. You are perfect."

"I need to be seen by a doctor. I am in too much pain."

"You know you cannot do that. What are you going to say? If you talk, do you know what would happen to me? Answer me!"

He was screaming with his face close to mine.

I was too weak to be assaulted again. I panicked.

"Okay. But please, I can't breathe."

"The only place you are going, Carmen, is my office."

"Okay. I will go to your office."

"Go tomorrow, and I will see. Is that clear?"

He was screaming all the while.

When I went to his office, he did an X-ray and said I was fine.

"It is nothing. It just needs time. I promise you it will go away, you little cry baby. I love you."

I will never know if he told the truth or I did indeed have a broken rib.

For months, I could not breathe right or cough. It took a long time for the bruises to go away. He was sleeping in the guest bedroom, where he had been most of the time for the last two years. Of course, he blamed me for that.

Life in Italy was more than fun. The people were fun loving and enjoyed life in a way that not even Venezuelans can. And, believe me, in Venezuela we are fun people. But the Italians were different. It was probably my Italian genes that made me feel right at home. I have Italian, German and indigenous genes from my mother's side. And from my father, I got Spanish and French.

I was in no hurry to get back to Venezuela, so I kept postponing my return. In all I stayed in Italy three months during the whole summer break. My dad knew better and wanted me to get on a plane that had no stops in another country. The options were Rome-Caracas or Rome-Lisbon-Caracas.

Dad had an uncle who was the Ambassador for Venezuela in Portugal. I had it all planned. If we stopped in Portugal,

I could stay and just go to the embassy. At least that would give me a couple of days in Portugal. But no! My father could read my mind and told my sister to send me back on a non-stop flight.

However, I kept postponing my trip. Twice my parents went to the airport, and I did not arrive. Until one day the phone rang!

"¿*Pronto*?" I said in Italian.

This is the way Italians answer the phone, but "*pronto*" in Spanish means "fast." Next thing I know, my father said, "*Pronto* is how you are going to come back."

Oh my God! He sounded furious.

"I have gone to the airport twice and you not only did not come, you did not care enough to let us know."

I was laughing because there was nothing he could do at the moment. We were on different continents. Soo mischievous of me.

"*Sí, Papi*! I will be there on the next flight."

Alitalia flew a nonstop to Caracas twice a week. And that was the end of my Italian adventure.

That morning's horse was Rosalinda. I felt like she was looking at me with disdain. The feeling was mutual. I did not like her, and she did not like me.

Carota said: "You know she feels you."

"But I am learning to like her."

"Yeah, right."

We were working on polo exercises. I needed to learn to do them before I was able to hold the mallet. The exercise was to gallop, then lean down and touch the front of her neck and so on. This used to scare me, but I was excelling at it and was proud of myself. We were working inside a round ring and I was controlling Rosalinda quite well when suddenly she changed from a gallop to a fast run. It was so fast that I could not sit upright. When we got to the fence, she stopped abruptly and I went up in the air, up, up, then down against the fence. I was between the fence and her!

In so much pain, I had scratched my back and bumped my head on the fence. I could see *Carota* running toward me and hear him screaming "Are you okay?" in Italian. Helping me up and seeing that I was fine, he said: "Get back on the horse! If you don't, you will never be able to mount her again."

CHAPTER 29

The Suicide Threats

I WAS IN THE office as usual in early October 2009 making calls and going over papers. I typically used Alejandro's desk when needed, but was not the type that opens drawers and boxes like Alejandro was. I found this intrusive and abusive. It was the way my mother had taught us.

But that day, while on the phone, I was appreciating the brand-new desk I got for Alejandro. Opening the middle drawer, I saw a checkbook. He never had checkbooks because he had left that responsibility to me since the beginning of our marriage. I opened the checkbook and saw that it was an account in Alejandro's name with an address close to our home from a bank that is not where we bank.

Alejandro was busy with patients, so I took the checkbook and went to the address listed on the account. It was a box at a UPS store. When Alejandro came home, I gave him the checkbook. His face fell and he went pale.

"Alejandro, can you please explain?"

"I...I...I..."

"What?"

"I wanted to have my own money."

"What? How old are you? You have your own money."

This went on for a while until he finally admitted: "I am using that money to go to the Men's Club with my friends. That way you would not realize it."

Back then, he said he went once in a while with friends or was invited by pharmaceutical companies for fun or business. I had never liked the idea, but did not want to be a crazy, jealous wife. I had always wanted to give him his space. But having this account meant he went there often. Why? Or was there something else he was paying?

Then, I also learned a debit card was attached to it.

"How often do you go there? I did not know you went there with your friends."

"Not often, but I did not want you to know."

"Where do you get the money for this?"

"Some checks I pulled out of your pile."

"How about taxes?"

"Becky puts the 1099 in the 1099 lot at tax time. There are usually too many for you to realize it."

"Alejandro, I don't like this. I cannot take it. Why hide? There is more to it that you won't tell. I think we have come to a dead end. I really want you to leave."

"This is my house and my children. I will never leave."

"Alejandro, you need to move into the guest room in the meantime, but you need to leave."

He started to cry.

"I cannot, Carmen, please."

This was a first: instead of going on the defensive, he was pleading with me.

I stopped talking to him or answering his calls. When he came home, I was already in my bedroom and did not allow him to come in. I left early in the morning with the kids, so I was gone when he came in to take a shower and get dressed. I was ice cold with him and determined. It hurt, hurt a lot. He was my husband, my love, but it was time to put my foot down and end something that was only getting worse. Still, I was impressed with his attitude. He was not his violent usual. Probably, it was because he felt weak after the Stanford loss of his investments.

Once again, I made appointments with lawyers, a difficult task because I did not know anyone who had gotten divorced and could give me a recommendation. I just looked in the yellow pages.

One Thursday afternoon, Alejandro called me. This was his light day of the week, when he usually finished early. I let his call go into voicemail. Once I got home from a meeting with a family lawyer, I played the message: "Carmen (his voice was weak, almost crying), I cannot take this anymore. I have too many responsibilities and losing you just adds to them. I bought a gun, and I am going to end this."

OMG! I was between incredulous and nervous since his brother had killed himself.

After waiting for a while, I finally decided to call him.

"Alejandro, please stop this act. I don't believe anything you said."

"Carmen, please…I am not lying. You know my brother killed himself, and I will do the same. You are making me do this."

He said all this in the same weak, nearly crying voice.

Suddenly, I felt cold and nervous. I felt guilty. What if he really did it? Was he really suicidal? Like he said, suicide ran in his family.

"Where are you, Alejandro?"

"I will not tell you."

"Alejandro, please! Where are you?"

"Some hotel on the 59 freeway."

And he hung up.

I called his brother Mario. They are a year apart and had always been very close. He lived in College Station, a little over an hour from Houston. When he answered, I went straight to the point, not knowing how much time I had to explain myself.

"Mario, I have a problem. Alejandro is in a hotel. I don't know which one or where, just that he said he was going to kill himself."

"What happened?"

"I want a divorce. I found out he had a bank account used to cover payments for those whores at the Men's Club and God knows for what else. This is it!"

"Carmen, I noticed Alejandro seemed very depressed with the Stanford loss. You guys have a family and a big responsibility. Thank God I don't."

"Do not make excuses for him. This is the time to stick to what is real, Mario, and that is family."

"You never know how people are going to react. But standard procedure when someone says they want to kill themselves is to call the police. They will institutionalize him."

"I could not do that to him. He is the father of my children. Please call him. Try to make him calm down. Please!"

I called Alejandro again. He was crying.

"Alejandro, please, where are you? Where did you buy the gun?"

"At the Academy store on the 59 freeway."

I went to Academy to see if that was true, showing my ID so they could see I was his wife. They confirmed he bought a gun.

I called Alejandro again.

"Alejandro, please tell me where you are."

"No, you would come here to try to take away the gun."

I felt guilty. I felt terrible, not understanding at the time that this was one of the many forms of manipulation: trying to make me feel guilty to distract my attention from the reality of the situation.

Finally, he told me which hotel he was in and I went over there intending to disarm him—something I tried a month later that went bad.

I knocked on the door. When he opened it, he looked sad like he had cried. The gun and bullets were on the bed. Crying and hugging me, he then started to kiss me. I hated what he was doing, but I was focused on trying to take the gun. What was I thinking? Did I think I was Wonder Woman? I was never going to get far from there. As soon as he realized what I was trying to do, he grabbed my hand.

"See, I knew it! That was all you wanted. You just did not want to feel guilty if I killed myself. You just wanted to get the gun and leave. Well, Carmen, I would just buy another one, but first I would kill you and then myself."

I was scared.

"No! No! That was not what I wanted. I wanted for you to be safe. Think about the children."

I remembered how many times a gun had been touching my head or inside my mouth. I did not want to be in that position again. I thought about options. What should I do? How could I get out now?

"You came here to trick me or to get me."

"What? What do you mean?"

"I thought you came because you love me."

"I do love you, but I am not putting up with what is happening."

"Get in the bed, Carmen."

"What?"

"We are going to make love or someone is not walking out of here. Probably neither of us would walk out of here."

I was convinced he could kill himself, but I also knew he could harm me. For years, he had talked about how he could be like his brother. He actually romanticized the idea.

Then, the Hotel ZaZa incident happened. But it was not until we were in the new house and I had found out about the affairs with the prostitutes, that he wanted me to call the insurance agent and find out if Alejandro's life insurance would cover suicide.

I was not an idiot.

"No, Alejandro! I am not calling to ask that. If something happens to you, I could be blamed. God knows what could happen. If you want to know, call him yourself and ask."

CHAPTER 30

The White Stuff

SEARCHING FOR SOME CLIPPERS to cut my son's nails, I looked in my bathroom and then opened Alejandro's nightstand drawer. There it was. I was floored to find a big bag filled with white powder. Right there in the nightstand! Any of my kids could have seen it.

Seen it? My baby son was only five years old. He could have tasted it, swallowed it, God knows what!

Suddenly, I was scared. How long had this been there? Had my children seen it? My God, the worst could have happened. I went to the bathroom, emptied the bag in the toilet, and flushed the whole thing.

Just back from the gym on an early Saturday afternoon, I was still wearing gym clothes: a jogging bra and yoga pants. I braved myself and went down to face Alejandro about this.

He was watching television as usual, sitting on the infamous black sofa, cleaning his teeth with the toothpick, something I hate. He had the most beautiful teeth, and I had always liked his perfect smile. But now, he had holes in every molar, and when he smiled you could not see a full set of teeth. His back teeth were receding, but he would never go to the dentist. Instead, he was always cleaning out the food that got stuck in these holes. But more than cleaning, it had become a tic. He always had something in his hand cleaning his teeth. I showed him the empty bag.

"What is this, Alejandro, and what is it doing in my house?"

He looked at me, speechless. He stopped cleaning his teeth and slowly pulled the metal thing out of his mouth. He was motionless.

"Tell me! And in your nightstand. Juan Diego could have taken it."

"Where did it go?" he finally said.

"What?"

"The cocaine, Carmen."

"I flushed it."

"You flushed over 600 dollars?"

"I didn't know how much it was worth. I didn't want it in my house. Alejandro, I don't like what has been happening here. You suddenly want to use drugs and you brought this into the house. You want to spend every night out going from bar to bar. We are respectable people. It is not okay anymore to go out dancing at those bars you like. They don't even have danceable music. We have three children."

Annoyed, he looked at me with a lot of hate.

"Shut up!" he said, throwing the toothpick at me. It got stuck right under my bra and hung there.

"Ouch...! You are crazy! You had this in your mouth. I could get an infection."

When I removed it, there was blood and a big hole in my skin.

"Listen, Carmen, this is what you are going to get!" And he threw a karate kid kick right on the same side where the toothpick was, sending me to the floor.

I could not breathe with the pain. I was coughing and started to cry.

"Don't cry, bitch. See what you made me do!"

He had kicked the air out of me, and I could not talk. I laid on the floor of the study trying to gather the strength to get up before he hit me again.

"You just like wasting money. You throw it around like it grows on the trees. That was good quality stuff, and you flushed it. Do you have any idea how much I have to work to pay for that? To pay for the clothes you wear, for the car you drive? You are not even thankful. You should be kissing my feet and the ground I walk on. You are nothing without me, Carmen. And now on top of it all, you are old. Look at you. Stop causing problems. What do you want? To be a divorced old woman? What would your friends say about you? They will stop talking to you. Stop it, Carmen, Stop it!"

He said all of this while I was lying on the floor coughing. I had expected another hit while he was raging, but my son called me. His room is on the second floor and opens to the family room. He can see into the study.

"Wait a minute, Juan Diego! *Tu mamá* is busy with me now."

Then he stormed out of the room and went upstairs. I was finally able to get up and sit on the couch. Alejandro's shoe was tattooed on my skin.

Juan Diego came down. I put my best fake face, crossed my arms over my stomach to cover the red mark, and asked him: "What is it, Baby?"

He hugged me. I think he saw something and that was why he called me as a way to stop what was happening.

"I am hungry."

"Okay, Baby. Go to the kitchen. I will be right there after going to the bathroom."

I got up and started walking toward my bedroom when I saw Alejandro leaving the house with a bag. Once again, he used whatever excuse to hit me and leave with the rented sports car of the weekend to show off and pick up girls. This time it was a white Ferrari.

This was new to me. He suddenly wanted to use cocaine and other drugs. I had no idea when he had started this, because for a while he had been leaving me by myself, waiting for him. Now, he was acting mysterious and going to hiding places at the bars. Had he always been using and I just did not know, or was this a new modality?

He had started trying to encourage me to try cocaine. He would say, "Carmen, come on. Let's try this. We are getting old and what else is there to do?"

The truth was that he could drink like a fish and never got drunk. I had no knowledge of how drugs and alcohol work, so I never paid attention, until a friend mentioned it: "How weird that Alejandro can drink so much and not get drunk. It is as if he is counteracting the alcohol's effect with cocaine."

She had not known what I knew. But that was the answer!

Once, I mentioned it to him, and just like the big liar, he denied it, even though I had already flushed the cocaine.

"Carmen, I am going to tell you the truth. What happened is that when I feel I am getting drunk, I go to the bathroom and throw up."

I could not believe his excuse … unbelievable. I already knew he was a bulimic. Everybody in the house knew it. Even the maids used to make fun of it because he would eat and then go straight to the bathroom to throw up. They could listen easily. One of them used to tell him every time he had his afternoon salad: "What a waste, eating to go flush it." But using this as the reason why he did not get drunk was incredible.

One night when we were coming back home from one of the bars, as soon as we pulled into the driveway, police lights were behind us.

"Oh shit!" he said.

It was the weekend, and he had gotten a Lamborghini. Of course, he was speeding and drunk. But that was not all: He also had used cocaine and still had a small bottle in the left pocket of his pants.

"I am in trouble!" he said.

The officer came to his side of the car and said: "Sir, you were going 95 miles per hour."

"Really? I am sorry, sir. I was just going home."

"Is this your house?" the officer asked while looking at the magnificent three-story contemporary home."

"Yes, it is our home. Our children are in there."

"Well, I will let you pass with a warning since you were coming home."

"Thank you so very much," Alejandro said. "Would you like to come inside for a drink?"

"Sir, I cannot drink. I am on duty."

"I understand, but you can stop by if you ever decide."

I do not know how, but you better believe that the police officer got not only one drink but two. A picture of this ended up in my daughter's Twitter account. I wondered what would have happened if I had done as he had wanted. He would have accused me of being a drug addict during the divorce, but could never have proved it. But if I had used, as he had wanted, that would have been another story.

CHAPTER 31

The Foundation

Once I was back home in Venezuela after the Miss Universe pageant, it was all about engagements with the Miss Venezuela organization and Miss South America. I was traveling a lot. However, after all the work before the pageant, I was a little bored, always accustomed to be working and studying. My schedule had always been 100%-plus full.

Remembering what my mother had told me right after the Miss Universe pageant, "*Mi amor tu país te necesita más* (My love, your country needs you more)," I decided to use my Miss Venezuela power and put my crown to serve others, especially the needy. I knew I wanted to form a foundation, but was researching my country's biggest needs.

As Miss Venezuela, I was invited to visit hospitals, retirement homes, foster homes for children and many more. But it was the pediatric hospitals that attracted my attention the most. It was sad to see that in such a wealthy country as Venezuela there was so much need at that level.

Children had always been my biggest concern because they cannot help themselves. I realized how big the need was when on a tour of a pediatric children's hospital in my hometown of Maracaibo, I was told not to enter the area where the children were bathed because I could catch an infection. The area was in very poor condition. I was shocked. I could catch an illness or an infection, but what about the children? That stayed imprinted on my mind: What about the children?

This feeling was confirmed while as Miss South America I also visited many pediatric hospitals that specialized in different areas. All of them had needs. It was as if the whole continent of children had been abandoned. I had to help them!

I had always worked in charitable causes since I was a teenager, collaborating with the youth program at my church, so helping was second nature for me. More than that, it was a need. I saw a need and had to help to fix whatever it was.

I had already met with the President of Venezuela, Jaime Lusinchi. The following Monday after the pageant on Friday, I was at his office in a meeting. He asked if I wanted to help the country in some way. To which my answer was a solid "yes." Entering the competition for me had a bigger purpose than just winning.

Then, he asked where I wanted to help. I said the children. Though I was only nineteen years old, I knew at the time that I had to pay my rent on this earth for the many privileges I had been given. And winning Miss Venezuela certainly was one of them.

My father was a great inspiration in developing the foundation, both in the idea and the whole organization. When I told him what I wanted to do, I saw pride in his eyes when he looked at me. I think that also helped him ease into the idea of allowing me to enter the pageant.

My father wanted all of his children to be the best in any endeavor we undertook. This foundation was something he felt was also part of him. He rolled up his sleeves and helped me like the biggest and most robust working bee.

He especially helped me in putting the Board of Directors together, enlisting his friends, all recognized businessmen in

Venezuela that were involved in helping the community also. The list was a dream come true for any organization: Enrique Delfino, Manolo Muchacho, Domingo Coronil, Lorenzo Mendoza Senior.

I hired a lawyer to develop the organization's bylaws, the most consuming part of the whole project. Meanwhile, I talked to different health organizations and companies to establish connections and communications for donations to the hospitals. I also formed contacts with corporations that could help with donations and developing ideas for fundraising events.

While doing all this, I was fulfilling my duties as Miss Venezuela and Miss South America. I went on a month-long tour as Miss South America to Peru and Ecuador. As I visited different cities in both countries, I also went to hospitals and pediatric hospitals, explaining to my boss over there what I was doing in Venezuela with the foundation. He loved the idea.

During my tour, it was announced that a chapter of the Las Misses Foundation would open in Peru and Ecuador. I was so proud of what I was accomplishing, especially since it was giving a different face to beauty pageants.

Back in Venezuela, Las Misses Foundation opened its doors with offices at Parque Central in Caracas, Venezuela, courtesy of one of our Board members, Enrique Delfino. Now, we were open for business and could put our hands to work.

In addition to enlisting former Miss Venezuelas and participants, including Paola Ruggeri, Neyla Moronta and Pilín León, I also recruited many of my partners from my pageant, like Mariela Salma. Their mothers also were part of the organization because they wanted to help us with this project just as they had helped us become beauty queens. Even one of my aunts, Ruth Ávila, became part of the organization.

The idea was for all former and future participants of the pageant to be part of it. The current Miss Venezuela was to serve as the president and the first runner up as vice president of the foundation. The Miss Venezuela and first runner up from previous year were to be part of the Board with a tenure of two years.

In the first year, we donated to the pediatric hospital in Maracaibo. In less than a year, we were giving away our biggest donation to the Hospital J.M. de los Ríos. By the second year, we were donating to the pediatric hospital in Guárico, the state that my successor represented.

All of the girls were interested and happy to participate in the project and we saw the result. The Board of each hospital was approachable and very thankful. When our donation was presented, each hospital organized an event with the children to receive us. Nothing could compare with this feeling of giving and knowing that it was so very needed.

Within a year, one of the biggest stars in the Spanish language music world chose the foundation as the recipient of a 20% donation from all his appearances in a tour of Venezuela. At the time, Juan Gabriel from Mexico was the best and brightest singer for the Spanish speaking world, and I was there with him at every stop, every concert.

My father and Alejandro were not happy to have to go see him. But it was opening night in Caracas, and a table had been assigned for me and my guests. They learned that he not only had a special voice, but was also a natural and complete showman. My dad and Alejandro became his biggest fans after that night.

It was in Maracaibo that I learned why he was unique and the best. He was singing one of his most heartbreaking songs, one that he wrote to his mother "Tear under the rain." That song got to everybody. You could feel the sentiment as he sang with that voice that wrapped around everyone. But the sound went off in the middle of it. The audience and I could see him moving his lips, but nothing could be heard. Juan Gabriel stopped singing and looked toward the audio people, clearly not happy at all. The sound came back immediately, but he put down his microphone and ordered the orchestra to stop playing. Everyone was silent waiting to see what would happen as we could see he was mad. At that moment, without microphone or music, he finished the song a capella, just his voice and nothing else. His voice filled up the space and got under our skin. That day, I knew I had witnessed something beyond spectacular!

Later, Paola Ruggeri and I were invited to the foundation's inauguration in Peru. It was incredible to see how the Peruvians were even more receptive to the idea than the Venezuelans had been. The event gathered all the former and current Miss Peru winners, starting with the first one, who was 80 years old at that time.

I was 20 then and could not believe what a difference I had made. Paola and I kept looking at each other with satisfaction for what we had accomplished.

CHAPTER 32

The Thief

I WAS INSIDE THE WARM WATER of this wonderful beach, where the sand is as white as salt and the water is crystal blue, so clear that I can see my toenails. Banks of clear blue fish swam around me. It was hard to distinguish them from the water. It was peaceful and quiet. No words could describe this beauty... only "paradise" could be like this.

The alarm clock sounded interrupting my dream. I was between the dream world and reality. Was I dreaming? Was I there? Oh! Yes. I would be there in two days.

Early in the morning, I thanked God that I lived three minutes from school. This was the best decision of my life. It was Friday, the last day to take the children to school before Easter vacation. Like always, I would drop the children at school and go to the gym. After today I would have over a week's break from my gym routine and work. Although, I was planning to do some yoga at the beach. We would see if that happened.

Tonight, we were going home to Venezuela, where my husband and I were born, for vacation. Venezuela had the largest Caribbean coast. All the beaches were beautiful, some more than others. But they were all beautiful. The Caribbean is a jewel in this world.

So much to do. The kids were packed. We were not. As much as I tried, we never seemed to be able to pack on time. Well! I had the whole day. We had to be at the airport around midnight to catch our flight that departed at 2:45 a.m. It was a short flight, just a little over four hours. For that reason, it was a killer, because they served dinner and by the time they finished we only had two hours to sleep. We always arrived tired.

After my spinning class of 45 minutes, I did a partial upper body workout. I am so pleased with the way I have kept my body in shape.

Back at home, I did the usual chores before going on vacation... pay bills... dreaded bills.

Then, I started packing. Afterward, I picked up the children from school and went to the movies like we do every Friday. When we got home, I instructed the children to take a shower and get ready for dinner before we left for the airport, while I finished packing.

Alejandro arrived. He had been working all day, or so I thought. He had not even started to pack, but he finished his bag fast. Well, in reality, all he did was pull out his clothes so I could pack them.

"Are you ready?" Alejandro asked. "Is that what you are wearing for the plane?"

"No," I answered. "I am going to shower and wear something comfortable. How about you?"

"I will shower also."

We took a shower and dressed comfortably for the night flight. Though we were not talking to each other, deep inside we wanted this trip. Our lives had been so difficult during 2011, the previos year. It was very hard to forgive him.

Knowing this flight was worse than a red-eye and we would arrive in Venezuela very tired, where we would sleep most of the day, I thanked God we were not going to Los Roques until Sunday.

On the way to the airport, I was day dreaming again.

"Paradise" for me had such a special meaning. When I thought of paradise, I was a little girl again on a beach with the whitest sand you could ever imagine and crystal-clear blue water. I walked on this soft, warm, white sand. It was soothing to my feet. The horizon, sky and water came together to a point, making it hard to tell what was water and what was sky since both were the same tone of blue. Getting into the water was another sublime experience. The water was perfectly warm and calm. You could walk and walk... and the water would be a little over my waist. And I saw my dad looking at me, watching my face full of fascination, as he said, "Paradise must be like this." He used to say that whenever we were on those gorgeous beaches.

I know he has been there... At that beautiful beach ever since he left us. And as of Sunday, for a week I would be close to him.

"Here we are!" Alejandro said.

We were at George Bush Intercontinental Airport, the five of us. My children were used to traveling the world. They were very familiar with passports and the whole horrible experience that had become traveling. I remembered when traveling was a luxury. When people dressed to get on an airplane. And because you were traveling international, they treated you like royalty. Not now! Not even if you traveled first class. Now we were treated like suspects of a crime... whatever that crime could be.

It was past midnight when we got to the counter, checked in, and went through the torture of passing security. What a pain now. My six-year-old son was a pro, putting his Nintendo, backpack and shoes in a bin before going through the machine himself.

The airport was like a ghost town. Everything was closed, even the Presidents Club. So, we went straight to the gate where the airplane was departing. The children were thirsty, but there was nothing around, until we saw someone pulling a cart with sodas and water. We all went for it. The girls got their sodas and went to find a seat. Alejandro, my son and I stayed. Juan Diego, as usual, could not decide what he wanted.

That was when I noticed a man looking at us, observing what we did, what we said, every movement. I blinked and thought I had become paranoid and seen ghosts ever since the burglary of my house. I think to myself, "Stop! Snap out of it!"

I went to the counter and tried to get upgrades to first class for our children. The gate agent informed me that it did not look good, but we were near the top of the list. We all sat together waiting. I entertained myself with my Blackberry, chatting. I loved my Blackberry and could never change to an iPhone. My Blackberry allowed me to stay connected to my friends and family in Venezuela.

We were going to my cousin's house at Los Roques. That was a luxury! Nobody had a house there because it was a national park. I had invited two couples to meet us there with their children. I was chatting with Zoraida, who asked me to let her know when I got on the plane.

I was also talking with Gustavo, my childhood friend. He was making me a white swimsuit for the beach, which impressed my daughter, Alexandra.

"MOMMMMMM...he is making you a swimsuit!"

"Yes! Why?"

"*Mami*, does anybody sleep in Venezuela?"

"Well, it is Friday."

At 2:15 we started boarding the plane. Finally! Alejandro and I were in first class. I got the children seated and returned to our seats 2E and D. There, across the aisle from us, was that man I saw at the beverage cart. He started a conversation with us, but we were busy taking care of our children. We still hoped to get them in first with us. But this man will not stop talking.

The flight attendant told us that we got one upgrade. However, my children did not want to be separated and decided to stay in the back. This man was still talking. Alejandro was in the aisle seat, while I was at the window. Oh my God! Cannot he stop talking…blah, blah, blah?

Finally, the airplane departed. I had been hoping to sleep a little, but it looked like that would be impossible. This man was still talking! From Venezuela, he had found a common ground, talking about the government, Chávez, blah, blah, blah.

When suddenly, strike one occurs! This man asked my husband, "Do you know Alejandro Latuff?"

I looked at him in disbelief. Where did that come from? I did not like it; men and their big egos! Or Alejandro and his big ego.

My husband answered with "I am Alejandro Latuff," so very proud. Turning and looking at me, he said, "See…everybody knows me."

I sat there thinking, what was that all about? How this person, who obviously wanted to talk to us, asked my husband about himself. This cannot have been random.

Well, at this point, we introduced ourselves.

"Gustavo Reyna-Zubillaga," he said.

"Ah! Gustavo, like my dear friend from childhood," I added.

Of course, when I said my name, he said, "I know a cousin of yours!"

Well, that was possible. I had the largest family one person on this planet could have had. As a matter of fact, after 27 years, my husband still felt he could not graduate in that topic. So, this Gustavo went on and on about my cousin, whom he said he dated. And he added that he met me at Le Club with her years ago. Here comes strike 2! Mary lived in the US for years and when she moved back to Venezuela, I got married and moved to the US. I never went out with her when we were adolescents or adults. However, he insisted on it. I have always had a wonderful memory and was quite sure I would remember that!

Then, he proceeded to strike 3.

"So, you are also related to Pedro Méndez?"

"Yes, he is my first cousin."

"Well, he is in deep trouble," he said.

"Really? People talk too much, and you need to stop. I do not tolerate people talking about my family, especially if I don't know you."

I think my attitude toward the topic finally made him stop. Gustavo had been very loud. The flight attendant from the back came and said the passengers were complaining of the noise, and added he could no longer serve more alcohol. The two of them had been drinking whiskey during the whole flight. Gustavo proceeded to tip our flight attendant so he kept serving him whiskey.

It looked like we became best friends with Gustavo or he thought we had. The conversation got personal. He was divorced less than a year ago and had one son. Suddenly, he said: "Let's get together tomorrow at Barandas."

It was the "in" place in Caracas. He and Alejandro exchanged numbers. We were staying in a hotel, but had local cellular numbers in Venezuela. He was staying at his parent's house.

We landed at 7:45 a.m. Venezuela time. Our extravagant president had changed the time to half an hour earlier compared to most of the world. It should have been 8:15 a.m.

We cleared customs quickly and our dear driver, who had worked for us for the last 20 years, was waiting outside. Exhausted, I had not slept at all. Another 45 minutes of driving and I would be in bed. This time, we had decided to stay in a brand-new hotel, The Embassy Suites. All five of us went to bed at 9 a.m. I would not communicate with anybody until I was rested. However, I needed to be at my dermatologist's office before 3 p.m., so I set the alarm on my Blackberry for 2:00 p.m.

Everybody was still sleeping when I got up. After my appointment, back at the hotel, Alejandro said that his new friend, Gustavo, was coming over. My friend, Gustavo, also was bringing my swimsuit to the hotel. As soon as he arrived, I told Alejandro I was going down to meet him and he decided to tag along. We got together in the bar, ordering drinks and *tequeños*.

Then, the new friend arrived and started talking to Alejandro like they had known each other for years. It all looked too strange to me. Even Gustavo asked me when they went outside to smoke if they were longtime friends.

"No, we just met him on the airplane coming here."

"What?"

"Yes! But Alejandro gets enamored with people like that."

When they came back from smoking, the new friend said: "We have to do business together."

My friend Gustavo, answered: "For that, you have to talk to her. She is the one that handles the money here."

Alejandro was rude to me all night, to the point that the new friend told my Gustavo while waiting for a taxi, "Pretty couple. I want to help them."

After spending a week in Los Roques, Alejandro and the kids left while I stayed to attend Ángel Sánchez's 25th Anniversary Fashion Show. Then, I went to Miami since I was looking for an apartment, flying back to Houston on Wednesday. As I landed, Alejandro's new friend was already in Houston trying to do business. I did not like this at all.

Of course, Alejandro had not picked me up at the airport because he was with his newfound friend. I arrived at the restaurant where they were having dinner. Alejandro was rude and entitled. He felt bigger with Gustavo.

Alejandro said Gustavo wanted him to get two MRIs for him from the Venezuelan government that would earn $1.2 million and he would split the proceeds in half with Alejandro just for helping to fund them.

"You are very generous, Gustavo, giving us 50%, and you just met us."

"Carmen, come on. This is a business opportunity," Alejandro said.

"I don't like this, and I also don't like you accusing my cousin of wrongdoing. Let me tell you, if you want to do business with us, you can never again mention anybody from my family."

I left and went home to see my children. Alejandro did not make it home that night using the excuse that I got mad. After that, Gustavo, who supposedly lived in Washington, practically moved to Houston. He even drove Alejandro's car, which he never allowed anybody else to do ever. More often than not, Alejandro used any excuse to avoid spending the night at home, always getting mad and blaming me for his absence.

The $1.2 million business became an extra $80 million business with a new deal. They were going to sale paperless medical records to the Venezuelan government.

"How is the government paying that, in dollars or bolivars?" I asked since there was no way to convert to dollars in Venezuela.

"Bolivars!" Gustavo answered.

"How are you going to convert that into dollars? We don't need bolivars here in the States."

"Well, that is the problem we are trying to solve."

More and more, this man sounded like a con artist to me. At one point, Alejandro said we were going to have to put up some money for this deal.

"Alejandro, I do not give a penny for any deal that has to do with Venezuela. If Gustavo is so sure this is a good deal, he has to foot the bill. I don't care. I can take less of a percentage."

We went to Venezuela in May 2012 for a meeting with the government without me knowing we had paid for everything with a credit card Alejandro had gotten for Gustavo. All they did in Venezuela was see prostitutes while I waited for Alejandro. I learned that after the divorce was filed.

With my resistance to invest in these deals, Gustavo decided to keep me busy back in Houston. He gave me two assignments for me to make money for myself, telling Alejandro it would be for me and me only as a way to try to befriend me. He knew I did not like him at all.

One of the businesses was transportation of some construction material and the other was getting thousands of HP tablets for the paperless medical system deal in Venezuela.

The first one I got within a day with my cousin, Lexy, who worked in transportation. And the second one took me two days with a friend I had that worked at HP. Gustavo was frustrated that he could not keep me busy or distracted for long.

My cousin investigated this man, calling me and asking how long I had known him.

"Two months," I answered.

"Where is he from?"

"Venezuela, but he said he lives in Washington."

"Well, Carmen, this company of his was registered in Houston in October 2011."

I was floored. That confirmed my suspicion: Alejandro knew Gustavo before the airplane. Was Gustavo determined to get rid of me or was it Alejandro? Alejandro became ruder and more enraged with me for every little thing. One day, I had reprimanded my oldest daughter. Since Alejandro hardly ever spent the nights at home, he did not know what had happened. Suddenly, he showed up at the house, took my daughter and screamed at me: "You are going to jail! I am going to the police to report you."

I looked out, and Gustavo was driving the car. Calls went back and forth between us. On one occasion, he forgot to hang up and I could hear how he instructed my daughter to lie and say I hit her. My daughter was crying, saying she could not do that.

"Of course, you can!" Gustavo said.

They were talking, and I could hear my daughter sobbing in the background. Gustavo finally told Alejandro that if she could not accuse her mother, he would find a way to get me into jail.

"Believe me," he said, "I know people, and I will find the best way to get rid of her."

I could not believe what I was hearing. Conducting an Internet search on this man, I found he had many complaints in the Ripoff Report and was a close friend of a New Yorker that was in prison for fraud. He also was involved in manipulating a fraudulent election in Central America.

Still, I could never have imagined that Alejandro and he were involved in all of this. That was a reality I came to understand later, as this had started way before I met Gustavo in March 2012 on our way to Venezuela.

Hours later, I called Alejandro and told him what I had learned. Gustavo grabbed the phone from Alejandro and insulted me.

Two days later, when Alejandro came home, I showed him everything I had printed about his friend. He acted surprised. But it took over a month for him to finally believe me. So I thought.

Gustavo never came back, but left us with more than a $20,000 American Express bill. He had not been able to get a check from me, but managed to leave a big bill on a credit card that I had never approved.

It became clear that Alejandro continued with Gustavo's recommendation to get rid of me, nearly succeeding with the plane incident that he himself had created.

How much of everything that had happened to me was Gustavo's idea? If the company had been registered in Houston in October 2011, he must have been here before then.

CHAPTER 33

The Blackouts and Medications

WE WERE IN a discotheque or bar as they called it here. In the last years of our marriage, Alejandro wanted to be in those places from Wednesday to Sunday, and would have been there on Tuesdays too, if he could. It was exhausting! I liked to get up early in the morning and take the children to school, then go to the gym, but with this new routine it was impossible.

He blamed me for that, saying I had become lazy. But he was getting up around noon and only working afternoons, while I took care of the kids, the house and the business.

Alejandro was always the gentleman getting my drinks. Usually I waited for him while he went and came back, most of the time staying with people I knew and talking. But this particular night I stood by myself and decided to follow Alejandro. Standing right behind him, I saw him take my glass and put a white powder inside. He had no idea I was watching, and I said over his shoulder:

"What did you put in my drink?"

He jumped!

"Nothing. You are crazy!"

"Alejandro, I saw a white powder coming from your hand fall inside my glass."

"Carmen, don't be paranoid. I put nothing in it. You want to fight, as usual."

"I am not drinking that."

"Well, it was something to make you happy. You look a little down."

"What?"

I asked the bartender for a sealed bottle of water and told Alejandro I wanted to go home.

"See! You are down. Now you want to go home. See, I am right! That is why I have to make you happy! You are going to stay here with me, and we are going to have fun."

Fun? I could not even look at him. I started to realize this could have been happening for a while. Could this be the answer to my memory loss? Could this be the answer to my freak accidents lately? Could this have been what happened in Colorado?

In the meantime, he was looking at every woman. I felt so disrespected and helpless. I could not escape from my misery.

I was suspicious from then on and avoided taking drinks from him if I had not seen where they came from.

Sometime later at the house, he served wine for both us and I saw him again pouring something in my drink. I locked myself in the bathroom and called Gustavo.

"Gustavo, this is the second time I have seen Alejandro putting things in my drink."

"Don't drink it."

"I know, but I am afraid of what is happening. How long had he been doing this?"

My life was so difficult, and I was under his spell. He had manipulated me so much for so long that I was not thinking clearly. It was not until I separated from him and healed over time that I started to understand every incident.

Ever since I had started dating Alejandro, he had tried to medicate me. This was very difficult for me because I come from a family that never used or abused medication. I wondered how long he had been poisoning me or keeping me under the influence of drugs. For years, he had tried to see which drugs would control me, using a real medical excuse to make me take them. My family has never had problems sleeping and only visited doctors when it was necessary. I was treated for my asthma, as was my sister, by our pediatrician even when we were already adults.

When we were dating, Alejandro gave me a bottle of Sinogan and told me to take one drop at night. I questioned why should I take it as I did not have problems sleeping.

"It will help you sleep better and function better," he said. "You do a lot, work and school. You need the help. We all take it at home, my brothers, Dad, even my mom and grandmother. Believe me, my dad is an expert on it!"

Yes! At the time, his dad was the doctor everybody who was anybody in Caracas went to see, or so he said. But at the same time, using help to sleep was fashionable, which my dad never agreed with. I was young and did not think anything was wrong with it. I just thought we were not like that and we would never take pills as a solution or to fix anything.

So, I tried it! And got the opposite reaction. It was terrible! I actually spent the whole night with my eyes open. And of course, I was miserable the next day.

Of course, all proud, he asked me: "How was it?"

"I could not sleep at all."

"Then you need two drops."

I never tried it again. After we got married, I noticed that Alejandro took Sinogan every night. Over time, just drops were not enough. He took half a bottle or more. Later, he had to take Sinogan accompanied by other medicines, which he said his dad's research had found to be very good.

His father was lucky! He had started seeing *la crème de la crème* in Caracas as patients. These women felt great with his treatments and referred their husbands. And these men brought with them the political figures of the time. He became an instant celebrity on the social circuit of Caracas, and those friends helped him fit in.

Not only was he able to join the Caracas Country Club, but also society women created a foundation for him to support his research. However, he critiqued the same people who supported him as the worst humanity had. I never understood how he could say those things about the people who fed him.

He purchased the best and biggest office in a new hospital, Hospital de Clinicas Caracas. Membership in this ultra-modern hospital, built and run by Jewish doctors, was a privilege. All of this came as a favor from his new supporters. He, the Lebanese doctor who hated Jews. With his new social status, he could now discriminate against everyone.

He felt he was a blue blood and looked for castles in Europe with his last name to prove he was a French immigrant—not an Arab immigrant—that had come to Lebanon in the Crusades as the "Hospitallers."

Many people in the medical field said he was a crazy man. But of course, he brushed off those comments as pure envy. So, of course, whenever Alejandro mentioned a treatment used and/or developed by his dad, it was like Jesus had spoken. And I, who knew nothing about medicine, should just respect that.

Around 1990, by the time I had been married for two years, Prozac came out on the market. It even made the cover of *Time* magazine. We were living in Johnson City, Tennessee. Finishing my degree in Broadcasting and Spanish, I had an overload of 21 credits per semester, which required keeping up a GPA of 3.94 in order for the dean to approve my overload.

Once again, Alejandro decided I needed medicine to help me. And of course, this time it was Prozac. I refused, but he insisted. Once again, I tried, and the reaction was terrible. Those medications definitely did not agree with me.

In 1992, we were in Houston and had purchased our first home. Since I was working full time at Telemundo, I planned to move on a Saturday. I had the weekend to get the house ready.

On Friday night, I organized as much as I could so everything would be ready when the movers came early in the morning. I had been moving nonstop since arriving from the newscast after 10:30 p.m. and it was after midnight. I asked Alejandro to help me. He was watching television.

"Please help! I cannot do this alone. And I still have to get up early to be prepared."

"Carmen, you are super stressed. Take this!"

"Alejandro, those pills don't agree with me."

"This is different. It will help you not have asthma tomorrow. I know you. With all of this, we are going to end up in the emergency room tomorrow instead of moving."

I believed him and took the pill. Next morning, I could open my eyes but I could not move. I tried repeatedly and could not. I could not even talk. My lips would not move.

The doorbell rang, but I could not get up. Alejandro started shaking me. Even though I felt it, I was not reacting. Inside my body, I was scared.

"Carmen, I am going to open the door."

He went down and came back up telling me they had started packing. I could hear everything but could not respond. And I was very sleepy. He went back to bed. He was not mad at me because he knew what he had done.

I thought someone needed to handle this, but fell asleep. Until Alejandro came and said: "Carmen, they need to start packing the second floor. I will dress you."

After dressing and helping me down to the living room, he put me on the sofa, until they needed to move it. Then, he put me in his car, and I continued sleeping all the way to the new house, where I slept until the next day.

On Sunday, I was finally able to wake up. The house was a mess and I did not know where anything was. I had not been part of the move.

"Alejandro, what happened to me?"

"Carmen, you definitely don't react well to those things."

"What did you give me? You said it was to avoid getting asthma."

"I cannot explain why you reacted like that. I never expected it."

I was mad. How could he? The movers had packed the trashcans with trash inside. The plates were dirty. Everything I had left to do in the morning did not get done. It was a mess.

In time, I learned when he drugged me like that it was so he could leave and go party. Apparently, he was accustomed to drugging women he was with. In 2012, I found a recording he did of Cara, the prostitute from Treasures, to scare her because she was blackmailing him about going public with their affair. In the recording, she complained that he had drugged her. Some parts of the recording went as follows:

"…the way you behaved last Friday," Alejandro said.

"What? Alejandro, you put something in my drink. That never happens to me."

He was silent, and she asked again: "What did you put in my drink?"

"The same thing you take every day to go to work."

He left me alone for a while or so I thought. Until he found a way to medicate me again using the excuse of treatments developed by his father.

At some point after the year 2000, Alejandro started giving me Stablon, supposedly the treatment his father found to "cure" asthma. He said he could assure a cure. Stablon is an antidepressant.

I took the medication for months and it never did anything favorable for my asthma. Though Alejandro knew I did not react well to this medication, he kept giving it to me. Later he started giving me Amantadine whenever I had a cold or felt I was catching one. Amantadine is another antidepressant and a medication used for Parkinson's disease.

Later, before I left for a trip to Venezuela by myself, he gave me Ambien and advised me to take it with wine. The result was that I passed out before I buckled my seat belt and reclined the chair, arriving in Venezuela with neck pain and totally disoriented.

When I told Alejandro what had happened, as usual his answer was that I reacted so differently from everyone else who took the medication.

He always found a way to make me feel at fault or inappropriate, until one day I saw a *Law and Order* program dealing with a case about a woman who had a car accident after taken Ambien. During the show, they discussed how the woman drank a glass of wine on the same day, and that mixing Ambien with alcohol "can make people randomly to pass out." At that point, I had a flashback of what happened on my flight to Venezuela. How could he advise me to take Ambien with alcohol? As a doctor, he must know about it. I questioned him, but got his usual answer: He did not know. Could this have been the first setup for the airplane event?

Then, when Stanford Bank crashed in 2009 and we lost millions, while building a new house and a commercial building, I was understandably depressed and stressed out. This was another great opportunity for him to medicate me.

A friend of mine was worried about me because of how bad I was doing and how down I was. I told her Alejandro was medicating me, and she did not like it at all. She took me to a Chinese doctor so he could get me off the medication with acupuncture, and he did.

I was in the hands of my husband, the person that I loved, the one supposed to love and care for me more than anybody, the one who is on top of it, a doctor. Of course, I trusted him.

After the Stanford crash in February 2009, he started drinking heavily and wanted company. Never much of a drinker, I had only been a light social drinker. But after Stanford, Alejandro needed a drinking buddy, and I had to drink with him or I was punished. Later I discovered what he was doing to my drinks. By then, the damage had been done.

As time passed, I wondered if the headaches I suffered while working at Telemundo were caused by medication. I had developed a chronic headache and went to doctors to cure it, and then to a neurologist, his former professor.

During couples therapy in 2011, I discovered he had been cheating since back then. Was he already drugging me, so he could leave the house without me knowing?

I even wondered if I had ever had West Nile virus, but actually the illness I suffered for six months in 2012 was caused by medication Alejandro was giving me without my knowledge.

He had sent me to the hospital to be tested for West Nile since there was an epidemic and I was having headaches. I never saw the results, but he came home from work and told me that my test results were positive and I had West Nile virus.

The only incident where I could imagine a mosquito biting me was when I had the car accident. Yes, a freak accident. That also could have been caused by what he was giving me. My car flipped, and I ended up in a ditch near my house. How I ended up there? I did not remember, but I had spent time in the ditch and it had water. The mosquito must have bitten me at that time. Or did it?

For months I could not function. I had a chronic headache all day long. It was so bad sometimes that I wanted to die. Life was not worth living like that. I felt worthless and could not get out of bed. I could not take care of the children or myself.

A few months later, in a fight, Alejandro said: "You are so crazy that you have invented a case of West Nile virus for yourself."

"What are you talking about? I cannot invent the pain I had."

"Yep! You never had West Nile virus."

Were those headaches the result of his medication? I will never know.

My friend Fernando always celebrated his birthday with a summertime party. In 2012, the party was at a local bar/restaurant on a Saturday.

Alejandro had joined a luxury/sports car club and rented these cars on weekends. It was always those cars that men dream about having: Lamborghinis, Ferraris, etc. He was so proud when he drove them. I could tell he felt like God! But he really wanted to be picking up girls instead of having me beside him in those cars. He tried to get rid of me so he could go out and show off the cars to young girls, always picking fights to have an excuse to pack a bag and leave. Or if that did not work, he just drugged me.

On Saturday, we left for Fernando's party in a black Lamborghini. I was wearing a short black dress. After we arrived, Alejandro got our drinks as usual. I was not supposed to drink, but he always made me. Caught in the middle, I had become his prisoner after what he had done in Colorado.

I had not even drunk a full glass when I had to sit down. I could not stay on my feet. When Alejandro came to ask what had happened, I could not even speak. Feeling weak, my tongue was heavy just like it had been in 1992 when we moved into the new house. Right away, Alejandro said we had to leave and he would take me home. I could not walk. He made me wrap my arm around his neck and he held me by the waist. Like that, we left the party that had just started.

The goal was not only trying to get rid of me, but also trying to make me look bad in front of other people.

As soon as I got in the car, I passed out. I did not remember how I got to bed. The next day, I had to take my son to a morning soccer game. I woke up totally disoriented, but responsibility was more important than staying in bed. After breakfast with the three children, we all left while Alejandro was still sleeping.

I noticed that the Lamborghini was parked in the carport, not inside the garage. That was odd. And when I pulled into the street, a pickup truck with young boys was trying to get it out of the ditch. All around my neighborhood were ditches on both sides. These kids were not from our neighborhood. What were they doing here? Like the movies, I slowed down when we passed and looked at them. I felt like they had not liked me looking at them and were trying to hide. But I had a game to get to and kept going.

Two years after that, I got the answer. Our new neighbor, whom I did not know at the time, remembered that Alejandro had fallen in one of the ditches with a black Lamborghini one night while leaving the house. He got some kids with a pickup truck and a rope, and they had tried to get the car out. What ended up happening was that the truck went into the other ditch across the street.

When I heard the story, I had a flashback: the kids in the green pickup truck when I had left my house. That was confirmation that during this time, Alejandro had been trying to get rid of me!

Just like he did in the summer of 2010 in the Bahamas at the Atlantis Hotel. That summer we had taken the kids to Atlantis. The three of them wanted to go after the commercials got them all excited. It was an exclusive family vacation all about letting the kids have fun.

We had only been there for two days when walking back from dinner one evening we came across the casino with a staircase and people in line. Alejandro asked a guard what that was, and he was told it was the discotheque. He came back and said: "Let's go, Carmen!"

"What about the kids?"

"They can stay in the room."

"That was not the plan. We are on a family vacation."

"Carmen, you are really becoming old and boring. Come on! If you don't come, I am going by myself."

So, we walked the children to the room, made sure they were watching television, and left around 10 p.m. When we got there, Alejandro walked past the line and paid the bouncer $100 to let us in. He wanted seats next to the dance floor that were surrounded with a red ribbon and asked how we could sit there. He got the typical answer: Buy an expensive bottle. So, he ordered a bottle of champagne and a whiskey for himself as we sat down in the exclusive seats by the dance floor.

Two women dressed very provocatively were seated at a nearby table in the same area. Alejandro kept looking at them.

A couple drinking beer sat next to us. Alejandro got mad that they were there without buying an expensive bottle. He called the waiter and complained, but he did not care and brushed him off. Alejandro kept complaining, but the couple did not leave and no one attempted to move them. By now, Alejandro was very mad and started to throw small pieces of strawberries at the back of the woman. She was wearing a white dress.

They sent us a couple of beers as a peace offering. I do not like beer and never drink it. Plus, why drink beer when I had a bottle of champagne. I only toasted with them and then proceeded to drink the champagne until I felt sick. Running to the bathroom, I turned to find Alejandro when I was about to go in and he was talking with those two women.

I did not remember anything after I entered the bathroom and went into a cubicle, not even how much time had passed when an African American female opened the cubicle: "Honey! Honey! Are you okay?"

The next thing I knew, I was sitting in a wheelchair in an office. Opening my eyes, I tried to see where I was when I passed out again. It felt like a dream. I was moving in a wheelchair; someone was pushing me through hallways, elevators, and hallways again, until they stood up in front of a door and knocked on it.

Then I sat up! Alejandro opened the door as I got up out of the wheelchair and walked into the bedroom. Once the door was closed, I asked Alejandro what time it was.

"It is past 4 a.m.," he said.

"All of these hours and you did not care where I was?"

"Carmen, we were drugged by that couple."

"Alejandro, I did not drink that beer."

But I was still drugged and got in bed passing out again. Next morning, we woke up around 10 a.m. Alejandro was defensive.

"How could you? I disappeared and you didn't care."

"Carmen, I thought you were mad and left because you saw me talking with those whores."

It was true; I did not dream it. He was talking with them.

"Really? I was going to leave without my handbag? And by the way, where is it?"

"What?"

"My handbag."

"I don't know."

"You must have been pretty distracted to not care about me or my handbag with all of our credit cards and cash."

"Carmen, we were both drugged."

I could not believe this. The kids were next door listening to the whole conversation.

"Carmen, let's get the problem with the purse fixed."

He called the front desk: "I need to report a crime."

He had to make it look real so he reported a crime. The hotel sent a security officer. He told them his version of what happened, acting as if he was worried.

"They drugged both of us."

The hotel put out a report on the incident. With that, I had to notify all the credit card companies. Great! We were on a trip and now had no credit cards. He convinced me that they drugged us.

These incidents also were a way for him to verbally abuse me and make me feel bad.

He would say, "Carmen you are so crazy that you lose your memory every time you have a drink!"

It was not until after he had moved out of the house, and my oldest daughter had come back after the terrible experience she had with him that one evening after dinner she said: "*Mami*, he drugged you so he could go with those women."

"What? What are you talking about?"

"In the Bahamas, *Mami*, remember? When *Papi* said those other people drugged the two of you."

Alexandra lived with him for two months. When she came back, she knew a lot.

It was as if light started to appear in my life. Time and healing myself, along with the distance from him, had started to show me what had been really happening to me. Everything that had no explanation started to make sense.

How many times had he drugged me? I had no idea. I had just passed out without noticing anything.

Many times, I had woken up in bed not knowing how I got there or how I had on my pajamas. These things never happened after he left and I was no longer under his control.

CHAPTER 34

The Second Setup

In 2012, it was the time for my daughter Kamee, to go to camp in Switzerland to improve her French. As I had done with my oldest daughter, I sent her and then went to pick her up.

The plan was that I would fly by myself to Geneva, take the train to Montreux, stay a couple of days with her on a mommy and daughter trip, and come back.

At the last minute, Alejandro enlisted himself to come with me, using the excuse that became his signature: "I will go with you to show you that I only want to be with you and I am not misbehaving."

This was the same excuse he gave me a year later—after Gustavo Reyna-Zubillaga was in our lives and gave him ideas on how to get me in jail.

With no direct flights to Switzerland from Houston, the best way to get there then was to fly to Amsterdam and from there to Geneva.

As with all European flights, the plane left around 6 p.m. Alejandro loves to be at the airport early, and we were. He was always looking for an excuse to be mad at me, and that day was no exception. He was unhappy, complaining about everything, even the fact that Kamee went to Montreux.

"Alejandro, really. We had agreed to do this just as we did with Alexandra."

"Nope," he said.

I decided to ignore him. It was better that way. At the Presidents Club, Alejandro was having his regular whisky and drinking from my wine, too. I did not know how he could do that and never look drunk.

We boarded the plane and had dinner as usual. After dinner, I was looking for a movie to watch, when Alejandro said we should watch the same movie.

"Okay," I said. "Which one?"

"*Resident Evil.*"

"I want to see *Abraham Lincoln*."

"No, that is boring."

"You know I don't like those movies."

"*Coño*! See it with me."

"Why don't you watch yours and I'll watch mine?"

Big mistake! That set him off.

"You never do what I want. We are traveling together, but it is as if we are alone."

"Alejandro, you are the one that has been mad and ignoring me all this time."

While I was speaking, he got up and went to the galley where the flight attendants were working.

He talked with a male one. I knew he was hoping the man would empathize with him. I do not know what he said, but could only imagine he was complaining. I saw the flight attendant point to the seat as he told him: "Sir, you cannot be here; sit down."

Alejandro came back to our seats, but before he sat down, he got close to me and punched me in my left eye with his fist. I still had some wine in my glass and threw it at him. The wine went all over his seat and smelled, of course.

Going back to the flight attendant, he complained I got him all wet.

The man looked at me and saw me covering my eye. The gentleman seated next to us across the aisle saw the whole thing. I asked him to please be a witness, but he said he wanted nothing to do with it: "Ma'am we are on a plane. This is dangerous."

In the meantime, the flight attendant told Alejandro to take a seat. Alejandro asked to change seats, then came back to me and said: "See what you made me do. Now I have to change seats."

He gathered his stuff and left.

A woman came and sat next to me. I did not know who she was nor did I care. I turned and fell asleep for the rest of the flight, waking with the announcement that we were getting ready to land.

Getting up, I went to the bathroom, washed my face and brushed my teeth. While looking in the mirror, I realized I had a bruise around my eye, the result of Alejandro's punch. I went back to my seat, got my sunglasses out of my handbag and waited for landing.

Once we landed, I got off the plane and did not even look or wait for Alejandro. I am familiar with the airport in Amsterdam; it is big and complicated, but I knew my way around.

Looking for Customs, I suddenly bumped into Alejandro. Ignoring him, I kept going. But he was lost and did not know where to go.

"Carmen, come on."

"Alejandro, leave me alone please. I am going to pick up my daughter. You go do whatever you want."

I kept on walking.

"I don't know where to go."

"Your problem."

He grabbed me by the arm to stop me.

"Don't you touch me again!"

I looked at him and removed my glasses to show him what he did.

"I did not say anything on the plane, but I can now. Leave me alone!"

And I kept on walking. He kept walking next to me without talking. As I walked, I was thinking what I had to do. I had to get a divorce as soon as I got home, but how? How with all this mess he created? I was trapped and I did not know how to get out. I kept moving, passed through Customs, and went to get my luggage to make the connection to Geneva. He tagged along and did as I did. I just ignored him.

"Are you planning not to talk to me anymore?"

"Alejandro, I have something to do. That is why I came, to pick up my daughter, and that I will do. That is all."

But as luck would have it, one of our bags did not arrive and I had to go report it at the airline counter. He tagged along.

While there, he looked at me and nodded his head negatively, finally saying: "Please forgive me."

"Leave me alone."

"Please, we are here to pick up Kamee. We cannot show up not talking to each other."

"We? I am going alone. I have been there before and know where I am going. You can do whatever you want."

"Well, I am going with you. Let's see how you can get rid of me."

The airline said the missing bag would be sent to the hotel. Since we had a connection to make, there was no way that we could have waited for it. After that, I made my connection. He followed me. We boarded the plane, but I did not talk to him.

Once in Geneva, after getting our luggage, I proceeded to pick up the rental car I had reserved. This time, the plan was to drive to Lausanne instead of going by train. As soon as we got there, he took over and requested the car. I took my luggage and started to walk. I thought: I could go by train, so I did not have to go with him, plus he had no idea where he was going.

He never knew about anything that had to do with the children, not even school related activities, studies or grades. He never met their teachers or went to a parent-teachers conference. Their camps were even less important to him. I could have sent my children to China, and he would have never known or cared.

As soon as I started walking, he ran and stood in front of me.

"Where are you going?"

"I am going to catch a train."

"No, you are not."

I looked the other way.

"Listen, Carmen, you are going to do as I said."

"And I am going to show my face."

"Please, please forgive me. All I want is to make Kamee happy. If you continue with this, it is your fault that this is ruined for her."

Once again, he put the blame on me. If the children were not happy, it was my fault. If anything bad happened, it was my fault. Now, I was responsible for ruining an incredible summer for Kamee. I felt terrible. Kamee had been so looking forward to spending time in Europe together, and now this.

I just nodded and left with him.

CHAPTER 35

The Police

I HAD JUST ARRIVED in Houston from New York after leaving Alexandra at her summer camp, which also meant that I had new clothes.

Every year, my friends from Venezuela and I would take the girls to summer camp in upstate New York, then would stay a few days for shopping, dinner and fun in Manhattan, a tradition that we baptized as "*Mami* Camp." The first year, it was only Ariana and me, but each year the group had grown, until we had become 13. While many took their children to the camp, others simply came to join the fun. These days coincided, most of the time, with the 4th of July, United States' Independence Day, so we had incredible days that were not so hot in the Big Apple.

I had bought tickets for The Police concert in Houston before I went to New York; in fact, I had bought them as soon as they went on sale. Of all my friends, only one was in Houston at that time, and she was dying to go to the concert. Already by June 29, 2007, most of my friends were out of town on vacation.

Although we bought the tickets early, we did not get seats close to each other. Alejandro and I were in the third row on the floor, while Thelma, her husband, and a girlfriend of hers from Mexico were sitting much further back on the floor. Since I had just arrived from Manhattan, I had not had time to see Thelma, but we had talked on the phone. Alejandro told me to invite them to dinner after the concert at my favorite restaurant, Mark's. Thelma's Mexican friends had come to Houston exclusively for the concert.

Thelma had not sounded very happy about the idea of going to dinner. The last time we had gone to dinner with other couples, Alejandro practically took me by my hair at Da Marcos after he had fought with the chef and his wife. The scene was so embarrassing that the next day I had called everyone to apologize. For a while, I had kept my distance from the couples, only seeing the wives when we went out for lunch.

Making a scene in restaurants was Alejandro's custom. Years before, he had fought with the chef of Ruggles, located inside Saks Fifth Avenue in the Houston Galleria. That night, we had gone out to dinner with his brother and a friend of his. I knew her; she was a friend of a friend and had met him on a blind date. At that time, Ruggles was new and one of the restaurants of the moment.

Arriving when the restaurant was full of people, we were the last in the restaurant and were still there when it closed. We asked for the bill, which the waiter brought in a leather notebook. Both brothers put their credit cards inside, and the waiter returned them with receipts ready to sign and a pen in each of the two notebooks.

The notebooks were dark brown with the name of the restaurant in golden letters on the front cover. They both signed the receipts as we kept talking. Alejandro had been playing with the pen while talking, when suddenly he began painting black ink over the golden letters, thus covering the name.

"Alejandro, what are you doing?"

"What?"

"You're scratching the notebook."

"So what? How much can this cost? We ate and paid around $500. Leave me alone!"

He continued scratching the notebook while I stood up and went to the bathroom with Mario's friend. Like many women who visit the bathroom together, we retouched our makeup and talked about female stuff. How did she feel? What did she think of Alejandro's brother?

As we went out and walked down the corridor connecting to the restaurant, I heard voices. I thought it was strange since nobody besides us was there. The voices were louder as we got closer. Someone was arguing. As we passed the bar, we saw Alejandro and his brother standing with a man dressed in white with a chef's hat. While Alejandro and the man in white were arguing, his brother had that uncomfortable look on his face that he wore in embarrassing situations with his brother.

Mario tried to calm both Alejandro and the chef. I grabbed his date by the arm and stopped her from walking over to them. I preferred not to get closer. The tone went up.

Alejandro asked: "How much did you pay for this?"

"That's not the point," the chef said with a heavy French accent. "It is your lack of respect."

I thought they were going to start fighting. But all bullies are cowards. When Alejandro saw that the situation had worsened, he took a $100 bill, threw it on the table and ran off saying: "Let's go."

Despite other incidents like this, Thelma agreed to go out to dinner with us, and I made the reservation at Mark's as late as they accepted. I dressed in black for the evening, with black skinny pants, a black shirt with open shoulders by Anne Fontaine, and yellow and black shoes, all New York acquisitions.

When we arrived at the Toyota Center, I called Thelma to locate where they were. I had to stand and turn around. I did not see her! It was quite behind where we were sitting. She got up and signaled to me.

Before the concert began, Alejandro had gone upstairs to look for drinks. He brought me a white wine, but I did not like it and put the glass on the floor under my chair. Why drink this terrible wine when we were going to Mark's later and will have a good wine.

The lights went out and the music started. When they came back on, Sting was lit on the stage. I was like a little girl fulfilling my dream. I could not believe it. I was watching The Police live! When they had separated, I thought that would no longer be possible. But they met for a world tour and came to Houston. I almost pinched myself to make sure I was not dreaming. I did not blink. For me, there was only the stage. I was so entertained.

Alejandro was never a man who liked music very much. We all have favorite youth groups, but not Alejandro. I thought he did not know much about The Police since he spent the night getting up and down. However, I was not paying much attention because I was in my own world, watching and listening live to The Police.

At one point, he said something to me that I could not understand because of the music. When he repeated it, I got closer to hear.

"That *mona* is ruining my night," he said. "She is a fat woman. Look at her! I want her to see you so she sees the *mujerón* (great woman) that I am with."

I turned around and saw a security woman who looked after the staircase. Apart from taking care of the place, she was in charge of not letting people who did not have seats on the floor to come down. Every time Alejandro had gone up and down, I figured he had to show his ticket to prove he was sitting on the floor. Since he hopes people will treat him like a king, I was sure it made him mad. He went up to the bar several times.

Alejandro had always consumed alcoholic drinks like they were Coca-Cola.

We had left quickly after the concert ended to get to the restaurant before it became crazy. We tried to go up the stairs next to where we had been sitting, where the female security guard was, but the woman stood in the middle and blocked the stairs with her arms on each wall when she saw Alejandro.

When I saw that, I turned around and walked to the next staircase. Alejandro was following me when I heard: "*¡El coño de su madre!* (mother fucker!)"

Already climbing the stairs, I turned but could not see him. I looked around and saw a group of security men on the neighboring staircase surrounding a person who seemed drunk. It was Alejandro! They had arrested him.

I was paralyzed. Never in my life had I experienced something like this. I had no idea where they had taken him. I went down again and asked the woman who had blocked the stairs what had happened.

"They arrested him," she said.

"Where did they take him?"

"Ask the security people above."

She let me through to go up. At the time I thought: "The problem is not with me. It is with him. She did not want to let him go."

When I reached the top, I found a guard who told me Alejandro would be at the police station there. I never knew there was a police station at Toyota Center. But of course, it was obvious one was needed in a place with thousands of people, both for sporting events and concerts, drinking and God knows what else.

On the way to find him, I called Thelma and explained what had happened.

"They took Alejandro."

"Why?"

"I don't know."

"Tell me where you are and we'll go there."

"When I get there, I will let you know."

I arrived at the door and knocked. A policeman opened the door.

"Who are you looking for?"

"My husband."

While talking to him, I looked under his arm for Alejandro and saw him sitting behind the officer.

"There he is. He is behind you sitting down."

"Wait a moment."

He closed the door, and I waited there, calling Thelma to tell them where I was.

Thelma and Nizar arrived, saying their friends had gone on to the restaurant.

"Well, we will not go," I said. "Who knows what's going to happen here."

I stayed at the door waiting while Nizar and Thelma went to get the car. They told me they would stop in front of the exit closest to where I was. My feet were already hurting from standing there when the policeman came out and told me they were going to take Alejandro to jail. He gave me the name of the place, but it was unknown to me.

While I was waiting outside to find out where to go, a friendly patrolman stopped and I explained that they were taking my husband. He told me where they would take the people detained there and to look for a "bail bond" office to get him out. I asked if he could get the car key from my husband for me.

"Yes, lady. Let me see what I can do, because in addition, they will tow the car if it stays parked all night."

After a while, the officer came back with the key. I waited there until I saw that Alejandro had been taken with other men. Nizar accompanied me to a bail bond office. I had never done anything like this in my life. Those offices are open

24 hours a day. I apologized a thousand times to Nizar that the night had turned into a tragedy. Thelma had gone on to dinner with her friends, something that Alejandro criticized when he found out.

Upon arriving at the bond office, I got the paperwork started and paid. They informed me that it was necessary to allow time for those detained to arrive at the station and be processed so they could obtain bail.

After I had done everything, they had asked me to do, they told me to go home and they would call me when they had everything ready to tell me where I had to go next and what steps to follow. I did not know how long it would take, so it was better to leave and wait at home.

Nizar took me to get my car at the concert venue and from there I went home. When I arrived, our maid, Stella, was awake. It was almost two in the morning.

"Stella, what are you doing up so late?"

"Madam, they do not stop calling. It looks like Doctor Alejandro but I do not know if I should accept the call."

Stella, along with every person who worked in the house, had to call him doctor. Even his engineer brother, who is not a doctor, had the employees call him doctor.

"Stella, what happened is that he got arrested. I came here to wait to see when I can get him back."

The telephone rang again, and I ran to take care of it.

"Hello."

On the other side, I hear a recording: "You have a collect call from the Harris County Jail from…"

And I hear Alejandro's voice.

"Do you accept the call?"

After saying yes, immediately I hear: "WHERE THE FUCK WERE YOU?"

"On the street, waiting to see how I could get you out of there."

"Listen, Carmen. Listen to me well. I already found out everything. This is what you have to do."

"Alejandro, I have everything ready."

"What? You know nothing at all. Here I am with these prisoners who do this all the time. They told me what to do. LISTEN."

It had always been like that. He knew everything, and I was an idiot who knew nothing. It was so frustrating to talk to him. I kept quiet as I always had and let him talk without paying attention.

After all, on my part there was nothing more to do except wait. When he shut up, I told him: "Everything has been done."

"Then why am I still here?"

"Because you have to be processed so the bond company can ask for you. And that's what I'm waiting for. When they call me, I will come looking for you."

"How long will that take?"

"I don't know."

And the authoritarian changed to a scared puppy: "Get me out of here, please."

I was exhausted. The day had been longer than long, all this uncertainty, in addition to the mental stress. I lay down on the bed, but not before I had put on something more comfortable and less flashy, so I could be ready to leave whenever they called me. I tried to sleep but could not because Alejandro called every 10 minutes.

"What happened?"

"Nothing, I'm still waiting."

"Did you call them?"

"There's no case, Alejandro. They said they would call me."

"CARMEN, you call them." And he hung up.

When I called the bond office, they informed me that they had already located him and his release was being processed. I hung up and tried to sleep but no! Alejandro called again. I told him it was being processed and they would call me.

"If they do not call you in half an hour, you call."

"You'll call me before half an hour."

"Carmen, understand. I do not want to be here," he told me almost crying.

I hung up and tried to sleep again. But between Alejandro's anxiety and his calls I could not. Finally, they called me from the bail bond office.

"Everything is ready. You have to come here to collect some papers and then we will tell you what to do."

I got up, brushed my teeth, poured water on my face and left. Not without first telling Stella that if Alejandro called to say I had left. When I stopped by the bail office, they gave me a document that I had to take to the courthouse, where I paid. Then, I could go to the prison to pick up Alejandro.

It was still dark when I left the house, but the sun had started to come up by the time I got to the courthouse. I looked at the clock, and it was 6:00 in the morning; the courthouse office did not open until 7:30, so I sat down to wait, my eyes closed. I was fighting sleep because I did not want anyone to get ahead of me once the office opened. I closed and opened my eyes, suddenly noticing that the office was open. I stood up and walked fast, managing to be the first one at the window where I paid.

It took about half an hour to get to the prison, a place I had never seen, in an area of Houston I had never been in before. I went to the window and gave the papers to a policewoman who told me to sit down and wait.

I had lost track of how much time had passed when Alejandro finally emerged. It looked like such a little thing, but I still trembled from the experience. We embraced and left in the car, arriving at the house after 10:00. While he went straight to bathe, I sat down to eat breakfast with our two youngest. Alexandra was at the camp in New York.

After finishing my coffee, I went to sleep exhausted from fatigue. We spent all day in bed because we were so tired.

On Monday, it was my job to contact our attorney to see what we were going to do about this. I was always in charge of everything in our lives, along with cleaning up the messes Alejandro made. Although our attorney practiced civil law, he would recommend us to someone else who would take care of the case.

I explained the version of events that Alejandro had given me since I never saw what happened. Everything that happened with Alejandro was abnormal. And so, it led my life to abnormal events. According to him, he had only passed under the woman's arm. Our lawyer told me that most likely the case would be annulled since it was a first offense.

As the months passed and the case was not canceled, I learned in a conversation with the lawyer that the Toyota Center and the woman were saying that Alejandro had beaten her. And the Toyota Center was willing to go to the end. If only I had known then what I know now. Alejandro had spoken with the lawyer, so there were many things I did not know.

Finally, one day he told me he was going to trial with this.

"I'm playing it because I could lose my license. Even if I do nothing, I put my medical license at risk."

"Is there no other alternative?"

"I cannot plead guilty. That woman is accusing me of hitting her. At least the charge is for public intoxication."

"And you hit her, Alejandro?" After all, he had hit me several times, so it was possible that he hit another woman.

"¡CÓMO CREES, CARMEN! (Don't even say it!) Do you not know me?"

How well I know you, I thought.

"Carmen, you have to go testify because do you know what happens if I lose the license? Do you know? YOU DIE OF HUNGER AND THE CHILDREN ALSO."

"What I'm going to say if I did not see what happened?"

"That I did not hit that woman. I DID NOT DO ANYTHING. You understand, nothing happened. That is what you are going to say."

"But how could I lie under oath?"

"CARMEN, a lie that is said a thousand times becomes true. So, start repeating it in your head."

I was trapped. I did not know how much, until he told me that Thelma and Nizar would have to come testify, too.

"But Alejandro, they did not see anything. They were well behind us."

"They have to testify or the children will not see theirs, and you will not see Thelma again."

Alejandro asked me every day if I had talked to them.

"They do not want to testify," I told him. "They say they saw nothing, that they were far behind, and it's true."

"Incredible that you can help people, but they cannot help you."

"What have you done for them?"

"What? Ask me what I have not done for them."

"What?"

"Well, I've treated them at the office."

"And you've taken insurance payment from them, so they paid us."

"Didn't I sign the form that got Thelma the handicapped label for the car? So, she owes me, Carmen. And you're going to tell them. We're done doing favors if they cannot do one for me. And if they do not testify, this friendship ends."

I was dying of shame at the thought of telling Thelma that. Every day, Alejandro asked if I had spoken with Thelma and if they were going to the trial. Finally, armed with courage and seeming like a madwoman or at least malevolent, I mentioned the handicapped label to her.

Thelma had breast cancer a few years before. While she was doing chemotherapy, the doctor gave her the papers to get the handicap permit. When it expired, and she mentioned to us that she needed to renew it, Alejandro immediately offered to give her the documents to do so. With that, she could park easily and not so far from the places she went.

It was one of those illegal favors that impressed everyone because of Alejandro's good "intentions." What they did not know was that he charged more than enough for these favors when he needed them.

When I told Thelma that, she was quiet and told me she would talk to Nizar. In effect, she called me later and told me that they would be witnesses.

However, on the day of the trial, Alejandro called me a thousand times to make sure they had come. When we arrived at the courthouse, we could not listen to anything because we were witnesses. We sat outside for a while, until they called Nizar first. He did not take long and left. Then they called me.

They made me raise my right hand and swear I was going to tell the truth. And actually, I had told the truth. Although I went there to defend him, I had not seen anything. I did not even see what he did when he went up the steps. I had been happy watching my concert.

The prosecutor asked me: "Is it possible that when he went up, he had a drink or two, and then went back down to you with one in his hand?"

She wanted me to agree with her in a supposed situation, and that cannot be done. I looked scared at Alejandro, who looked like he wanted to kill me. Finally, after much questioning, I told her that it was not possible. It was not until years later that I realized Alejandro drank when he was anxious, so it could have been possible.

They asked me if Alejandro had hit the woman. But in reality, I had not seen anything and that is what I answered: "I don't know. I did not see when he left. I thought he was behind me."

Alejandro left the trial furious with Nizar because he said he had not seen anything and with me for not lying. I did not understand what he wanted us to say. In spite of Nizar's testimony, it served him.

Years later, he used this to threaten them if they testified in my favor in the divorce. He told them that Nizar would be accused of perjury for having lied in the 2007 trial if they testified in my favor, but he did not lie.

Alejandro did the same with Kika, who was ready to testify in my favor. But after Alejandro called her, she refused. Kika had also had breast cancer a few years before with no health insurance. She had to undergo an emergency mastectomy, and they did not have money to cover such an expensive intervention. She and her late husband were desperate. We were all seeing how we could help her.

One night at a dinner shortly before the operation, Alejandro proposed to save the situation with an offer that was as impossible as it was illegal. But what mattered to him was to appear to be a great man willing to help. This happened to be one of those unpayable debts that he charged later.

Kika's operation was set for the following week; it was necessary that it was that fast. However, Alejandro said he could put her on the insurance plan for his office staff. I looked at him in shock, because he knew what he was saying was impossible. I also worked with him and, as a journalist, I knew everything that is needed to add someone to a group insurance policy, besides the fact that the person needs to work there.

"Alejandro, how are you going to do this? She needs to work in the office."

"That does not matter. I say she works here. Do not worry. I will do whatever I have to do to make it possible."

We were facing one of Alejandro's many illegal actions, though I knew he never intended to carry this out. He knew she would have to wait a few months, once he said she was his employee, before she would be eligible for the office benefits. Not to mention that we would have to give her a salary, even if she did not go to the office.

The insurance company would never fall for this. It would be obvious that she knew about the cancer before she had supposedly started working for Alejandro. Knowing right away that he would make me look like the bad one if I gave him the reasons why this was impossible, I stayed silent. Alejandro told them not to worry, that he would do whatever it took.

In short, I knew he was talking nonsense. And of course, nothing happened, nothing. No one ever questioned what had happened to Alejandro's promise. However, Kika always remembered the generous offer that Alejandro had made. Every time she mentioned it, I laughed inside to think how Alejandro had made fun of her.

Alejandro continued seducing her. Kika suffered from migraines and once commented that she had not been out of the house for days because she had run out of the pills she brought from Venezuela. Since she did not have health insurance, she did not have a doctor but needed a prescription. Once again, Superman came to the rescue.

"But you have me," Alejandro said. "Give me the name of the medicine and the number of your pharmacy, and I will order it for you."

This was illegal. But what did it matter when you were the invincible Alejandro? He used these facts in times of crisis to manipulate people. Actually, they were not favors. They were loans. Loans to be paid at any time he needed to collect.

That was the night of The Police. I never knew it would become a real police night.

CHAPTER 36

The Plane

He had been trying to set me up, so he could succeed in getting rid of me somehow, but not really get rid of me. What he did on this flight almost gave him what he had been looking for.

The plane left at 11:58 p.m., which meant we had to be at the airport between 9:00 and 9:30.

I got home from lunch with my friends. As usual, we had a great time and some heart-to-heart talk.

Alejandro hated nothing more than me having fun. Needless to say, he got mad when he saw me so happy.

I had not had that much fun in a while. There was nothing like silly girl talk, and I had been avoiding luncheons, just staying busy trying to save my marriage, family and my life. Avoiding people was the best way to avoid talking about reality.

After getting home, I took a shower and got in some comfortable clothes. Since it was a red-eye flight, I wanted to be comfortable to sleep. I had already packed my bag that morning. Even before the flight, I felt a little uncomfortable because I had planned to go on this trip with only my daughter Kamee, who had a *quinceañera* party in Colombia. But at the last minute, Alejandro decided to tag along. He was trying to convince me that he was behaving like a good husband by traveling with me instead of staying in Houston.

We had dinner with all of the children before heading to the airport, where we checked in and went to the Presidents Club. There, the three of us sat on a sofa while Alejandro got two glasses of white wine.

I started to tell him about the afternoon with my girlfriends.

"By the way, Alejandro, today I was told that Roberto was telling everyone that he was not the one with the womanizing problem; you are."

We had discussed this many times. In an effort to look like an angel, Alejandro had always said that it was his friends—Roberto and a long list of others—who were driving him to cheat.

"What? Carmen, you know that is not true."

"Alejandro, I don't know who has told the truth. I am just telling you what people are talking about."

Alejandro went for other two glasses of wine. I was not drinking mine beyond a few sips. This was his standard behavior: He would drink these two, plus the one he had already had.

"Roberto owes me everything he is today," Alejandro said. "He travels a lot and has all the freedom to do what he wants and the connections to get girls for all of us."

He went on and on obviously very mad.

"Remember, Carmen, the texts you read from him that said he had a discharge after using two condoms with another woman. He is the guilty one. I have many, many more texts about him and what goes on."

There was nothing he hated more than being discovered. He had a persona that he did not want anyone to know about. He left for more wine. As predicted, so far he had drunk three glasses of wine and now had two more.

When our plane was ready to board, Alejandro saw that my glass was still almost full and drank it down. The count was now six glasses of wine before we even boarded the plane.

The three of us are seated in first class, with my daughter in 1E, me in 2E and Alejandro in 2D. As soon as we sat down, the flight attendant asked if we would like something to drink. As was customary, Alejandro ordered red wine for him and white wine for me. As soon as we were served, he started drinking from both glasses. I was so used to this, but hated it. I never drank or ate solely from my glass or plate. He always took my glass and picked from my plate. He opened his iPad and started writing a threatening email to Roberto. He read it to me.

"Alejandro, I do not see the need for this. Don't do it."

"Moreover, I am adding that you have a file on him and I am going to use when I sue him."

"Stop it. I don't have a file for him."

"Well, you are going to."

He sent not one but two emails to Roberto from the plane. He was mad as hell.

The plane departed and the crew started the meal service. It was almost 1:00 am by then, and I was starving as usual. He ordered another red wine for him and white for me. Nuts had come with the wine. He had finished his in seconds and had started on mine. I took them away, saying "Sorry, I am starving."

Toward the end of the meal he said, "See! You did not finish your nuts, but no, you could not give them to me."

"Here, now you can have them." And I put the nuts on his tray.

Like a petulant child, he returned them and said: "I don't want them anymore."

Alejandro was in a terrible mood. He was reading a brand-new book, but I could not tell what it was because I was seated on his right side and it was dark. All I could see was the back cover. Later, I learned the book title was *How to be an Abused Husband*.

He was not talking to me, and if I spoke to him, he would not answer. He was ignoring me. I decided to sleep, but needed a pillow. So, I called the flight attendant and asked for one.

"Ma'am, there are no pillows."

"But this is a midnight international flight. There must be a pillow somewhere around."

"The airline does not carry pillows anymore." (This was and still is a lie.)

Airlines had been taking away privileges from all of us since September 11, 2001. It was even worse when gas prices went up, but even when the price of gas went down, they never adjusted ticket prices or stopped charging extra for everything.

Looking at the flight attendant, I said: "What else is the airline going to take away from us?" He got mad; I could tell.

"I can give you two blankets," he said in a rude tone of voice.

"Please," I said.

After he brought the blankets, I put them between my shoulder and the window, but they scratched my face and it was uncomfortable. I decided to lay my head on Alejandro's shoulder and closed my eyes, until I felt pain on the right side of my face. Something had hit me hard right on the temple.

Alejandro had hit me! So typical of him to be mad, mad at everything or anything and I was the one who had to pay. I sat up and pushed him.

"*¿Qué te pasa?* (What is with you?)"

Not even answering, he pushed the button calling the flight attendant.

"She is invading my space," he told him.

"I saw that Ma'am," the flight attendant responded.

"You did not see the whole thing," I insisted.

The flight attendant left.

"Alejandro, what are you doing? You hit me and called him to say this idiotic thing. Are you crazy?"

He called the flight attendant again.

"She is bothering me."

This time, the flight attendant left and then came back with a piece of paper that he asked me to sign.

"What is this?" I asked.

"It is an incident report. You need to sign it."

Alejandro had grabbed it from the flight attendant and was handing it to me.

"Carmen, please sign."

"I am not signing anything. I have done nothing."

Once the flight attendant left, I told Alejandro to stop it. Big mistake! He called the flight attendant again.

"She won't stop. I need to change seats away from her."

"There are no more seats in first class, sir. Probably you can change with your daughter."

So, we changed seats. Alejandro moved to Kamee's seat, which was in front of me, and I decided to move to Alejandro's seat because I did not want to be behind him. Afraid of what was happening, I preferred to sit on the aisle and be seen by the flight attendants.

As soon as we changed seats and I was with my daughter, I started to cry. I was so nervous. Where was Alejandro going with this? Based on previous experience with him, I knew this was not good. He was up to something.

Alejandro again called the flight attendant.

"Now she is bothering my daughter. Make her stop."

The flight attendant left. I stood up, touched Alejandro's head and said: "Alejandro, please stop it. What are you doing?"

He called the flight attendant again.

"She won't stop."

I kept crying and talking with my daughter. Alejandro went to the galley and had a lengthy conversation with the flight attendant, who then came to my seat and said I had to move out of first class.

While crying, I asked why.

"If somebody has to move, it should be him. He is the one creating this problem."

A female flight attendant came from the back and knelt down to talk to me.

"What is happening?"

Explaining everything to her, I even mentioned we were having marital problems, that my husband had been cheating and was punishing me for that. She looked at my daughter, saw that we were both well and went to talk with the other flight attendant.

Later, I learned she had told the male attendant that everything was under control and she did not see any problem.

He replied: "I have already decided to arrest her."

Everybody was sleeping and the plane was dark. Suddenly, the male attendant came to my seat with two short, stocky men. Each of them must have weighed over 300 pounds. One of them said: "Ma'am, come with me."

"What? Where?"

They had some type of plastic cords.

"I have not moved from my seat, and I have done nothing."

"We can do this the easy way or the hard way."

And he took me by the neck and yanked me out of my seat, while twisting my arm behind my back. They took me to the galley right behind the cockpit.

I was crying, feeling completely violated and assaulted.

"Please, please don't do this. My daughter is in there. I have done nothing."

They were trying to put plastic handcuffs on me.

"Alejandro, tell them what you did," I pleaded. "Tell them."

"Carmen, don't create more problems. Let them arrest you."

My daughter was crying.

"Please, I beg you, don't do this."

"Carmen, stop it. Let them arrest you."

Once I realized there was no way out, I let them put on the plastic handcuffs and take me to the back of the plane. I kept telling them to stop.

"Please, don't do this. My daughter is here. I have done nothing."

They were practically carrying me, which was so easy for them as I was only 115 pounds. While we were going down the aisle, suddenly a woman with a Houston Police badge stood up and said: "Police, how can I help?"

"Thank God you are here," I said.

Finally, someone who could see the injustice of the situation, I thought. She joined us and sat down with me, asking what happened. I explained everything from the beginning. She shook her head in disbelief. Later, she told my daughter that none of this should have ever happened. That if she had known what was going on and had gotten involved, the plane would have got to Bogota. But what she had not known that night was that the plane would not have been able to get to Bogota anyway due to weather!

I had told her I had already filed for divorce back in November and that I needed to communicate with my lawyer. She said she would go to the front of the plane to get my handbag. While she was gone, they announced that the plane was returning to Houston. Everybody on the plane sounded disappointed and unhappy. I could hear the two men seated behind me saying in Spanish: "Come on, couples have fights. This is not necessary."

At that point, I realized that no one had a clue about what happened. After a while, the female officer came back with my handbag, giving it to me. However, my hands were tied, and I had to ask her to get my cellular out.

Recently, I had moved from Blackberry to iPhone and was still learning to use it. There was no connection, but I asked the officer to help me put in a message that could be sent once the connection was activated.

I texted my lawyer, telling him what had happened, and as soon as the plane got close to land, I pushed send and my message went off. It was then around 4:30 a.m. We texted back and forth. He said he would find me and take care of everything. I thanked God I had hired him in November last year.

All I could think about was how devastated my daughter would be, about her well-being and her brother and sister. Also, she had so been looking forward to going to her friend's party. Every vacation since 2011 had been ruined.

Later, I was told that Alejandro had been trying to get on a flight that was leaving later that day without any care for me or what had happened, but the airline would not let him.

Back home, while the children cried and were mad at him once again for what he had done to me, he sat at the kitchen island laughing while wiggling his legs in a celebration expression.

CHAPTER 37

Men Behaving Badly

Around this time, men lost respect for their families and their own careers—getting involved in behaviors that once revealed would create an explosion of atomic proportions and put everything at risk. Or were they always like this? No more secrets forever. Sex scandals of renowned persons splashed all over the media had become regular occurrences. The only question was who would be next?

Alejandro applauded them. He believed it was their personal life and nobody else's business, or would criticize them as being evil and point to himself as an example of great behavior.

Some lesser individuals became famous by their actions, like the genius Houston doctor who found a solution to sweaty hands. Once the truth had emerged, his four wives had talked about their experiences with him involving alcohol, drugs and prostitutes. He became an instant personality, not as the family doctor he tried to portray in his TV commercials, but of a crazy doctor gone badly.

There were simple indiscretions like the one of British actor Hugh Grant, who stopped on Sunset Boulevard to pick up a prostitute while engaged to a British actress. Others went all the way to destroy families and careers.

One of the biggest offenders was Bill Clinton. The fact that an acting President was caught with his hand in the cookie jar was not only disappointing, but also grounds for impeachment since he lied to cover it up. Here you have the president of the most powerful country in the world claiming on live television: "I did not have a sexual relationship with that woman." Only to come back later and admit he had made mistakes. Clinton went on to destroy Monica Lewinsky, finished his term and worked on Hillary's political aspirations. Still, Clinton will be remembered as one of the best presidents of the United States, not as a liar and the president with the biggest indiscretion ever.

Of course, there had been talk about other presidents with indiscretions. But Clinton was in office at the beginning of this new era of communication. After everything that was said about Kennedy, no one ever came out to confirm anything. And boy, there were stories within that clan.

Spritzer's story could be the most hypocritical one. The governor that fought prostitution rings in New York—and vowed to punish everyone involved in them—was their biggest client. Probably he thought that if he was fighting them, no one would ever suspect him. Spritzer started a witch hunt all over New York, but was the hunted one at the end. In the meantime, he utilized the services of a high-class, high-pay prostitution ring, where some of the women charged $5,000 per service, traveling to Washington to have his rendezvous.

Also, in New York was Mr. Weiner, whose name by now is self-explanatory. He even came back and tried to clear his name, only to do it again! The congressman would text women with sexual innuendoes. And when he did it again, it was with underage women.

Actors and public personalities always seem to be forgiven for their bad actions. However, when the indiscretions of Sandra Bullock's husband went public, people were stunned. It was not so much about his behavior but about how could he do that to America's sweetheart. Sandy had married late and dedicated her life to her husband and his children. Probably, everybody thought their marriage was a mismatch. Here you had a beautiful, successful woman married to a biker whose body was tattooed all over. Yes, he was successful in his own right with his biker show, but what did they have in common? However, she seemed happy. The problem was that once that can of worms was opened, women came out of the woodwork to talk about Jesse. He was unfaithful by the numbers to sweet, beautiful Sandra. She had to face this public embarrassment, and every day there was a new one.

How about Arnie? Arnold Schwarzenegger impregnated his wife and his maid at the same time, destroying the picture of a perfect family life overnight.

Tiger Woods had been the best golfer of the world until his career ended when all his indiscretions were uncovered. Alejandro criticized him the most, especially when he dated the Olympic skier. "How can she?" he would say. "He is a cheater."

Well, and what was Alejandro? But he went above and beyond cheating. It was abuse at all levels. He wanted to destroy me or get rid of me.

During that time, there were many doctors who had killed their wives in order to get rid of them. They would get away with it for a while, but eventually they all got caught.

Alejandro knew what he was doing to me. He was completely aware of all his misbehaviors, but was not stopping. One day in a drunken depression, he cried out: "I don't want to end up like the hand doctor!"

CHAPTER 38

The Trial

"ONE DOWN, one to go!" the email read.

The day before the trial started with good news coming our way. The second charge, filed just a few months before accusing me of attacking Alejandro, had been dropped.

When I read the email, I called Andino.

"Well," he said, "it is starting to look good. They know they cannot support that charge. They did it to scare you, scare us, and force you to take their deals. But it did not work."

The next day, September 29, 2015, we started a trial that had been completely handicapped. The judge had allowed the prosecution to enter unconstitutional evidence, as well as eliminate evidence and our expert testimonies, which was also unconstitutional. However, I was still feeling sure that no matter what, we were going to demonstrate the truth. I did not know how, but I was at peace.

I could feel Andino and Zack's frustration because of the court's behavior during preparation in the last days before the trial. A few days before the trial, when Andino and I had a meeting, I could not believe the person that received me. I am waiting in the lobby when a man I had never seen before came up to me and said hello. He looked like one of those Andes survivors with a beard and long hair. I looked at him in disbelief.

"What? Where is Andino?"

He laughed and said, "This is what your case is doing to me."

"My God! Now I am worried. Look at you!"

He laughed again.

A few days later, when we were in front of our judge in court, she was like a mother to him. He told me he had pictures of her with his newborn children, and I could tell she really liked him. That woman never smiled, but ever since Andino had been on the case, she looked relaxed and smiley.

However, that day after the hearing ended, she signaled to Andino to cut his hair. He smiled and told her it would be cut by trial time. She smiled in return and nodded. All I could think about was: you did not see everything. You should have seen him with his beard like I did a few days before.

My sister and my friend Lilly arrived in Houston to be here with me for the trial. It was good to have the house full so I could keep my mind off the real issue.

When I spoke with Andino, he said to remember to be there earlier than requested. We needed to be there before the prosecution, to get the side next to the jury. That was always beneficial.

Sure enough, we got there before everybody and sat on the side next to the jury. When the prosecutors arrived with Miss Congeniality, they wanted to take it away from us and did not unpack any of their belongings because they expected to move to our side. I looked at Andino, and he looked back at me in a way that I understood meant it was a lost cause for them. Finally, the clerk told them it was first come, first served when she came out.

Then voir dire, which means "tell the truth" in Latin, or jury selection, started. Over 30 people were on the list that Andino and Zack were studying. They paid close attention to the ones they thought would be better for us and how they acted during the questioning process.

Andino pulled out a visual aid and the prosecution objected. The judge sustained it. Every step, every attempt we made was overruled by the judge. There were a couple of people that neither side wanted. Even the judge said they were trouble. Andino, Zack and I went over the candidates we liked. It was good to see that the three of us liked the same people. There was not much disagreement with the prosecution and the judge about them. This would prove to be the smoothest part of the trial. At the end, we had a jury we were comfortable with and that I liked.

The prosecution opened the case making me look like a lunatic. The interesting thing to be discovered down the road was that, if I had really been like that, why they did not have any passengers as witnesses? If it happened like they said, the whole plane must have been awakened and aware of the incident. But only the people that had been enlisted by the flight attendant to arrest me knew about it. The rest of the people had become aware after I was arrested. No one could testify about the craziness they were accusing me of because they had all been sleeping!

Andino opened the case saying we would prove that the flight attendant overreacted—and acted under Alejandro's guidance—and that the prosecution had the power of the government behind it, while I only had the two of them and the truth.

The court was fully active, with people coming in and out. Trials are public, but my experience in family court has been that unless you invite people or are a public figure yourself, people were not around. While I was a public figure, that was in my country, not here. That is why all of this movement in court caught my attention. People were entering in pairs or by themselves, sitting down, observing, taking notes, talking to each other.

I kept notes about the people and later asked Zack and Andino during breaks if all this movement was normal. At one point, one of them reminded me that the prosecutor was on probation. In time, I would learn that they were just trying to put me at ease. While it was true that he was on probation for mishandling another case, that did not require all these people to be there. Remember, the government never loses.

My Hoopla Team (my friends and family) noticed everyone, made notes about them and paid attention to what were they doing. They also paid attention to every reaction from the jury.

During breaks, they were informing me about it, checking to see if I knew them. We also asked my lawyers about them. We could not account for 100% of them, but could conclude that something was going down. Something we did not know about.

The prosecution started their case, calling the Houston Police officer that got involved when I was arrested and moved to the back of the plane. I was so thankful to see this woman on the plane, the one person who could not believe what had happened. However, she had changed her story after the government got involved. But we had all the records, interviews and voice recordings. So, if she lied, it would be way too easy to catch her.

She entered the courtroom in full Houston Police uniform, even a bulletproof vest as if she was on duty. She was from Colombia and had been on the flight with her husband, whom she had now divorced. Lucky her, I thought. Mine was still going. Easy answer why? My husband was hoping I would be going to prison.

From the prosecution's questions, the jurors could see she was lying. She said she took that Houston-Bogota flight two or three times a month. How could she go to Colombia that often on a police officer's salary? We could tell the jury was not buying it. First strike! The rest of the questioning went smoothly.

My support team also was describing the jury's reaction to me during breaks, since I was looking at them with normal limitations. In addition to showing signs of disbelief at times, some jurors looked at the floor and moved their heads in a negative manner. The common feeling among my people was that the jury was asking themselves what they were doing there and why?

Then it was our turn, and Andino went for the jugular. A good attorney does not review the obvious, but unveils what is not as obvious, providing a different perspective for the jury or judge. And that is what Andino did.

"We called you and you did not answer our calls. You know you have the duty to also communicate with us as you did with the prosecution, as you said in their examination."

"Yes, I know."

"Not only did you not answer at one point, you said to us, and I quote: 'You were instructed by the prosecution to NOT talk to us.' Is that true?"

"Objection, Your Honor." (the prosecution)

"Overruled. Answer, please." (the judge)

"Can you repeat the question?"

"Do you know they cannot do that? Instruct you not to talk to us?"

"I did not say that."

"You did say that. I have a recording here of that conversation with you. Do you want me to play it?"

At that point, the woman started to sweat. She looked at the prosecution like she expected an answer from them. Clearly, she was asking for help. Her eyes looked like they would pop off her face. She was breathing heavily and fast. She was pulling her bulletproof vest up, like she wanted to take it off there in the middle of the courtroom. You could see the sweat coming down her face. It was so obvious that the bailiff handed her a few tissues at first, but then gave her the whole box of tissues. She was caught lying, and the whole courtroom could see it.

Andino proceeded to another example of her ability to lie.

"However, you talked with our investigator two years ago willingly."

"I don't recall."

"Let me refresh your memory," Andino said as he pulled out a bunch of papers.

"On June 15, 2013, you said the following, 'There was no noise until I noticed three men bringing a woman from first class to coach. At that point, I stood up and showed my badge. I did not understand why she was arrested or why the plane was returned. If I had been able to get involved, we would have landed in Bogota.' Is this correct?"

"That is not correct."

"Again, I can play the recording of that conversation. Do you want me to do that?"

Once again, she looked at the prosecution for help. Impossible, they cannot help her. Once you walk inside the courtroom and into disaster, you are on your own. She again started pulling on her bulletproof vest up and sideways. She was sweating profusely. They kept passing tissues to her but it was not enough.

At that point, Andino said: "No further questions."

He did not need to ask her anything else. He had proved she was lying and that meant her entire examination by the prosecution was now TRASHED.

During the next break, I noticed that the associate lawyer for Alejandro's family law firm, or at least the one defending him in the divorce, was there taking notes. At every opportunity, she went to talk with the female prosecutor.

CHAPTER 39

Oliver

W HEN HE ENTERED THE COURTROOM, he looked just as I remembered him. He was wearing his flight attendant uniform, which was odd since he was not on duty or an officer of the law. Not even the military wear their uniforms unless they have to. But that was the prosecution's game, just as they had the Houston Police officer wear her uniform.

He was thin with tanned skin, bold with thick eyebrows. Obviously, he was from Brazil. It was as if I had a photograph of him forever imprinted in my brain. Though he tried to be poised and show he had a good command of the situation, my lawyer was going to get under his skin, and he did not know it yet.

The prosecution kept trying to get him to paint me as being a crazy lunatic that deserved to be arrested and sent to prison. Yet everybody on the plane was sleeping. They made many mistakes. For example, he referred several times to the many times he had met the prosecution.

The prosecution asked: "Was she a problem since you met her?"

"Yes, I could sense she did not like me. You know, she did not like my type."

He was trying to say that I did not like gay people. Apparently, they forgot to check my background. As a beauty queen, it was second nature for me to have gay friends. I love them! They are the best friends I have ever had. Things were going to get interesting as soon as the defense took over.

By the second day, one of Alejandro's family lawyers was present in the courtroom—where she remained during the entire trial—talking with the prosecutor whenever possible. That added to the prevailing mood in the courtroom created by people coming and going, taking notes, and being so interested in the case that it was crazy.

Andino took over, and the cross-examination began. He pointed out the many complaints that the flight attendant had in his record. Of course, Oliver denied them.

"These are all written complaints," Andino said to show the flight attendant's capacity to lie.

In one complaint, he opened the door of the plane when they were ready to depart, causing the slide to open. The incident caused a major delay because the airline mechanics had to be called. His report said the door jammed and malfunctioned, but the mechanics said nothing was wrong with the door.

Andino read the whole report in court, showing the jury he had just lied to them. My lawyers were ahead of the game, knowing the prosecution would come back and throw out all of the airline's latest efforts to counteract the complaints against Oliver. In the three months leading up to the trial, the airline had given all types of awards to the flight attendant. Too obvious!

Andino moved to ask him about the nature of his meetings with the prosecution. Of course, the prosecution objected. Andino was trying to establish that he was trained for his interrogation, so the jury could see the power and advantage the federal government had.

Andino decided to move on to the incident itself.

"What was your first contact with Carmen?"

"When they boarded the plane. As was customary, I offered them drinks."

"Did they have any?"

"Yes, he ordered red wine for him and white for her."

"What else happened?"

"After the plane departed, dinner was served. They had dinner."

"Did she have a drink again?"

"I served her a glass of white wine with dinner and refilled it, but when I picked up the tray there was still wine in the glass, around half a glass."

"So, can you say she had a glass and a half of wine?"

"That or less."

Andino kept asking questions.

"How long did this process take, the process that ended in her being arrested?"

"It was 40 minutes."

"I am sorry. I thought you said to the prosecutor it was 20 minutes."

"It was 20 minutes."

"I am confused. You said a little while ago it was 40 minutes. So, what is it?"

"Oh! It was 15 minutes."

"Fifteen? So, now it is 15? What is it: 15, 20, 30 or 40? I better make a chart of what happened because you keep on changing the time."

Andino got an easel with paper and a red pen, making a chart that started at "0."

"Okay. Here is time zero. What happened in time "0"?"

"She called and requested a pillow."

"Okay."

Andino wrote, "'0' Carmen calls and asks for pillow."

"What happened then?"

"I said there was no pillow. She was mad, so I offered two blankets. And I gave her two blankets."

"When did you hear again from them?"

"Around five minutes later."

"Who called you?"

"Her husband called."

Andino wrote, "5 minutes, Alejandro calls flight attendant."

"And what happened?"

"He said she was invading his space."

Everybody in the courtroom started to laugh. Even Andino could barely contain his smile.

"Her husband calls you and complains about her invading his space, and you did not think that was strange?"

"I did not know they were a couple."

"You did not know they were a couple? You saw them come in with their daughter and interact, and you did not know they were a family?"

"No."

"Isn't it part of your job to know the names of the passengers?"

"No."

"No?"

"No."

He was lying, and the jury could tell. My lawyers were doing an incredible job.

"When did you hear from them again?"

"Within a minute or two."

"Who called you?"

"Her husband called me."

Andino wrote, "7 minutes, Alejandro calls Oliver."

"What for now?"

"He said she was still bothering him. So, I got an incident report and handed it to her. She destroyed it and threw it on the floor."

"Can you specify what she did to it?"

"She made it into a ball."

"She destroyed or just wadded it up? I am confused. Which one was it?"

"She destroyed."

He was contradicting himself, going back and forth changing his answers.

"And then what?"

"She threw it."

"And what did you do? Did you pick it up? The pieces?"

"I don't remember."

"You remember certain things very well, but not others."

"Yes."

"Then what?"

"I went to my post in the galley. And within another two-three minutes I was called again."

Andino wrote, "Minute 9."

"Who called you?"

He was about to answer, but stopped and thought, realizing this was not looking good. Finally, he answered: "I don't remember."

"You don't remember. Was it Carmen?"

"I don't remember."

"Was it Alejandro again?"

"I don't remember."

"What happened now?"

"He said she was still bothering him and needed to change seats."

"So, it was Alejandro who called you?"

"I don't recall."

"But he was the one with the complaint, not her."

"I don't recall."

"So, he called you. Not her."

"I don't remember," he insisted. "But I saw her putting her feet on the back of the front seat."

"She did what?"

"She put her feet on the back of the seat in front."

"How? Can you explain, because Carmen is 5 feet 9 inches?"

"She just put her feet up and was bothering the passenger in front of her."

"But the passenger in front was her daughter."

"I did not know it was her daughter."

"Anyway, how did Carmen put her feet up?"

Andino proceeded to mimic ways to do it, but they were all impossible. It looked funny and the jury and everybody in the courtroom started to laugh.

Andino continued, asking: "They changed seats. Where did he go?"

"He sat in his daughter's seat, and I don't remember how it was that Carmen and her daughter changed seats."

"Carmen and her daughter, and Alejandro and her daughter…those are your words, sir. But you said you did not know they were a family."

"I did not at the time."

"So, how was it that it was natural to change seats with the teenager?"

"I don't remember."

"Perfect! And what happened next?"

"I was called again."

"What minute is that?"

"Probably another five minutes."

Andino wrote, "Minute 14."

"Who called you?"

"I don't remember."

"What happened now?"

"Her husband said she was now bothering the daughter."

"The daughter! Those were his words?"

"Not exactly! I don't remember how he said it. The fact was Carmen was bothering a passenger."

"A passenger that was her daughter."

"I did not know."

"But you changed seats with her, because it was the right thing to do. Why didn't you change seats with someone else?"

"They were sleeping."

"Sleeping? If people were sleeping, how is it that you thought this was disturbing?"

"It was disturbing."

"And what did you do?"

"I went and asked a female flight attendant to help."

"Did she do it?"

"Yes, she talked to Carmen."

"What happened next?"

"I had to go again to her seat."

"Why? Who called you?"

"I don't remember."

"Sir, I can give you a couple of minutes in order for you to regain your memory. Do you want to take a recess?"

"My memory is fine."

"What happened then?"

"I had orders from the pilot to arrest her."

When he said that, Zack, who was sitting next to me, smiled and gave me a bad-boy look.

"Why?"

"She was disturbing the passengers."

"But you just said they were sleeping."

"She was disturbing a passenger."

"You mean her husband?"

"I did not know at the time."

"How did you proceed to arrest her?"

"I got two able-bodied men to help me."

"Why two? Carmen only weighs 115 pounds or less."

"I was afraid she was going to run."

"And go where?"

Everybody in the courtroom, including the jurors, broke down in laughter.

Andino kept him on the stand for almost two days, grilling him to the point that you could see the flight attendant was losing his patience and cool.

Throughout the interrogation, Andino questioned him about his reasons to arrest me. When he could not come up with a real conclusive one under the law, in frustration he finally said: "She hit me!"

"What? She hit you?"

"Well, she touched me."

"This case has gone on for over two years," Andino said with his voice rising and his motions getting stronger and more convincing.

"You admitted under oath that you had met several times with the prosecution. At no point during this long time, have you ever said, not then, not now with over two days of cross examination, and not under the examination of the prosecution that Carmen touched you."

The flight attendant looked frustrated that once again he had been caught lying. He was silent.

"The truth is, you arrested an innocent woman!" Andino screamed while pointing at me.

It was like the best part of a movie, a standing ovation moment. I could see Andino's excitement. With that, he said: "No further questions."

He sat down next to me and asked: "How did I do?"

"You were fantastic!" My Latin self wanted to hug him, but I was in court.

CHAPTER 40

White for Dinner and Black for the Opera

I WAS WALKING FAST trying to catch up with him. Why did not he park in the Wortham Theater garage? Instead, we had parked two blocks from it. Alejandro started walking, completely forgetting about me.

I wore a beautiful and elegant black dress with super high Jimmy Choo stilettos. As much as I tried to keep up, Alejandro got farther and farther away from me. When we crossed the street, right before I got on the sidewalk, I fell. It hurt.

I looked up to see if Alejandro had noticed and was coming to help me, but no, he kept on walking. I had to get up by myself, and my knees were bleeding. Nothing I could do but keep on walking. When I finally made it to the door of the theater, Alejandro was standing there waiting for me and was mad.

"So tall, with these long legs, and you cannot walk fast."

"I fell."

"What?"

"Look at my knees. They are bleeding."

"Oh, I did not realize."

"Why didn't you wait for me? My father used to wait for us women."

"Oh, Carmen! Yes. I am terrible. But hurry up. We need to get to our seats."

"Alejandro, I have to clean my knees. These could get infected."

This happened years after Earl and Diane Marks, our first friends in Houston, introduced us to the Houston Grand Opera. Earve, as everyone called him, had a jewelry store near our home that is run by his son today. We got together for dinner and had become good friends after Alejandro took care of him as a patient while doing his fellowship. Diane was the person I trusted to talk girl to girl.

They had invited us to the opera to see *The Barber of Seville* with Cecilia Bartoli, the greatest opera singer at the time. Not only she was the best soprano, but also her facial expressions added to the whole experience.

Our seats were in the third row. After I sat down, I was so taken by Cecilia that I do not think I even blinked. This was better than any opera I had seen before. When it was time for intermission, I looked for my clutch, but it was not between me and the chair armrest where I thought I had put it. Then, I saw that the nice gentleman sitting next to me held it in his right hand and was handing it to me.

While I looked at him in surprise, he said: "You put it right there in my hand when you sat down!"

My God, I could not have been more embarrassed!

"Did I? I am so sorry."

"Well, you were so taken and entertained, I could not bear to interfere with you."

"Sir! Thank you so much."

His wife was looking on, amused by the whole thing. Earve and Diane were laughing at the situation, while Alejandro started criticizing me.

"Oh, come on Alejandro! That was cute and funny," Earve said. "Besides, anything Carmen does is forgiven once you look at her."

"Thanks, Earve. Oh, wow! You made my day."

"I am telling the truth!"

Alejandro and I started buying season tickets to the opera soon after. It was always something we enjoyed together unless it was in German. Alejandro hated those.

Over time, Alejandro lost his self-control and exposed himself as a rude, verbally abusive husband and person more and more.

A few months before we finally separated, we were invited to dinner with my Middle Eastern group. During my years in Houston, I had befriended many of them through friends and my charity work. I was part of this group and the Latin group, comprised of local Americans and mixed-race individuals. It is the nature of being an immigrant, many of whom stay within their own group. I opened up to everything, however, probably because of the pageant or my nature as a communicator, but also because I have always been very sociable like my father was.

The dinner was at Brenner's on the bayou for only about 60 people. All of the guests were Middle Eastern except for us. Friends with all of them, I introduced Alejandro to everyone.

I wore a brand-new white cocktail Chanel dress with an open back.

While mingling with everyone, Alejandro was his usual self, behaving like a clown and trying to attract attention. We decided to sit with two couples I knew. One of them was a doctor that Alejandro knew, but they were not friends. I was and still am friends with his wife.

Two younger girls, who looked to be in their twenties or thirties, sat with us. It was obvious they were good friends. We met a couple from Lebanon. This woman was not only beautiful, but also had a wonderful personality, outspoken and smart. She was obviously much older than me. She had mentioned she had grandchildren, and I thought: "This is how I want to look when I am that age." Although I did not know how old she was, I guessed she was around 60. I was 48 years old at the time.

And then, Alejandro directed his first assault toward me in front of everybody. It was one of those things he did to impress people, trying to compliment them while insulting me.

"You are so beautiful," he told Noor.

"Oh, thank you."

Since Alejandro's father was from a Lebanese background, he was desperately trying to appeal to them. He said he had been in Lebanon many times by himself and with me, an outright lie. I was quiet because neither he nor I had ever been in Lebanon. I do not lie and could not have a conversation about being in a place I had never been. I was looking at him to see how this conversation would unfold.

Suddenly, he said: "You are around Carmen's age, right?"

Everyone at the table went silent. The look on my face must have shown how humiliated I was. Even Noor was impressed because it was obvious that she was much older than me.

"Oh, come on," she said. "Carmen is much younger than me."

"Impossible!" he said. "And if she is, then more power to you. Cheers!" he said, while raising his glass.

The mood at the table started to shift, growing cold when at first it was happy and cheerful. Alejandro was commanding the conversation. Seated across from the younger women, Alejandro looked at them and said: "You are so beautiful. Why are you alone?"

One of them said: "My husband is sitting over there. I am here with my friend, Jasmine."

Noor said: "Hanna is married to the son of the general counsel of Lebanon."

"I see! And you, Jasmine, what do you do?"

"I am an engineer."

"WOW, smart and beautiful. See Carmen, she is an engineer."

"But Carmen is beautiful also," Noor said.

"Well, she is no engineer," Alejandro replied.

"But I am a journalist!"

"Come on, Carmen. That does not compare to the type of studies she has done."

Alejandro continued, "Now, do you work?"

"Yes, in the oil and gas industry."

"See, Carmen!'

Embarrassed, I decided to drop the subject, as usual, hoping that people did not see it as I saw it. He went on and on complimenting her to the point that it felt like he was flirting with her.

Continuing to talk, he finally said: "Beautiful and smart, then why are you still single? What is wrong with you?"

I could not believe my ears. I am used to this verbal abuse toward me, but now he was directing it at another woman. The table went quiet. I could see the facial expressions of everyone at the table. There was a moment of silence that I thought would never end.

"I am divorced," Jasmine finally replied. She was pale, and her friend was obviously uncomfortable, but I was quiet because I knew that if I opened my mouth, he would turn on me.

Alejandro started to apologize, but the more he did, the worse the situation got. I was wishing that he would shut up. Finally, Jasmine said something in her girlfriend's ear, and the two of them stood up and left.

"I am so sorry. I never imagined she was divorced," Alejandro said.

But that was not the problem. The problem was the way he had said it and what he had said.

Someone came back to the table and said Jasmine was sick in the bathroom.

Noor commented: "Poor thing, she has too much on her plate. She works and has to take care of those little boys."

"I feel ever so sorry," Alejandro said again.

All I could think was: How could you? That was so un-called for.

Finally, Amal came to the table and told us they were taking Jasmine to her house because she was just too ill to stay.

CHAPTER 41

The Trial II

AFTER TWO LYING scumbags, it was the time for the class act, all courtesy of the federal government.

I had not seen the pilot—a statuesque man of 6 feet, 5 inches tall— until he entered the courtroom.

He wore a dark gray suit, in contrast to the flight attendant and police officer, who wore uniforms. He was what you would expect when you imagined a true American man, what people called a good old boy.

Elegant and well spoken, he was a former US Army pilot who had defended our country and was now part of the airline after the merger. He was so tall that he had trouble getting his legs to fit when he took the stand to testify. Affable man, I liked him already!

He had refused to press charges when the plane landed. Would we now find out why? The prosecutor went through the facts with him, but did not go over the legal aspects of the case.

"You heard noise in the cabin, sir?"

"Yes."

"Were you able to tell what was said?"

"No."

"Did the flight attendant inform you that a passenger was causing problems in the cabin?"

"Yes, he did."

"Is it customary for events like this to call for restraining a passenger with plastic handcuffs?"

"Sometimes, if the incident gets out of hand."

The prosecution had not had much to ask him and passed the witness. Sometimes, I wonder why they had him testify at all if he really served no positive purpose for the prosecution. I could only imagine that they could not make a case without the pilot, the ultimate authority on the plane.

But he was to serve a very positive purpose to us. We had decided to subpoena him in case the prosecution ended up not using him.

Zack Fertitta cross-examined him with all the respect a former military man and ultimate authority on a plane deserved. The flight attendant had lied on the stand, saying he had orders from the captain to arrest me, so Zack went directly to that and more.

"Sir, you said you heard noise. Did you hear those noises before or after the flight attendant called you about the troubled passenger?"

"Not before. I heard the noise once I believe she had been arrested because it was coming from behind the cockpit's door, which is where I was informed the arrest took place."

"Did you hear any noise?"

"No."

"Was there any noise that could have caught your attention before the arrest?"

"No."

"Did you order the flight attendant to arrest the passenger?"

"No."

"Did you authorize the flight attendant to arrest any other passenger?"

"No."

"But he informed you that there was a problematic passenger?"

"Yes."

"And what did you say?"

"I told him to keep me informed."

I could see from the corner of my eyes how some of the jurors nodded in disbelief and disliked what had happened. That was it for the pilot's examination. The important facts were established: The pilot had nothing to do with the arrest, which meant he never thought the events required such measures. Also, the flight attendant had lied and the pilot, with the ultimate authority on the plane, had not ordered my arrest. The pilot's testimony would also prove that the next witness was lying.

So far, I was feeling good that none of the testimonies had proved their case. And the law said that the crime had to be proved beyond a reasonable doubt. This case had doubts all over the place.

My lawyers moved to request an acquittal based on the fact that the prosecution had established doubt already. The judge denied it.

The prosecution then called one of the men who the flight attendant had enlisted to arrest me. He was as I remembered him, short and overweight. He was almost 400 pounds.

My lawyers were never able to locate the other man who had restrained me, and the prosecution was not using him. This witness, however, had been interrogated by my lawyers over the phone, and they had caught him lying. The conversation had been recorded and could be used during the trial.

He sat down with an arrogant attitude, acting like some sort of Rambo! During the examination from the prosecution, he confirmed many lies.

"Do you recognize the woman you arrested the night of the flight to Bogota on June 6, 2013?"

"Yes."

"Is she here in this room?"

"Yes."

"Where?"

"There," and he pointed at me.

Obvious, since I was the only female sitting opposite the prosecutor.

"What was the first memory you had of her?"

"I saw her come onto the plane with her husband and daughter."

He knew just by looking at us that we were family, something the flight attendant said he never knew.

"When did you notice her again?"

"When the flight attendant came to tell me that the pilot had ordered me to arrest her."

"Had you noticed anything about her until then?"

"No, I was getting ready to sleep."

Another strike! He was getting ready to sleep when a passenger, who was so disruptive that she needed to be arrested, was practically sitting next to him.

"What happened next?"

"I started to pay attention and realized they had switched seats. Her husband was now in 1E. She got her hand between the seats and hit him."

"What happened next?"

"The flight attendant came to get me, along with another passenger, and we went to her seat and told her to get up."

"Did she get up?"

"No, she said she had done nothing. So, I told her we could do this the good way or the hard way. At that point, I grabbed her by the neck, yanked her off her seat and twisted her arm behind her back," he said very proudly.

I saw and heard the impression he had made on the jury. This man had just admitted under oath that he had assaulted me.

He proudly continued.

"It was easy. After all, there was a difference of over 250 pounds between us. I was 350 pounds and she was around 100 pounds."

The jury and people in the courtroom were gasping out loud.

The prosecutor asked: "If you were in a situation like this again and were asked to arrest a passenger, would you do it?"

"Yes!"

The prosecution passed the witness to the defense. Andino started the cross examination.

"How did the flight attendant ask you to arrest her?"

"He told me, 'Mr. Torres, the pilot ordered you to arrest Carmen.'"

This question had been asked to establish that the flight attendant had not known our names, or so he said, but he had known the name of this witness. Also, to confirm that either he was lied to or he was lying, since the pilot never ordered anyone to be arrested.

"Where was she sitting?"

"Not behind her husband. She was sitting on the aisle in the second row and her husband was by the window in the first row."

"Where were you seated?"

"In the first row on the other side of aisle."

"Your statement was that she put her hand between the seats and punched her husband?"

"Yes."

"And you knew that was her husband?"

"Yes."

"I am going to show you a picture of the seats in question. Do you recognize this?"

"Yes, it is a picture of the space between the seats."

"Can you see the tape measure?"

"Yes!"

"What number does it show?"

"2.5 inches."

"So 2.5 inches was the space between the seats where you said she pushed her hand and arm in—it had to be her arm also—to punch her husband, who was sitting on the right of her, and she was sitting on the left of him," Andino said while mimicking the motion and action.

"Now, don't you think this is impossible?"

"Well, I saw her doing it."

"There was also a seventeen-inch depth. So, even if she had pushed her arm, probably from her elbow, the wrist would be between the seats still."

"I do not know about that."

"But would you agree with me that this is not natural?"

"Objection. The witness cannot be asked to agree with the counsel."

"Sustained."

"It is also impossible for a person, even as thin as she is, to get her arm through and still be able to punch someone."

"But I saw her doing it."

But the doubt had already been shown to the jury. A trial was like a theater show, and it needed to be done like a waltz. You needed to be smart enough to show the lies and important points during questioning. The point was made with the witness, and I thought the jury had not liked him. After all, he admitted to committing assault on the plane. He had assaulted me after my husband did. I was assaulted by four men on that plane!

The prosecution called their final witness, a US Marshall they said was on a flight I took with my husband back in July 2012—the second setup.

My lawyers objected to this witness because it was unconstitutional to call someone that had not been present in this case, especially if that person was from an alleged case before. You can only be prosecuted for the current action; everything else in your life does not count. Also, there was no incident if it was what was called "heresay."

The judge overruled. And my lawyers called for a mistrial. It was denied.

The female US Marshall entered the room. She was wearing civilian clothes, not a uniform, in contrast once again to the flight attendant and the female Houston Police officer. Funny how people with higher ranks did not wear their uniforms in court, but lower ranked people did.

"In July 2012, were you on a flight to Holland from Houston?" the prosecution asked.

"Yes."

"Did you see the defendant on that flight?"

"Yes."

"What were the circumstances?"

"I was asked to change seats with a gentleman."

"Did you witness any disturbance or noise on the plane?"

"No."

"You were only asked to changed seats?"

"Yes."

"Can you elaborate?"

"The flight attendant told me to switch seats, because there was a problem with a couple and the man wanted to switch seats. When I gathered my possessions, I looked up and saw a man waiting for my seat. I moved to the front of the plane and sat on the aisle in the second row, where she was sitting by the window, but not before they cleaned the seat where I was to sit because there was something spilt there."

"Did she say anything to you?"

"She mumbled some words that I could not understand."

"What else?"

"It smelled like alcohol."

"Then what happened?"

"She turned and fell asleep."

"Was she loud?"

"No."

"Did you witness anything else?"

"No."

"Pass the witness."

Andino stood up and said, "No further questions, please."

Andino felt he did not need to ask anything because her testimony was not relevant. It had proved nothing and was unconstitutional besides. With her, the prosecution rested.

CHAPTER 42

My Daughter, My Savior

T HE BEST TESTAMENT to a parent is who their children are and how they behave. My daughter was the best witness in the trial at only sixteen years old. We only had two witnesses. When you are accused, the burden of proof is on the government to prove beyond a reasonable doubt that indeed a crime had been committed. The government had not done so. Therefore, not much was needed from us.

During the break, Andino told me to get Kamee to court as soon as possible, because he was going to need her at any time. She was home because she was so stressed that she could not go to school that week. My friends Marisol and Lilly went to get her. My sister María Eugenia wanted to stay with me, and I did not want her driving anyway. She was so frail those days that I was afraid she would have an accident.

We had picked out what she was going to wear for court a week before the trial, choosing a dark blue pencil skirt and white blouse. The blouse, from her older sister, was a bit too big for her.

She had everything ready and was prepared when she got the call.

"Hello, Baby."

"How is it going, *Mami*?"

"Fine, my love! Baby, it is time."

"It's time?"

She sounded nervous. I could tell by the tone of her voice. I will never forgive Alejandro and everybody involved in this for doing this to my daughter.

"You don't have to do it, Baby. I insist!"

"*Mami*, I will never forgive myself for not telling the truth, if something happens to you."

"Okay, Marisol and Lilly are going to pick you up. Be ready! Remember, you can always change your mind about testifying."

Back in the courtroom, Andino stood up and asked for acquittal once again, citing that the prosecution had not been able to prove their case beyond a reasonable doubt.

"Denied," the judge said.

Andino called the only expert witness that the court allowed us to have. It was the person who took the photographs of the plane interior with the measurements. The other witness we would have called was an expert in flight regulations and procedures, as well as a US Air Force veteran and a former Continental Airlines pilot who flew for the airline. She was not allowed in the trial.

That questioning went fast, confirming that the pictures were indeed real and answering technical questions about the photographs to overcome the objections from the prosecution. The prosecution tried but failed to destroy her intervention.

The witness was excused, and Andino called Kamee.

My eyes burst into tears just thinking about what she would have to go through. She looked so beautiful and elegant in her super conservative clothes though skinnier than usual. Her long dark hair was pulled back into a ponytail, and she walked in poised and sure of herself.

I could see the jury looking at her, analyzing every hair, every movement, every blink of the eye. She got to the stand

and was sworn in. The jury had looked a bit bored that day, but suddenly came alive and sat up in their chairs to pay attention to what was coming.

"Hello, Kamee."

"Hello."

"May I call you Kamee? Is that your nickname?"

"Yes."

"How old are you?"

"Sixteen years old."

"Which school do you go to?"

"Awty International School."

"Which grade are you in?"

"I am a junior."

"How are your grades?"

"I am a straight A student."

"Who do you live with?"

"My brother and I live with my mother. My oldest sister is in college."

"Were you with your mother and father on the flight to Bogota in June 2013?"

"Yes."

"How old were you then?"

"Fourteen years old."

"Do you remember what happened then?"

"Yes."

"Was your mother drunk?"

"No."

"Did your parents have a discussion at some point during the flight?"

"Yes."

"Did it surprise you?"

"No. They were fighting often."

"Was your mother loud?"

"No."

"Did your mother called the flight attendant?"

"At one point, to ask for a pillow."

"Did she get it?"

"I don't know exactly."

"Did she again call the flight attendant?"

"No."

"Who called him again?"

"My father."

"Did your mother at some point call the flight attendant again?"

"No."

I could see the way the jury was looking at her, analyzing every word, every movement. After all, this was the daughter of a woman they were portraying as a lunatic. But this girl does not act like a daughter of someone like that. She is calm, well-spoken and poised.

"Who was calling the flight attendant?"

"My father."

"Do you know why?"

"He was complaining about my mother."

"Was your mother screaming?"

"No."

"You changed seats with your dad?"

"Yes."

"At that time you were sitting with your mother?"

"Yes."

"How was your mother?"

"She was not happy. She was crying."

"But was she screaming?"

"No."

"Does she get nervous often?"

"When situations like that happen, she does. And she gets scared and very, very nervous."

"Did she drink on the plane?"

"Yes."

"Was she drunk?"

"I don't know. I am not an expert in that."

"Were the people around awake or sleeping?"

"They were sleeping."

"Were you surprised when your mother was arrested?"

"Yes."

"Why?"

"Because I could not understand what was going on, why they were taking my mother."

"What did your father do?"

"He was telling my mother to let them arrest her."

Andino was being careful to not make us look like we were pitting the girl against her father.

"No further questions. I pass the witness," Andino said.

The prosecutor came over and started his cross-examination.

"Kamee, may I call you Kamee?"

"Yes, sir."

"What do you want to be when you grow up?"

"I want to be a lawyer."

He kind of smiled with sarcasm.

"Well, you are surrounded by many here."

All his questioning and the manner in which he was doing it was intended to confuse her. At one point he asked too many questions at once.

Kamee said: "Which one is the question?"

"Objection. Too many questions, Your Honor," Andino said.

"Sustained," the judge said and addressed the prosecutor: "Please, one question at a time."

Later, he was trying to make her agree with him, and Kamee answered: "Where is the question, sir?"

Then he added: "You said you could not remember when asked what had happened after the last call and your mother had been arrested. You were fourteen years old and now you are sixteen. So, you have a selective memory of what happened?"

"No. I said I didn't recall because nothing 'significant' happened, sir."

She did not fall into the prosecution's traps. She was calm and very professional. I had always been so proud to be her mother, but especially at that time. I was proud of myself as a mother and thought that I did a good job.

But the prosecutor could not stop himself, asking: "So, do you mean to say that your father created this whole incident?"

The court went silent. That was a question Andino had stayed away from asking. But he dared to ask!

"Yes!" she said.

The prosecutor looked frustrated, realizing he made a mistake, but the damage was already done.

"No further questions," he said.

Kamee was allowed to leave the courtroom. I saw her a little later during the break. There were no words between us, just the most beautiful embrace we had ever had.

That Thursday evening before saying goodbye, Andino asked me: "Car, (that is how he called me) is your sister staying over the weekend?"

"Yes, she is planning to stay for a while. Why?"

"Tomorrow is the last day. If they find you guilty, they will take you in right away."

"But they said they usually give you time to organize yourself."

"No, Car. They just came to tell me. Organize everything you can tonight, just in case."

I started to cry.

"Andino, are we doing that badly?"

"You can never predict a trial, Car."

I felt as if the world was falling apart. My life could end in prison. My children, my children, please God, do not allow it. I cried all the way home.

At home, Lilly was getting ready to get back to Orlando to take care of an emergency. She was worse than me, to the point that Kamee had to get control of the situation. I was desperate, crying and afraid for my children. I had a panic attack until I was able to regain control of myself and start planning. I called my sister to my bedroom and gave her a notebook.

"María Eugenia, please take note of all my passwords."

I told her of my bank accounts and safe deposit box, giving her the password and keys. I called the movers to have all the art moved out of the house, along with some important furniture pieces, first thing in the morning.

The movers were there at 6:00 a.m. I was ready by the time my son was up. I had decided not to take him to school because that would take time away from us being together. He was 10 years old then. I never told him what was going on, but I think he could feel something was wrong, unless his father had told him. I made a point of not asking him what he talked about with his father.

We had breakfast together. I sat with him and hugged him a thousand times. He was to stay with the nanny while Kamee came with me to court. I hugged the nanny and my son again. The movers had worked for me for years and witnessed all of this until one of them said: "It is as if you are not coming back."

I brushed off the comment, probably so true, with a smile. The nanny confessed later that Juan Diego said as soon as I left: "My mommy, I love her so much. I know she is in danger."

My little man so wise and perceptive. I am so proud of him. I hope none of what had happened would mark him, even if I ended up in prison.

I left with María Eugenia and Kamee for court. The rest, my brother and other friends, were meeting us over there. The judge had a full docket, so we had to wait. The jury was closed up in a separate room waiting. Friends and family were with me in the hall, where we joked and laughed with each other and the lawyers. This Caribbean thing that we have gives us the capability to always make fun even at the worst moments. Thank God for that. It made me forget why I was there.

I was relaxed and positive when we were finally let in. The judge said: "Before we proceed, I understand the defense had some motions."

"Yes, Your Honor." Andino stood up and continued: "I move to request an acquittal, Your Honor. The prosecution has not proved their case beyond a reasonable doubt."

"Denied," the judge said.

"I move to request a mistrial based on the mishandling of this case and unconstitutional actions."

"Denied. What else do we have?"

"Nothing, Your Honor," the prosecutor said.

"Well, are we ready for closing statements?" she asked.

Little did I know that after all the witnesses had lied, the prosecution would come down hard on me, repeatedly pointing at me saying I was crazy and made a mess on that plane. Even when it was clear that everybody was sleeping.

"She is not the woman you have been seeing sitting here these past few days. She is nothing like this. She is not this composed ever!"

The jurors had not liked his words, but all of the members of the jury really came to a halt when he mentioned my daughter. "And then they had Kamee."

My God, all of the jurors' faces changed. They looked like they would hit him if he said a bad word about her. It was so obvious and felt throughout the courtroom. There was a silence. The prosecutor stopped abruptly and said after a pause: "Isn't she sweet!"

When Andino's turn came, he described me as a woman put in a bad situation with four men deciding my fate. He asked the jury how horrible could I be if I was the mother of such a wonderful girl as Kamee, that in the midst of all of this mess I was able to be a great mother and raise wonderful and successful children. That proved I was not the crazy woman they were trying to portray.

He added: "The flight attendant has been caught lying many, many times. There were so many times that even I can't remember."

He concluded that the prosecution had trained their witnesses by their own admission.

"She was not perfect," Andino said. "But have you walked in her shoes?"

The female prosecutor came for a second round! Yes, the government's advantage. That is why less than two percent of the people win over the government. She was terrible, so mad and vindictive.

The judge instructed the jurors with final guidelines. Then, we were free to leave while the jurors deliberated. We decided to go for lunch. It was past 4:00 p.m, but we had had nothing since breakfast.

I called my son and talked to him. Marisol's mother picked him up and took him home with Oscar, his best friend.

The story was all over the news in Houston. I had messages from many friends giving me support who were mad as hell at Alejandro for doing this. Of course, none of those friends were the ones that at one point in my life were my every-day friends, the ones I thought were family to me. Not even one of them cared at that moment.

While eating, I got a call from Andino.

"Carmen, we need to get back to court. The jury has a question."

My brother took care of the bill while we all ran back to court. The judge came in, and the bailiff handed her a note. The question: "What was the definition for 'threat'?"

The judge had a big dictionary with her. After we had all agreed on a definition, the jury was let in. The definition was read to them, and once again we were free to go.

In the meantime, I was orchestrating Juan Diego's pick up by his father. Of course, he was almost an hour late. I thought about denying him the right to keep Juan Diego and being able to hug him instead when I got back home, but what if I did not come back home?

At around 7 p.m., we were informed that a verdict had been reached. My beautiful daughter, Kamee, hugged me and started to cry.

"I love you, Mommy."

"I love you so much, my baby. Make sure Juan Diego knows it."

"You will be there to let him know."

Once inside, I was at the front with my lawyers. My family and friends were in the back. Also, in the back was the reporter from the *Houston Chronicle* that was there every day. She was dressed that day all in red; even the cover of her computer was red. I wondered if she had a cover in every color for every fashion in her wardrobe. Her reports were hateful, as if I were crazy and had a personality problem with entitlement. And that I had a defense that only money could buy. Did she know my husband had left me with nothing?

As we waited, Andino and Zack looked at me with reassurance, but I could sense they were worried. Zack had said to me: "Whatever this verdict is, it does not define who you are."

Two marshals came in, looking like they were ready to arrest me. Kamee saw them and started to cry. It was as if she felt they knew something we did not. She was shaking and cold. Andino and Zack said it was normal procedure.

Suddenly, I remembered my car keys were inside my Fendi handbag. Taking them out, I went to back of the courtroom and gave them to my sister María Eugenia. She said: "You are driving this car back home."

Oh God! What would I have done without her my whole life? She had always defended me.

Kamee was shaking, almost passing out. Zack had a talk with my brother on the side. Later, I learned he had told him: "If Carmen is found guilty, take Kamee out of the courtroom right away."

"All rise!" the bailiff said.

We stood up, and the judge came in. She had this little ironic smile I hated. After her, the jury came in.

"Have you reach a verdict?"

The foreman of the jury said: "Yes, Your Honor." He handed it to the bailiff.

I was looking at this as if I was watching a movie in slow motion. Never in my life had I imagined I would be put in this situation, moreover in the United States. That white piece of paper held my life. What was inside of it would determine my fate and my children's, I thought. Every step the bailiff took felt like an eternity.

The judge took the paper. We had to stand to hear the verdict. I was between my two young lawyers.

The judge opened the paper and started to read: "In the case: United States versus Carmen...We the jury find the defendant...!"

She was all smiles. I saw her in slow motion. But her face changed and her smile was gone.

"NOT"...that is what I heard...NOT and I almost fell. Andino hugged me. NOT GUILTY.

Time was frozen! Or passed so fast that I was suspended in the air. I could hear my daughter in the back crying in happiness and relief. My two lawyers were hugging me. I looked at the jury and thanked them with my eyes full of tears.

The prosecution, including Miss Congeniality, was petrified. I decided not to look at them anymore. I looked at my family in the back. My daughter was finally smiling for the first time in a long while. The two male marshals were smiling. Even the newspaper reporter was smiling.

The judge dismissed the jury, ending the whole ordeal. Jumping with happiness, I walked to the back and hugged my family and friends. After more than two years, it was all over. Over.

The truth triumphs!

My sister's stress finally showed up. She started screaming: "This is a circus. This is your taxes at work. Prosecuting an innocent woman based on a lie."

"Perucho, please! Get her out of here," I said.

We walked out of the courtroom, and my lawyers and I hugged each other.

"We did it!" I said.

We took pictures. The most beautiful one was of the three of us, and another was with Kamee, who they called the first associate of the Reynal-Fertitta law firm, the new firm they were going to start within months.

With all our hugging, kissing and picture taking, we could not leave the building, and it was after 7:00 p.m. I had lost track of time. It was as if we were holding on to that triumph.

At one point, Luisa said: "Give me Alejandro's number."

"Why?" I asked.

"Give it to me."

"Do not call him."

I heard her call: "Alejandro? Just to let you know that you can call the press now and tell them Carmen María is innocent."

And she hung up.

Little by little, we made our way to the elevator. Still talking when we got to the first floor, we discussed every face of the jurors, the judge, everything. The officers on the first floor knew if I was there, I was free.

"Aren't you tired of being in this building?" one of them asked.

So, we left, but were still walking slowly and stopping and hugging. It was the best feeling of a lifetime.

Finally, we said our goodbyes. Zack said he was seeing Alejandro's criminal lawyer later at a cocktail party and was looking forward to rubbing it in her face. We walked toward the underground parking lot, and they walked toward the street. I turned and at that moment saw them embracing and celebrating one of the proudest moments of their careers and life. I was so proud that I made that happen for them, for me. "Look at them," I said. Just look at them!"

As we entered the underground parking lot, one of the female jurors that had smiled at me a lot during the trial was coming out. She was crying. I thanked her.

"Move on with your life," she said.

I got home, and it felt better than ever. While I wished my son had been there to hug and kiss him, I needed to rest. However, we went out for dinner, even taking the nanny. It was celebration time.

The next morning, when I opened my eyes, the day was so beautiful, the sky so blue it was like a dream. I got a text from Zack: "How does it feel today?"

"Like a rebirth!" I answered.

CHAPTER 43

Divorce Trial

"How should I call you, sir? General or Mr. Reynolds?" Bobby asked.

"Reynolds is okay."

"Reading your resume made me a little jealous, sir. What planes do you fly?"

The video was playing and everybody was completely attentive, even the judge. After all, he was a decorated officer. After the fourth mediation and my last attempt to solve this in a friendly manner—the law only requires two mediations—and an improved offer of 30% of the estate from 20%, there we were on August 29, 2016, ready to start the second trial. I could only imagine how ugly and unfair this would be compared to the previous one.

My side walked in ready to start, but Jacob Woods, Alejandro's lawyer, filed a motion asking the judge to grant Alejandro all of the estate because he was the breadwinner. This had to be heard before the trial started.

I looked up in disbelief. How could he do this to me? I had earned more money than him in our first years of marriage. And later I managed his practice and what I called our family corporation, the real estate investments, financial investments, bank accounts, all of it. At the end, what we were dividing was the real estate (my work) because all of the money in Stanford (his idea) was gone. In fact, we had lost money in every investment idea he had. I managed his life, not his cheating, but everything else.

My lawyer whispered, "Don't worry. This is going no place. No judge will ever favor that. It is against the law. By law, you get 50%. But you will get more than that for all the years of marriage and the damage he has done."

Sure enough! The judge denied the motion, and we were able to start.

Since I was the petitioner of the divorce, meaning I sued him, we got to start, and that was a good thing. It was a disadvantage we had in the other trial, but I still won. Bobby started his opening arguments. He was good. He made me look good, but did not overdo it.

In trials, the people lying usually put on a show, going overboard trying to convince the jury. But here we had no jury. The judge was to decide this. However, that did not stop Jacob from putting on a show.

Jacob's turn was a joke.

"I am proud to represent the doctor," he said. Either he did not know him well or probably bought Alejandro's story of "we were like the Kennedy family in Venezuela." I could not believe all he said.

They finished, and we took a break.

"That was an oversell and never works well," Bobby said.

When we came back, the trial officially started by us calling our first witness, General Reynolds. We had him ready to come in with airline tickets and everything when the trial first was to start in March. When it was postponed, we went ahead and took a videotape deposition of him, which was admissible in court.

The opposing side had objected to some parts, even though they were present for the deposition. This created a problem for how the tape was going to be played. Discussion went on and on until the judge told Woods: "The only way is to play the tape completely, and then I will take your objections under consideration."

That was a win for us. This way, the judge got to see the whole deposition, not just pieces of it. And that was always better. Even if they opposed it, the judge had already heard it.

As the tape was rolling, everyone paid close attention when Reynolds said he saw a man screaming at a woman.

"She was trying to leave, but he stopped her when he stood in front of the car. He started banging the hood of the car while screaming. I did not get out of the car because my wife was inside the grocery store buying diapers for our oldest, who was a baby then, and I wanted her to be inside the car safe. You never know what could happen."

"What happened then, sir?"

"He was screaming. He wanted her to open the window. He insisted. Apparently, she did not want to. But she did after all the screams. He put his hand inside the car through the window and pulled her hair. She was screaming in pain when he was pulling her hair. He wanted her out of the car. He continued to pull her and managed to open the car door."

"What happened next, General?"

"My wife came back, got inside our car and said: 'Do you see what is happening over there?'"

"Yes, I was waiting for you in order to be able to do something."

Continuing his testimony, he said: "The assailant, who I later learned was her husband, continued to pull and bang her. I could see she was struggling. I opened the door of my car, stood up on the border and screamed stop! At that time, he turned and looked at me surprised. Then, he forcefully wrapped her hair around his hand and threw her on the pavement. He hopped inside the Mercedes Benz and sped away from the parking lot, leaving her there on the ground."

"I started to scream while running to her: 'Are you okay?'"
he continued. "She was crying and nodded her head. I helped
her get up, and we slowly walked to our car. My wife had called
the police. She sat in our car crying, scared and obviously humiliated. My wife asked her if she was okay and if she could get her
water. Then the police came and we all reported what we had
seen happen. We offered her a ride, but she had called friends
to come get her."

When Bobby finished his interrogation, Jacob's associate
questioned the General.

"Did you see anybody else in the parking lot?"

"No."

"Nobody else was there?"

"No, only Carmen and her husband when he came to stop
her and assaulted her."

"This is a map of the parking lot. Can you mark where you
were and where Alejandro and Carmen were?"

Reynolds marked the map as requested.

Abusers typically act in hiding. Alejandro had been careful,
never attacking me physically or acting aggressively in front of
people, though he could be verbally abusive and rude. He never
had been physical in front of witnesses. But this time, General
Reynolds was there. That he never expected.

He was such a powerful witness, carrying the credibility
of a man in armed services fighting for our country and at the
US Pentagon now. Alejandro's lawyers would spend all of the
trial trying to discredit him, but how could they?

And now we were going to present the evidence.

After General Reynolds testimony, Bobby called me as his
second witness. He started with the abuse. He asked me what
type of abuse I had endured.

"It was of all types, physical, verbal and emotional."

"Do you have scars from the abuse?"

"Yes! Several."

Bobby pulled out pictures, putting one in front of me: "What is this?"

"The wound from a bite."

"A bite?"

"Yes."

"He bit you?"

"Yes."

"What is this?"

"Another wound from a bite."

"And this?"

"Another bite."

"How many times had he bit you?"

"Three that day."

"That day? Were there other days when he bit you?"

"Yes."

"Do you remember when this happened?"

"February 2012."

"Can you describe what happened here?"

"We were having sex and he called me by another name."

"Do you remember what name?"

"Cara."

"Who is Cara? Do you happen to know?"

"A woman he met at Treasures with whom he was having an affair."

"Treasures?"

"Yes."

I described the whole incident; it was painful and embarrassing. I wondered why Alejandro preferred to go to trial and have all of this come out. After all, what he did to me was public and everybody knew about it. But everything about him was going to become public knowledge with this trial.

"Is this one of the scars you have on your body?"

"Yes."

"When was the other time when he bit you?"

"The day before hurricane Ike."

"Another struggle?"

"Yes."

I could remember every assault, how it started, why, and how it ended. I had tried to forget about it, or at least not think about it, because it was too painful. But now I had to remember it all again to answer the lawyers.

Bobby proceeded to ask me about the incident that General Reynolds witnessed.

"Do you remember what happened the day that General Reynolds witnessed your attack in the parking lot?"

"Yes."

"When was that?"

"December 16, 2011, the Christmas party for our employees."

I reviewed that day's events and many others through all the questions and answers. Bobby went over most of the pictures, asking me about the incident, the date, how it started, everything possible to paint a picture to the judge. I had tears in my eyes at times remembering what happened to us, because this affected my children also.

Bobby went on to ask me about the infidelities. He asked as much as possible and I answered. We went over Alejandro's frequent visits to exotic dancer places like the Men's Club and Treasures.

We moved on to talk about the practice.

"Did you work with your husband?"

"Yes."

"What did you do?"

"I was office manager at first."

"At first?"

"Yes."

"Did your job change?"

"Yes."

"Can you explain?"

"When he had his only partner, which lasted two years, I had to leave the office because his partner wanted his wife to work at the office, too, or for me to leave. After the partner left, I went back to work with him."

"Why?"

"He wanted me back. Expenses were up. The practice had become very hard to manage, and I was good at running the practice effectively at a lower cost."

"So, you were the office manager again."

"No."

"No? Why?"

"I did not want to manage the employees anymore."

"Why?"

"Alejandro played 'good cop, bad cop' with his employees. Well, I guess with everybody."

"Objection."

"Sorry, Your Honor, what is he objecting to?"

"When she added 'with everybody.' She was asked about the office and her job."

"Sustained."

"He, Alejandro, played 'good cop, bad cop' with whom?"

"The employees and us."

"How come?"

"Well, I was the one that enforced the rules and regulations of the practice. I wrote and developed the employee manual. Many times, I had to deny requests from the employees and/or enforce the rules in the manual, while he went behind my back to tell them that I was tough and he disagreed with me. Then he undid what I had done."

"And you did not like this?"

"No. The employees hated me and it created an environment of disruption."

"So, what happened when you came back to the office?"

"I told him that I was going to take care of everything that had to do with the administrative part, but no employees. And most of my job I did from home."

"Who took care of the employees?"

"He did."

"Now he was both?"

"What?"

"He was the 'good cop, bad cop.'"

"Yes."

"Objection."

"What now?"

"Misrepresentation."

"Overruled."

"Can you better explain your new job description?"

"I was in charge of the bank, deposits, taxes, all payments, contracts, rents, equipment and/or furniture, the maintenance of the building once we moved to the office we had built. Everything administrative and maintenance."

"You knew the gross income and net?"

"Yes. I took care of deposits and provided all information to our CPA. I also made sure all filings were done at the proper time."

Bobby pulled out one of our tax returns. He handed a copy to me, others to Jacob and the judge, and kept one in his hand.

"Do you recognize this?"

"Yes."

"What is it?"

"It is our tax return for 2012."

"You provided all the information to your CPA."

"Yes."

"However, the income amount you provided is less than what it is here."

"Yes."

"Did you know about that?"

"No."

"Why?"

"I did not realize the discrepancy at the time. It was our expert who noticed it."

"Explain what you provided to your CPA every year."

"My books that I do on Quick Books with all deposits, withdrawals and payments. I also turned in all 1099s that come from every insurance company or entity that makes payments to us. They started coming in January. I verify that they belong to us and give them to our CPA."

"Did you calculate them?"

"No."

"Why?"

"It was a lot. I mean a lot. That was our CPA's job to match the 1099s with my book."

"Did he, the CPA, ever call you to report a discrepancy?"

"No."

"The discrepancy was less money or more money?"

"There was more money earned based on the 1099s. But my books showed less."

"How could that have happened?"

"The only way is that several checks were not given to me."

"Objection..."

"Your Honor, I am trying to see where the money went. I have not finished."

"Are you trying to get somewhere?" the judge asked.

"Yes."

"Overruled."

"Did you, Carmen, deposit the money in another account?"

"No."

"Did you find out your husband had other accounts?"

"Yes."

"When?"

"Before and after I filed for divorce, and a banking private investigator looked to see if there were other accounts."

"Did he find one, two, how many?"

"Several."

"Were you surprised?"

"Yes!"

Bobby continued to go over every property we had and everything financial. It took him two days. In reality, it was a day, half a day on Wednesday and a little more than half on Thursday.

Every night when I got home, I was exhausted. I would just hug my children, have dinner with them, and go to bed to rest for the next day.

By Thursday afternoon, the real nightmare had started.

"I pass the witness," Bobby said.

I saw Jacob coming at me with a half-smile on his face that made him look like The Joker. It was surreal. Every time he interrogated me, he was more than rude. There was a total lack of respect. But this time around proved to be the worst.

I had prevailed in the airplane case and most of the records related to that had been expunged. However, Jacob started by asking me about it.

"Objection," Bobby said.

"Your Honor, these are facts and I need to ask her about it," Jacob said.

"This had been expunged. Therefore, it would be a crime for him to use it."

"Sustained."

Jacob continued with his questions. He wanted me to be tried again for the the airline incident. Once again, he mentioned the expunged records.

"Objection, Your Honor. He is doing it again."

Jacob proceeded with the longest and most absurd explanation. I thought he would never finish. He makes things so complicated that either the judge gets confused or just cannot remember what is happening.

"Overruled."

"I am sorry, Your Honor," Bobby said.

"But if this is your ruling, then you have to allow me to use all of Alejandro's criminal records that had been expunged. And mentioning this again is a tactic to get this in the record, so I should be allowed to do the same when I interrogate Alejandro."

Jacob objected, but the judge said: "I think it is only fair that if I allow one, I have to allow for both. Please continue."

Alejandro and Jacob did not like this, but they were so desperate to further muddy my name that I did not know if they did not care or if it was too late since the judge had already ruled.

My father had never believed in psychological therapists. He always said: "In this family, nobody is crazy. Now go to a therapist, and you will be crazy after that."

The last years of my marriage, I had tried to fix and save it. I was trying to save my family. We did individual and couples therapy. I had thought I needed therapy myself because I was so weak. At the time, I did not know that Alejandro was medicating and drugging me. And I did not know the effect the entire verbal, mental and emotional abuse had on me. I just felt weak, when I had been so strong till then, that I thought therapy could help. Little did I know that opening my heart and being funny and exaggerated at times with the therapist, was going to end up becoming a completely different story in the hands of my ex's evil lawyer.

I was learning more and more that a trial is like a show. Sometimes I think the best show wins.

Therapists did not write everything down during a consultation. They write words, sentences, but nothing that you can make sense of, unless you remember everything you told them. Anyway, there was no time in trial to undo what Jacob was about to do.

He started filling in the blanks from those sketchy notes. I kept trying to fill in the blanks with the truth, but every time I did, Jacob would object to my answer.

"Objection, Your Honor. Argumentative."

"Sustained."

Anyway, it proved good because he was not getting anywhere. Alejandro had tried so hard to make people believe that I was an alcoholic. Those who know me well knew I never drank much.

Actually, when I was young, I never drank alcohol at all. Later in life is when I started drinking socially, and at the end of my marriage... well. Alejandro was putting things in my drink and medicating me.

So, Jacob tried to portray me as an alcoholic in front of the judge—even though I had been checked twice for drugs and alcohol in court, and the test was always negative.

"You can drink eight glasses of tequila," Jacob said.

"No."

He started to put eight tequila shot glasses on his side of the table. All of us in the room were wondering where he was going.

"Yes. You said that."

"I did not."

"Here! Here are how many glasses of tequila you drink."

"Objection."

"Your Honor, I am showing her drinking habits."

"Your Honor, this is not necessary. It could possibly be good if we had a jury, but there is no jury here."

"Sustained."

Jacob had to put the glasses away!

Friday morning, we took a break from my questioning to have Jake Thompson interrogated. Scheduled in court on Thursday, he was the sleep technician in our laboratory. Jacob objected to him testifying on Thursday, though he knew if Jake had to take more days off work it was going to hurt him. Bobby pleaded with the judge, but it could not be fixed. He was under subpoena and had to come back.

"Raise your right hand, sir," the judge said.

"Do you swear to tell the truth and nothing but the truth, so help you God?"

"I do."

"Did you work for Alejandro?"

"Yes."

"What was your position?"

"Head of the Sleep Lab."

"You were the Head of the Sleep Lab?"

"Yes."

"Were you working with Alejandro in 2012?"

"Yes."

"Did you discover that another employee was using his DEA number to order Vicodin?"

"Yes."

"How?"

"I was in the Sleep Lab one night when Becky Barra came in in the middle of the night."

"Was she supposed to be there at that time?"

"No."

"Did she work in the Sleep Lab or the practice?"

"The practice."

"Was she supposed to be there at that time? What was her schedule?"

"Objection," Jacob said.

"Why?" Bobby asked.

"He was not a supervisor. He could not have known this."

"Your Honor, he could say if she worked the day or night."

"Sustained."

Bobby rephrased the question in order to get around it.

"Did she work day or night?"

"She worked during the daytime."

"What happened next?"

"I paid attention to what she was doing."

"What was she doing?"

"She took the triplicates and wrote a prescription."

"What happened next?"

"She left."

"What happened then?"

"I started to observe if this behavior was repeated."

"And was it?"

"Yes. She continued to come several nights a week."

"What else did you see?"

"I saw on her Facebook page people were referring to 'that white pill' and how it could solve everything."

"What else did you find out?"

"She was writing prescriptions of over 500 pills a month for Vicodin to many different names."

"Who signed them?"

"She used the doctor's stamp."

"Did you report her to your superior?"

"Yes."

"You reported her to Alejandro?"

"Yes."

"Did he fire her?"

"No."

"Does she still work there?"

"To my knowledge, she does."

"Did he report her to the authorities?"

"No."

"Let's move on to another topic," Bobby said.

"Were you there when Patient C died?"

"Yes."

"Did he die at the lab?"

"No. But everything is related to the lab."

"Objection."

"To what?" Bobby asked.

"After 'No.'"

"What happened at the lab?" Bobby asked.

"The patient felt after his study was done that night at the lab."

"Were the doctors there?"

"No. They never are. But they are on call."

"Who was on call that night?"

"Alejandro."

"At some point, did you call him that night?"

"Yes."

"Why?"

"The patient could not sleep."

"What did he say?"

"He ordered me to give him Ambien."

The patient could not take Ambien. He said in his questionnaire that it was counter-indicated. As a result, the patient fell and broke his hip. He died two days later—when Alejandro was on call again—while in the hospital waiting for surgery. The answering service called Alejandro, but he never answered. He was drunk as usual.

"Was the medical record of the patient changed afterward?"

"Yes."

"Were you there?"

"Yes."

"Can you explain what happened?"

"Alejandro and another doctor discussed what pill they were going to exchange with the Ambien. They got into the system and Mr. C's record and changed the medication he had that night."

"Were you ever aware of any extra-marital relationship Alejandro had?"

"I cannot be sure, but a drug representative used to come often and spend long hours talking with him, until one day she left crying."

"Did you see him kissing an employee?"

"Yes."

"Where?"

"There were pictures of a party where he kissed a woman who worked with me in the lab."

"You were not at the party."

"No."

"But you saw the pictures."

"Yes."

"How?"

"The day after the party, my coworkers had them all over the office."

"Let's move on to another situation. After Carmen filed for divorce, did Alejandro instruct his employees in what to say if they were questioned?"

"Yes."

"Can you explain?"

"Alejandro had his lawyer on the phone, and every employee was called to his office and instructed on what to say."

"What was the purpose besides getting them to testify his way?"

"The ones that agreed were added to his witness list."

"Did you agree?"

"No."

"Pass the witness."

Jacob set out to discredit Jake.

"You were fired because you were a terrible employee."

"No."

Jacob presented a document to the judge and us and proceeded to show it to Jake.

"Have you seen this document?"

"Give me a minute."

"Yes. Take all you need."

"No, sir. I have not seen it."

"This is the reprimand that led to your dismissal."

"No. This never happened."

"Isn't it true that you were a difficult employee and always had problems with Alejandro?"

"False."

"You were disruptive."

"No."

"Did you ask to work from home?"

"Yes."

"Why?"

"The office was a mess. Alejandro was always screaming at everyone, especially his daughters on the phone. I could do my job from home."

"Isn't that too much to ask?"

"I was not asking to not go to the office. I was asking to work more time from home and less time in the office."

"Isn't it true that you are making this up because you are mad for been fired?"

"No, sir."

"Pass the witness."

Bobby came back and only asked one question. He took the supposed reprimand and showed it to Jake.

"I just want to make sure this is clear. Have you seen this document before today?"

"No, sir."

No further questions.

Jake left, and I went back to the stand. I was satisfied with Jake's participation. Bobby was able to show important issues.

Jacob was now moving to accuse me of cheating on Alejandro and to further embarrass me. He pulled out a picture, and I could see what it was. I knew they were going to introduce the private pictures I had sent to Alejandro; pictures just between the two of us, something I did to keep our marriage alive. My sexy pictures!

My face was red and showed my embarrassment. I had never imagined this would become public. He had asked for them and loved that I sent them to him. But this was low. Jacob gave me one of the pictures and was going to give another to the judge.

"Object vigorously," Bobby said.

The judge could see what it was and ordered Jacob to stop.

"Your Honor, this is private. What a couple does in intimacy has no place here but to embarrass my client."

Jacob insisted: "Your Honor, I am trying to demonstrate something with these pictures."

Bobby: "These pictures have no place here."

Jacob: "I cannot get where I want without these."

Judge: "You can ask the questions, but I will not admit the pictures as evidence."

This was a way Alejandro could expose those pictures and not be labeled as having done so. He liked to do things under cover, so he could say it was not his fault. If the pictures were admitted, then he had the excuse that they were public record, and then he would have splashed them all over the press.

Jacob was frustrated that he did not get to introduce the pictures and had to come up with a totally different line of questioning since he could not just abandon the subject. I was allowed to keep that picture and others in front of me in order to answer the questions, but that was it.

I was sitting on the witness stand when I saw Mr. Lilly walk in. Bobby's senior associate, he had started my divorce, but was now practically retired. He caught me by surprise. Walking inside of what is called the bar, he sat down behind Bobby. He was smiling and looked at me with approval. It felt as if he came to support me.

Jacob continued: "You sent this picture to Alejandro after you were separated."

"No."

"Isn't it true that after you separated and accused him of assault, you sent these pictures?"

"No."

"When did you send these pictures to Alejandro?"

"On many different occasions, but all months, months before we legally separated."

"No."

"You sent these right after, so how can you claim abuse if you wanted him?"

"Sir, the pictures had the date and so did the texts by which they were sent. We can pull that!"

"Objection. Too broad."

"Sustained."

It did not matter that the judge had sustained. I had already said it and that made Jacob stop that line of questioning.

It was late and I was tired. We were all tired. It was almost 7 p.m., and the judge called it a day.

Dismissed, I stood up and went to get my handbag. Mr. Lilly was talking to Bobby, but came to say hello: "You are doing great. I am proud of you!"

Once he left, Jacob and Alejandro were puzzled about his presence there. Jacob said: "He was a legend."

It was Friday, September 1, 2016, and next Monday court would not be in session. My son was off with his father, and Kamee had plans for the weekend with friends. My friends invited me to go to the beach for the long weekend to a house on Bolívar Peninsula. I thought it was a great idea to break away from the routine in the middle of this mess, but I did not have energy to pack. We had a menu plan, and I could even go to the grocery store. One of my friends wanted me to fight with her about the menu.

"Luisa, do you have any idea what I am going through? Do you think I care about the menu?"

The next morning, Douglas, Lourys and Jorge were at my door. The doorbell woke me up. Opening it, I said: "I have not packed or bought anything. And I need to take a shower."

"You take a shower while I see what I can pack for food from your pantry," Lourys said.

So, we left. But I spent the weekend like a zombie. However, we laughed, and I needed it.

On Tuesday, we were back in court, and I had to get back on the stand. I was not looking forward to that. What else was Jacob going to pull?

Little did I know today was going to be about trying to prove that now I was a whore. How could Alejandro get so low? He knew what type of woman I was. And only a few months before, he had said that he knew I had never cheated on him. However, he still was going to try that.

"How many times did you cheat on your husband?" Jacob asked.

"Never."

"Never? That is not true."

"Never, sir."

"You cheated at least twice on Alejandro."

"No."

"You admitted to dating two men since you separated, when Bobby questioned you."

"Yes."

"You cheated on your husband with one of them while you were still together."

"No."

Bobby said: "Objection. Time frame."

"Sustained."

"From when to when did you see Mr. M.?"

"This was already established with Bobby," I answered.

Jacob started pulling pictures taken from my Facebook page. Pictures with friends and at parties, pictures I put on Facebook because I have nothing to hide. He pulled out a photo of Juan José and I in costume at a Halloween party. He was an Arab sheik and coincidentally, I was a belly dancer. It was all by coincidence. We had laughed, taken pictures and posted them. We thought it was hilarious.

"Who was this?"

"Juan José."

"This is one of your boyfriends."

"No."

"Who is he?"

"We have been friends for over 20 years. We worked together then and now."

"Did you have sex with him?"

"No."

Jacob gave me another photograph. It was a beautiful picture of my dear friend, Luigi, and I. We were hugging at a party, and I was happy. Luigi had been a great support during this time, but he was gay. So, I was looking forward to questions about him.

"Who was this?"

"Luigi Santos."

But he did not ask anything else about him. He was trying to show the judge that I had photos with many men in his quest to say I was a whore. He knew that further questions about Luigi would not be good because my answer would have been: "I am not his type."

"What do you mean?"

"He is gay!"

Anyway, I would be able to do it later. I did not know how soon!

Jacob pulled out another picture with Luigi. There were four other men and two women: Claudia and I.

"Can you tell me the names of all the people in this picture?"

"Yes. Montero, Luis Hernández, myself, Luigi Santos, José Sánchez, Claudia and her boyfriend."

"Well, we have already established that Mr. Montero was the one with whom you had an affair."

"Objection, time frame."

After again repeating the time frame, Jacob asked the ultimate: "With how many men in this picture have you had sex?"

Containing my laughter, I could not believe they had walked right into this. I started to point with my finger to three out of the five men that were not Mr. Montero or Claudia's boyfriend: "Gay, Gay, Gay."

Bobby burst into laughter along with everyone in the room, even the court reporter. His face was red as was the judge's.

Jacob was so furious that he ended his cross-examination!

"Pass the witness," he said.

Bobby came back to clean up any damage that Jacob had done. This is why it was good to be the first to present their side of the case. Bobby had a chance to redirect in the questions that created confusion in my case.

After that, we took a break in the little room. I was furious with the way Jacob had treated me. How could Alejandro allow him to treat me like that, the mother of his children, with such little respect—treating me like a whore. It was established I had dated two people after I separated and that was it. In fact, during the divorce trial, when I knew they were saying I had cheated, one day I was so furious that I told Bobby: "Can I sue him for fraud?"

"Why?" Bobby asked.

"Well he is terrible at it, now that I know. If I had cheated on him, I would have left him long before."

Bobby told me while we were in the side room talking: "I am going to call Alejandro next. That way, I get to interrogate him twice."

"Great idea, Bobby! Take the thunder away from Jacob."

Probably Alejandro and Jacob thought we would call Beth Hurst, my forensic CPA, or another witness. But Bobby saved that for later. Alejandro was surprised when Bobby called him.

CHAPTER 44

The Prostitutes

ALEJANDRO TOLD AMANDA around 2011 that the first time he went to the Men's Club he felt like he was at Disney World for grown men. I never liked the fact that he said he was going to those places with friends to have fun. However, I never imagined everything that could happen there or that he would get involved with the women from those places.

He was having full-blown affairs with many of them without caring about getting diseases or passing them on to me. After he moved out, I learned he had been getting tested for HIV every six months.

Once we started couples therapy and he started to talk, I found out that most of his affairs were with prostitutes from the Men's Club and Treasures, clubs with exotic dancers that provided full services. These women were looking for a man or men to support them. The rest of the story I got from one of the women who sent me a message via Facebook that said Alejandro had many girlfriends like her.

In Texas, prostitution is a huge business, especially in Houston, which is the number-one port for human trafficking. Woman from all over the state and out of state come to Houston to participate in the business. Many of these women end up marrying well and becoming part of society in Houston.

Prostitution and substance abuse go hand in hand. I could only imagine that they enticed their clients to use. I wondered if these liaisons got Alejandro into cocaine, or was it something he always did that I just did not know about. After so many years of marriage, I found out that there were so many things I did not know about him.

Our marriage was so broken. He never stopped his cheating ways, though he swore he did. He kept getting other cell phones. One day, I found another one at his office, along with a recorder.

When I walked into the office, he suddenly hid something in a drawer and acted nervous. Once he left, I found a Blackberry that I had never seen before, with texts to and from different women. I left the office with both the phone and the recorder, playing the recording on my way back home. It was a conversation with Cara, a prostitute and mother that had an African American son, with whom he had an affair. She was the same woman I had finally found out about on our 23rd anniversary.

Alejandro said in therapy that he had reported her to the police because she was blackmailing him, and supposedly she had left town to escape the police. However, he was still texting with her. This is what he did to women, even his own wife: He reported them to the authorities to get rid of them, finding a way to get them in trouble with the law.

Cara was desperately in need of money. Apparently, Alejandro had stopped supporting her. In the conversation, she complained she had stopped working at Treasures since Alejandro had said she and her son were now his responsibility.

"What do you want me to do?" he asked.

"You probably want to tell me, 'Yes, bitch, go back to Treasures.'"

As the conversation continued, he also complained about the previous Friday, when I had gone to Austin. Apparently, he used the night off to go out with her, but he also was hitting on other girls and complaining about her behavior.

"I just don't like what you did last Friday. It makes me not want to see you again."

"Really? Tell me what you put in my drink, Alejandro."

He had laughed and did not answer.

She insisted: "Tell me what it was that you put in my drink."

Finally, he answered in a very sarcastic and cold way: "The same thing you take every day when you go to work."

A prostitute could tell much better than me that he was drugging her. That conversation enlightened me. Not only did he get women in trouble with the law, like he did me, he drugged them just like he had been doing to me.

When we subpoenaed the police records on him, we found many similar reports involving other women. And, of course, mine were there.

I found texts with other women, who my research showed had all worked at either the Men's Club or Treasures or both. Alejandro's own family lawyer confided to one of my lawyers that he had girlfriends, but always paid.

And then there were the prostitutes when he was with the thief! He kept taking these women to his apartment with one or more of my children present.

In July 2014, my kids came home saying their dad had a bruised eye, scratches and a problem with one wrist. He told them it was because he fell on the staircase going to the garage of his building. The kids had laughed, mimicking how their dad got a bruised eye by hitting the rail. Raquel, my friend, my sister in life, was in town. While we were having dinner together, we were all asking how that could have happened, laughing at the unbelievable story. But all his stories were like that, and the authorities believed him. Why? Well, he was a doctor!

A few months later, a friend of his now ex-girlfriend contacted me, saying she wanted to help me. She volunteered information about how Alejandro took all the men in her group of friends to an erotic dancers place north of Houston and went to a private room with one of them. He had always blamed Roberto. Well, two peas in a pod.

The girlfriend had forgiven him for that, but was mad because Alejandro had called the police on her. She described him as having both a mental and a drinking problem. Going on to mention the bruised eye, she said Alejandro had told her friend that he had fallen while drunk in his apartment breaking a glass table. And that fall on the glass table also had left him with pain in his testicles.

With Alejandro, it had been so easy to find out when he was lying because he could never remember what the last lie was that he had told. Once you had two versions, bingo!

I had not found out the truth or partial truth about this incident until later because he would not even tell the police the truth. Once again, he had reported another prostitute to the police at the same time when he got hurt. This time, he claimed he had brought two prostitutes he had met at Trulucks restaurant to his apartment. He said that after he finished with them, the women claimed he owed each of them $1,000. When he refused to pay, one of the women and an African American punched him and left him on the floor of his apartment. The woman was 5 feet, 4 inches and lightweight. How could she have overcome him and punched him to the point where he was injured and ended up in the hospital? The police report indicated that a pimp was involved, which would explain his bruised eye. The injured wrist was definitely a sign that he had tried to punch someone, not to mention the testicles problem.

During the divorce, after what had looked like an attempt to separate himself from the habit of sharing time with these women, he had dated two women as official girlfriends. He got engaged to the second one, a girl nearly 30 years younger than him. My investigators had found out she was part of an escort service, while he had said she was a lawyer.

They kept breaking up and coming back together. Each time he would propose again. She started telling him every time they had a fight that "this is what you used to do to Carmen" and also accused him of drugging her.

Until one day, after the divorce was finalized, he got her arrested.

CHAPTER 45

Divorce Trial: Him

Early in July 2016, Juan Diego and I were looking for Cristina, who said she was parked outside the club, but we could not find her. I had never met her before, so I did not know what she looked like. I was relying on Juan Diego. Cristina worked for Alejandro and was on his list of witnesses. Since this would be the first time I had seen her, I decided to videotape this moment and had started recording on my phone as we walked.

Suddenly, Juan Diego said: "That's her."

A woman started walking toward Juan Diego, asking him in Spanish: "Who is this one?"

"My mom," he responded also in Spanish.

I was checking my phone screen to make sure I had a good view. I made it look like I was just checking my phone so she would not notice what I was doing. I came close to her and extended my hand: "Nice to meet you."

"Nice to meet you," she responded in Spanish.

"What is your name, please?"

"Cristina López."

"I am Carmen, Juan Diego's mother."

"Oh...yes! Thanks."

"Please, take care of my son."

They both walked to the car and drove away.

In the summers, Juan Diego had to spend a month with his father, and this was the starting date this year. Our trial was to start at the end of August, and this video established that Cristina has never met me before, until that day. This was good, because Alejandro claimed she worked either for us or for me after he left. I did not know much more because he kept changing the story.

After getting in my car, I forwarded the video to my lawyers with a note: "This video is from today. As you can see, Cristina just met me. She did not even know who I was. Add this evidence to show how far they are willing to go and lie, to make a case that does not exist."

When Alejandro got on the stand, everyone could see how he could not stop moving. He was full of nervous movements. So much so that it was distracting! I noticed this toward the end of my marriage. Actually, it was Raquel who mentioned it to me. Since she lived in El Salvador, she did not see him for long periods of time, so she would notice anything new when she saw him again.

"Carmen, what is happening to Alejandro?" she asked. "All of this continued blinking and mouth movements…"

"Really? I had not noticed."

"Yes. The blinking is definitely a result of alcoholism."

"Since I see him every day, I guess I have not noticed."

But now I only saw him in court and had started noticing these uncontrollable movements that became more and more frequent. He blinked and moved his mouth and lips in many different ways. His shoulders would not stop. And at times it looked like he was getting off his chair. I wanted to go hold him down and tell him to stop. Later this would even bother the judge.

Bobby started out being soft with him about the financials, but little by little, he raised the tone. Of course, Alejandro tried to deny everything, saying he had been broke since the divorce started. How could the practice be so successful, then go broke as I filed for divorce?

Bobby pulled out a financial record from my books listing the gross income and net from the year 2012 and handed it to Alejandro, the judge and Alejandro's lawyers.

"Do you know what this is?"

"No."

"Have you ever seen one like it?"

"No."

"No? Carmen used to give you this information."

"No, she did not."

"You never got them?"

"No."

"So, how did you know how the practice was doing?"

"She told me."

"And it was doing well?"

"Objection," Jacob said.

"Do you see the gross and net income?"

"Yes."

"Can you read the gross?"

"$1,545,000."

"Can you tell me the net?"

"Objection."

"He is reading from a document that is part of the evidence."

"Overruled."

"Please, response."

"$900,000."

"And the numbers had not changed since then?"

"That is not true."

"Why is it not true?"

"The practice is not making that much money. I am struggling."

"I think I had asked you this before. Had you fired any employees?"

"Yes."

"Had they been replaced?"

"Yes."

"Well, you still have the same number of employees."

"Well, some of them are now part-time."

"Who? Please, tell us how many."

"One."

"Would you agree then that the practice was run better when Carmen was there?"

"Oh, no."

"No? But for years she was the office manager."

"She was terrible."

"Why didn't you fire her?"

"I couldn't."

"Excuse me. Can you explain?"

"She would not let me."

"But even after she ceased being the manager, once your partnership failed in 2004, you asked her to take her position back. Why?"

"She forced me."

"Sir, do you understand that what you are saying makes no sense?"

"She forced me."

Even the judge's face was incredulous. How could he believe anybody believed this?

As soon as Bobby was able to establish that, he moved on to the women.

"How many times had you cheated on Carmen?"

"Two."

"Can you please give their names?"

Alejandro went on to name them, but Bobby added more to the list: "How about Crissy and Triclyn?"

"Ah … well. I did not have anything to do with them."

Bobby distributed a piece of paper.

"Can you see what this is?"

"A message from Facebook Messenger."

"From whom?"

"Cara."

"To whom?"

"Carmen."

"Can you please read the highlighted part?"

"Alejandro was with my friend, Triclyn, after I left Houston."

"Can you read the second highlighted area?"

"Alejandro and his many girlfriends."

"Was Cara also mad that you were cheating on her?"

"I never cheated on her."

"But you cheated on your wife?"

"Yes."

"How many times?"

"I cheated four times."

"Oh, now it is four times? Does that include the night before your wedding?"

From the judge's face, you could tell he was in shock to hear this.

"What do you know about it?" Alejandro asked with anger.

"Sir, you are here to answer questions, not to ask questions," the judge said.

In fact, the judge had reprimanded Alejandro several times. He had been abusive and disrespectful during the interrogation. Clearly, Bobby was getting under his skin.

Bobby started pulling out the pictures of my bruises, bites, and others marks that were the result of many of Alejandro's assaults. We could not enter them all into evidence; it was too much. So, we decided to use the most dramatic. Alejandro denied every picture, but his arguments were worse.

"When did you punch Carmen in this picture?"

"I did not punch her."

"No? Then what happened?"

"She hit a kitchen cabinet."

He had an explanation for every picture, and it kept getting worse. The next pictures were about bruises on my body.

"Can you explain how you inflicted these bruises on my client?"

"These are not bruises."

"No? What are they?"

"Discoloration of the skin."

"Discoloration of the skin?"

"Either that or it is the printing of the picture."

"Is that your testimony?"

"Yes."

"You are aware, as my client said in her testimony, that these pictures were studied by a forensic expert?"

"I am telling what I see."

"Pass the witness," Bobby said.

Jacob's intention during his interrogation was to paint a picture that I was the abuser, not Alejandro. They also tried to devalue the practice, but did not have the evidence to back that up. Their tactic was mostly to paint a picture, then expect the judge to buy it. Thank God that Bobby still had a chance to come afterward and clean it up.

"Carmen was physical with you, was she?"

"Yes. Many times."

"Can you explain?"

"Yes. I had scratches on my head and arms. Many times, I showed up at the office injured."

"Did that happen often?"

"Yes. I was afraid for my life."

But that was it. There were no pictures or evidence of any of those attacks he was claiming, something the police should have taken into consideration. It was just his word. Not like me: Each question was backed up with a picture.

When Bobby came back, he went all in. There were things he had not used in his interrogation that Jacob had now opened the door for. Bobby handed documents to Alejandro.

"Could those marks have been from this fight you had?"

"What fight?"

"Once again, sir, you cannot ask questions," the judge said.

"In this police report, you called the police about a prostitute that you did not want to pay, claiming you were assaulted."

"That is not true."

"What is not true? The police report or that they attacked you?"

"I called the police because they took money from me and attacked me."

"Is this what you do? You call the police on every woman you want to get rid of?"

"What do you know?"

"Sir, once again. Please answer the question. I am growing tired of your behavior."

"In fact, you called the police on Cara," Bobby said while handing Alejandro that police report.

"She was blackmailing me."

"And you called the police on her."

"She was screaming on the phone."

"And well, we know about Carmen. Is it this what you do, to get rid of women?"

"No!" Alejandro screamed.

"This is what you do to women! You call the police on them, do you?"

"What do you know?" Alejandro said screaming again.

At that point, the judge called for a break. He was growing tired of this.

During the break, our topic of conversation was Alejandro's continuous nervous movements. We commented about the source. Drugs, of course. Bobby said he was going to use it when we got back to the courtroom.

The first thing he did was to go over Alejandro's expenses on women. That was important because it was money he took from our estate to give to other women. Bobby handed Alejandro documents from the bank that showed car purchases and money transactions. This account was not an account that we both used.

"Do you recognize this?"

"Yes."

"What is it?"

"It is a bank account I opened to cover some expenses."

"Expenses for other women?"

"Not necessarily."

"Did Carmen know about this?"

"Well, she discovered it."

"This is where some of the money does not match in your tax returns."

"That is not true."

"Yes or no?"

"Yes."

"How many of these accounts do you have?"

"Just that."

"Just this? How about these?"

Bobby pulled out records we had found with a forensic bank detective.

"These are not mine."

"No? Then whose are they?"

"Carmen."

"Carmen. So, she hires a forensic bank detective to find bank accounts that are hers, and she turns that in as evidence. Is that your testimony?"

"Yes."

As Alejandro answered, once again he could not control his movements. In fact, the movements of his mouth are making such noise that the judge asked: "Sir, are you eating in my courtroom?"

"What?"

"There is a noise coming from your mouth, and it sounds like you are eating."

"No, sir. I have food stuck in my teeth from lunch."

Oh my God, I was thinking: "How embarrassing this is. Was I married to this man?"

Bobby continued the questioning.

"Have you ever tried to commit suicide?"

"No."

"No?"

"Yes, once."

"Once? Only once?"

"Yes."

"Can you tell me the day or circumstances?"

"Well, I was depressed and bought a gun. Carmen had hidden all of them. I went to a hotel on the 59 freeway. I don't remember which one. I called Carmen to say I was going to kill myself."

"And that was it?"

"Yes."

"You did try to kill yourself at Hotel ZaZa on Halloween 2009. Didn't you?"

Alejandro face was comical, so obviously trying to show he did not remember.

"Oh, yes. There was an incident there."

"An incident? You tried to kill yourself."

"Yes."

"Or were you trying to kill my client?"

"Objection!"

"Sustained."

"And suicide runs in your family?"

"Yes. I had a brother who committed suicide."

Alejandro had still been moving his lips and the rest of his body. Bobby, who had been saving the judge's comment about Alejandro's moving mouth, now came for the jugular.

"In fact, aren't all of these mouth and body movements the result of your drug addiction?"

"You little prick! What do you know about me?"

"Sir, I am this close to ordering sanctions on you because of your lack of respect for this courtroom. During this break, I hope your attorney makes clear how this is going to be handled or I will dictate sanctions," the judge said.

And we went for a break on that high note!

During the break, I noticed his mother, brother Mario and two maids outside in the hallway. I knew one of the maids because she had done work for me, and Cristina was also there. Alicia had been working for me when the burglary occurred and had taken home a bag full of things she had stolen from my house. Many things had come to light with the lie detector test the police had given her. Apparently, she and Alejandro had forgotten about it. Bobby knew about everything and was ready to use it—and many other things—if she testified.

Bobby went to talk with Jacob during the break. I should not have allowed that to happen because, when we came back, the judge was furious and said he was ready to dictate sanctions.

At my request, my friend Luisa was outside as my witness. She talked with the maids to find out what were they going to say. Alicia told her that I had called her to my bedroom to ask her to be attentive to Alejandro's every move and conversation, and to report to me. The problem with it was that Alicia does not speak English. How could she be the person I was going to rely on to spy on Alejandro? She added that I had started hitting her when she had refused. Of course, since this had happened in my bedroom, there was no witness to corroborate her story.

Cristina's story was more surprising. At first, Alejandro told me in Colorado once that Cristina had worked for me after he was kicked out of the house. She said I was abusive toward the children. However, he had already given me custody of the children, making this irrelevant.

Domi, my maid, was able to question Juan Diego on the matter, since Cristina was working for Alejandro then.

"Juan Diego, did you know the woman that works for your father, Cristina?"

"No. Well, I know her now."

"Did you ever see her at our house with your mom?"

"No, but Daddy says she worked for us."

"When?"

"I don't know. I don't remember her."

"But did they say when?"

"The other house."

By now, I had already moved from the big house. After we sold it, I was granted the money to buy the house I was in now. Thank God, my house was paid in full.

"Which one? The big house or this?"

"I don't know. I don't remember her."

This proved they were trying to convince my son that Cristina had worked for me. But even my son said that she had not. Cristina's story now had changed. Now, she worked for us when Alejandro and I still were living together. It was not when Alicia was in the house, of course. I could not believe how Alejandro could pretend that I was not going to remember who had worked for me.

Bobby had questioned me about whether Cristina worked for me. During my testimony, he also asked me to name the people that had worked for me at the house in the last five years.

Luisa asked Cristina why she was there.

"The doctor asked me," she said.

"Are you getting paid for the time here?"

"Yes," the two of them answered.

"Did you work for them, Cristina?"

"Yes."

"When?"

"In the big house, when they were still together."

"And why is your testimony important?"

"One day, I saw how she grabbed him by his hair and dragged him all across the study."

"She dragged him?"

"Yes."

"By the hair?"

"Yes."

"Carmen and her 115 pounds dragged a man by the hair?"

"Yes."

"That sounds impossible."

The woman was silent.

"I bet she must have pulled most of his hair off."

Cristina shrugged her shoulders.

Luisa told me all of it during the break. It was good to know, just to be prepared. So, Bobby would be ready with questions, if we got there.

When we came back, Bobby started the interrogation. There was much more to cover, but he passed the witness.

With that, Alejandro was dismissed from the stand. I looked up in disbelief. How could he? Having Alejandro sent to jail for at least one night during the trial would be good for the case.

"Your Honor, I have a request," Jacob said. "I need to question two witnesses now because they are from out of town."

He was talking about Alejandro's brother and mother, who both lived in College Station.

The judge asked us if Alejandro could interrupt our order of questioning. Being the nice people we are, we agreed. Not like them, who made Jake Thompson lose two days of work. The judge should have had the same tough hand he had with

Thompson, but he did not. The judge's position had me so uncomfortable and worried about the outcome. I questioned whether I should have asked for a jury trial.

They called Mario to the stand, where he was sworn in.

Any questioning with Jacob was like a soap opera. Perfect! It moved with a flow so rehearsed it was obvious. Nobody ever understood the point of him being a witness.

"Do you know Carmen?"

"Yes."

"Since when?"

"Since they started dating back in the '80s."

"What can you say about Carmen?"

"Oh, she was very difficult. She always got what she wanted."

"But that is a good thing?"

"Ah...oh...Yes."

"Do you remember the day she called you because Alejandro wanted to commit suicide?"

"Yes."

"What did she say?"

"She was only worried about the money."

"What else did she say?"

"That if Alejandro killed himself, I would have to support her and the children because there was not enough money for her to survive."

The lies kept accruing, but you could see Mario was uncomfortable. Alejandro is a better liar, a natural liar, not Mario.

There was not much Mario could say. And the witness was passed to Bobby.

Bobby started his questioning. He pulled out a document, distributed it, and gave a copy to Mario.

"Do you see the figure at the bottom?"

"Yes."

"How much is it?"

"It is over two million dollars."

"Now, I am going to show you more documents."

Bobby pulled all of the life insurance policies and gave them to Mario one by one.

"Can you tell me what that is?"

"It is a life insurance policy."

"Can you tell me how much the benefit is?"

"It is two million dollars."

Bobby handed another one to Mario.

"Tell me how much the benefit is on this one."

"One million dollars."

"And how about this?"

"One million."

"So, four million dollars! Four million dollars in life insurance. So, he was better off dead than alive, wasn't he?"

Mario was mute. He could not answer. There was nothing else he could say. He had been exposed as a liar in front of the court.

"I guess," Mario said.

"No further questions, Your Honor."

Mario was dismissed. And we took another break. As usual, I went to the small room with Bobby. I high-fived him, we talked, and then went to the bathroom before we started again. While walking toward the bathroom, I saw Mario sitting in the hallway alone. His mother sat by herself.

He looked at me with sympathy. I knew! He knew! We had always had a connection. I knew he respected me and admired me somehow. I knew then! He had just realized that he was lied to. On my way back, I saw Alejandro's mom sitting on the bench not happy. Then I asked myself: Have I ever seen her with a happy face?

Then, while passing the little hallway that goes to the small courtrooms for the associate judge, I saw Mario hiding in there. Now he was mad! He was moving his lips, like he was talking to himself. It was important to see him away from his mother. This woman had zero influence in their lives because their father's manipulation took over. She had been so belittled; now she felt she could manipulate them. I had experienced it when she had tried. She felt that since the boys were not depending financially on their father, it was now her turn and she was trying her best to be "it," the "it" she never was. It was clear that Mario wanted away from her.

I walked by and kept going.

It was late! Alejandro's lawyer was trying his best to get Alejandro's mother or the maids to testify. But finally, the judge called it a day!

We had always had a meeting before calling it a night. I asked if they would interrogate the maids tomorrow.

"Probably."

"Well, one of the maids never worked for me. We have to have that video ready to show after she lies on the stand. Bobby, are we ready?"

"Where is that video?"

"I sent it to all of you back in July. I can look up the email."

Dawn looked at us like she did not know what I was talking about.

"If you don't have that video and you did not turn it in as our evidence, we are going to have a problem," I said. "I am leaving and expect an email with a confirmation later tonight that you have the video."

I was exhausted. I walked out of the courtroom and was looking forward to walking out of that building.

When I got home, I opened my computer and searched for the original email where I had sent the video to Dawn, Bobby and everybody in their office. There it was, the email from July 5, 2016. I sent it again with a note, afraid they had never turned it in as evidence and I would really be in trouble. We could never have proved they had lied.

As usual, I had dinner with my children and relaxed watching the news. For some that was not relaxing, but for me, the journalist, it was. I went to bed and rested to get ready for another day... another crazy day.

Getting to the courthouse the next morning, I did not see Alejandro's mother or the maids. Since we had to finish with our own witnesses, I figured they would probably show up later. We met before the trial started, and I asked if they had found the video. Dawn said with a sigh of relief: "Yes! I have the day and time I had sent it to them, and it is in our evidence. We sent everything to them in preparation for today."

Bobby called my forensic CPA. The interrogation was simple and to the point. There were questions about the income of the business, including our net and the misrepresentation between my books and the tax returns.

When Jacob's turn came, it was all about trying to make Beth Hurst look crazy. But Beth had been doing this for so long, he could not get under her skin. Still, Bobby came back and cleaned up anything that could be damaging.

Bobby called our case closed, and it was Alejandro's turn to put his case on. He already had his brother as a witness, and now we would see who else he had.

It was already afternoon, and I still had not seen Alejandro's mother or the maids. I could imagine what had happened to the maids, but not Alejandro's mom. Well, maybe I could: After Mario was caught lying on the stand, he got mad and left town with his mother in tow.

However, I was surprised to see Alejandro's employee, Eve, outside and my daughter, Alexandra. I knew Alexandra was on his witness list, but I never imagined that Alejandro would put her on the stand. Especially after I had cared for her during and after her bariatric surgery. Obviously, Alejandro did not care at all. Getting her to lose weight was something he needed for the trial.

I walked up and kissed her. She acted normal, but looked lost. Something was not right. Usually she was vivacious, but today she was in slow motion. She had lost some weight because of the surgery, but not much. She looked at me and said: "*Mami, can you get me water? I am thirsty.*"

Could that be the result of medication? I got a bottle of water and walked out to the hallway to hand it to her, sitting down next to her.

"Alexandra, you don't have to do this, you know."

"I don't want to hurt you, *Mami.*"

"I know."

Recess was over, and we had to get back in the courtroom. I left her sitting there all alone. I was worried about her. Bobby looked at me and could tell I was worried and hurt.

"Carmen, the judges hate when the children are used," he said. "This is going to backfire on Alejandro."

Jacob called Eva Leny, the second person in the Sleep Lab, as Alejandro's first witness. The whole line of questioning was about destroying the testimony of General Reynolds. How can you pit a regular medical employee against a decorated service officer? Suddenly, she was there to see the whole thing, which was against the General's testimony. Jacob showed Eva the map for the parking lot and made her point to where she was and where we were. It was completely different than what the General had said.

Eva looked scared, though it was obvious she had been trained for this. But she could never have imagined what was coming up with Bobby.

"Ma'am, I am going to give you the map of the parking lot," Bobby said. "Please, can you point out where Alejandro and Carmen were and where you were?"

"Yes. They were here, and I was there."

Her answer was completely different than her previous testimony. And Bobby said: "Let the record show that her previous testimony is different from the one now. The car is in different positions."

"You said Alejandro showed up at the office with scratches and marks."

"Yes."

Bobby pulled the police report and showed to her.

"Could those scratches have been the result of this attack?"

She was silent.

"Please, answer."

"I don't know."

"But it could have been?"

"Yes."

Bobby continued asking questions about women at the office and if she had witnessed any irregularities at the office.

"No," she answered.

But the ultimate question was coming. Would this show why she was willing to lie?

"Have you ever kissed Alejandro?"

She hesitated and thought about it, but finally said, "Yes."

I guess she knew about the photos and was afraid we would pull them out.

"Can you tell us when this was?"

"Sometime in 2010, at the farewell party of a coworker."

"And you knew that Alejandro was married?"

"Oh, yes."

"And it did not matter to you that you were kissing Carmen's husband?"

"Objection, Your Honor," Jacob said.

At that moment, without waiting for the judge's ruling, Bobby said: "No further questions."

Once Eva was dismissed, Jacob moved on to call the next witness, Alexandra.

His people went out and got Alexandra, who looked like a timid little girl when she walked in. I could tell she was afraid. Outspoken and full of life, she had never been a timid girl.

She sat down and was sworn in. Her testimony looked rehearsed. They had a witness to counter each piece of evidence in my case. Jacob shot himself in the foot with his first question: "Your father has not given you anything to come and testify here today?"

"No."

He pulled out the picture with a purple eye. That incident had happened in Miami in March 2013, the first time we had stayed at our apartment after it was remodeled. She had invited a friend from school that was living in England at the time to enjoy the Ultra Festival. It was Easter week and all my friends from Venezuela were in Miami.

We all went to a friend's house, and the girls stayed over there. Alejandro and I came back to the apartment. She was not there when Alejandro attacked me. Since it happened in our bedroom, she never would have seen it anyway.

Jacob handed the picture to Alexandra and asked: "Do you remember this incident?"

"Yes."

"Do you know how it happened?"

"Yes."

"How?"

"My mother was drunk and hit the kitchen cabinet."

I could not contain myself and gasped. I whispered to Bobby, "She was not there."

Alexandra's testimony was short and prepared. They did not want to overdo it for the judge.

Bobby said: "I have no questions," but he had been looking at documents when he said that, and added: "Yes, I do have questions."

He walked close to her, document in hand, but did not give it to her: "You were not at the apartment when your mother got her eye bruised," he said.

"Yes, I was."

"You were partying at your mother's friend's house."

"No, I was at the apartment."

"Is it your testimony that your father has not given you any money in order for you to come here and testify?"

"Yes...I mean no. He has given me no money."

Bobby handed her the document and said:

"What is it? Is it a bank statement? Look at what is highlighted on the first page, please."

"Yes."

"I will read it for you and please confirm that you see the same. On May 23, 2016, six thousand dollars to Alexandra. It looks like it is your bank account."

"Yes."

"On June 13, 2016, six thousand dollars to Alexandra."

"Yes."

"So, your father paid you?"

She was quiet, thinking how to answer this. Finally, she said slowly: "It was money to pay for school."

At that moment, Dawn jumped up and said: "He is whispering the answers to her," while pointing at Alejandro.

The paralegal stood up and said: "Yes, I heard it, too."

"Wait a minute," the judge said. "We have a problem. Are you done with the witness?"

"Yes," Jacob said fast. "Actually, she needs to go back to school."

"You are dismissed."

At this point, Dawn and Amy are telling the judge what they heard and saw. Alexandra was trying to walk out of the courtroom when the judge told her: "You need to wait outside in case we call you again after solving this matter."

Once Alexandra was outside, Dawn went to the stand and got sworn in. Bobby cross-examined her.

"What was the question?"

"If he (Alejandro) paid her to come and testify."

"What did you hear Alejandro say?"

"It was money to pay for school."

"And was that the answer she gave?"

"Yes."

"Pass the witness."

Jacob came up and asked her: "Do you have peripheral view?" Dawn was seated practically next to Alejandro.

"Yes."

"So, you are like a special human being?"

"Yes."

"Pass the witness."

Bobby said he had no further questions, and Dawn was dismissed. Now Bobby called Amy to the stand. She had been sitting on the side of the table, so she could see Alejandro straight on.

"Did you hear the defendant whispering to the witness?"

"Yes."

"Did you hear what he said?"

"Yes."

"And was that what the witness answered?"

"Yes."

"Pass the witness," Bobby said.

With that, we ended that day. My team and I went to the side room. Bobby was destroyed. He felt lost. I could not understand why. My daughter was caught lying and Alejandro whispered the answers to her, which proved that once they were off the rehearsed testimony, she could not answer because all of it was a lie.

The next day was the last. I dressed in a beautiful white, one-piece dress. Since I knew Bobby was devastated, I wanted to cheer him up.

"You look nice today," he said.

"I am dressing the part like the winners we are."

He smiled at me.

The last day, Alejandro tried to accuse me of fraud because I used to sign for him.

"Your Honor, we know that it is not right, but how many of us have done it? Especially when you have been married for so long and your wife is running your business," Bobby said.

The truth of the matter is that Alejandro never wanted to do anything, and I had to do it all.

He used to say: "Carmen, please don't bother me with this. You can sign." I now understand that it was all a setup.

They brought in an expert to say it was not Alejandro's signature, which is not always 100 percent certain. The witness was not necessary, and we moved to closing arguments. Bobby's closing arguments acknowledged that I was not perfect, but at least admitted my faults. Then he addressed why we had to go to trial: "Who would have wanted this to go on public record? There are serious accusations of even murder here."

Jacob's closing arguments were more of the same: Alejandro did not have to share the estate because he was the breadwinner. And, of course, his client had never done anything.

By 1:30 p.m., we were walking out of court. I was exhausted but hopeful that a good outcome was coming my way. It was September 9, 2016.

CHAPTER 46

Vindication

T HE DAY WAS so beautiful when I landed in New York on September 20, 2016. I was so looking forward to this trip to Italy. I have had this love affair with the country ever since I was fifteen years old.

I needed this. The divorce trial ended eleven days ago, and I was still waiting for the judge's ruling.

It had been over four years since I had been to Europe. In fact, I had not traveled much at all with the mess my soon to be ex-husband had created. I felt free, even though the final decision was not out.

It felt as if my life was starting over with this trip. I was hoping to celebrate in my favorite places in the world, New York and Italy. I would have six hours in Manhattan to sit in one of my favorite restaurants on Madison Avenue and toast with a glass of champagne. Toast that it was almost over. Little did I know that it was going to be a BIG toast!

Almost daily I had been asking my lawyers if we had a ruling. Finally, one day Bobby texted: "Carmen, believe me. When I get a ruling, I will inform you as soon as I have it."

The trial had ended on September 9 after nearly two weeks of testimony. That is what Alejandro wanted, to waste all the money on lawyers and leave me with nothing.

So, I decided to wait patiently and take this trip as planned. I was part of the charity organization My Way Events and we had put together four operas by now. I could not make it for the last one in Italy three years ago, but the first two were in Houston, when my marriage was going from bad to worse.

This year, we were donating the funds to a pediatric cancer hospital in Italy. Helping has always made me feel so good. We had become a good team, which included the tenor and soprano from Mexico, who had been part of our events since the second opera. We were to arrive around the same time from different places. The whole thing reminded me when I was working in my career and was part of events like this.

The flight was smooth and good. My phone was off since all cellular phones had to be turned off during flights. As soon as we landed, I turned it on. I am always worried about my children, so I needed to see that everything was fine.

Once the phone was on, I saw multiple messages from my two lawyers. OMG!

This was it. This had to be it, unless Alejandro and his lawyer had pulled another one. But at this point, it was pretty much a sit and wait time.

I was nervous! I opened the last one from the associate lawyer: "Carmen, are you getting my texts?"

I scrolled down and read: "We have a ruling."

I was going in and out of the texts while getting off the plane. I was shaking and excited. I went to my lawyer's texts and saw: "We have a ruling. It is good. You get a disproportionate share of the estate and he is guilty of cruelty and adultery. I am in a deposition and cannot talk."

Oh, my God! Oh, my God! Cruelty and adultery. Cruelty! I was still shaking while I walked, thinking: "He saw it! The judge saw it. Thank you, my God. Thank you!"

Tears started running down my face. I called Bobby, but of course he did not answer since he was in the middle of a deposition. I called Dawn, the associate lawyer, who answered right away: "Oh My God, Carmen, where are you? We have been calling you and texting for hours. We have a ruling. It is super good."

"I just got off a plane in New York. I read the texts. Could you explain it to me?"

"Well, you got what you wanted—a disproportionate part of the estate—and the judge found him guilty of cruelty and adultery. We won!"

"We did!" I said almost whispering.

"I am emailing the ruling to you. It explains the separation of the estate. That way, you can see it with your own eyes. I am also getting a certified copy."

Yes, I wanted to see it with my own eyes.

I was exchanging texts with my lawyer, since he was in a deposition.

"It is great, Carmen. Who is your favorite lawyer now?" He asked so proud.

That was an incredible statement because I had had all types of lawyers, but he changed the game in my divorce, while Andino and Zack saved my life.

I was still walking at JFK Airport. My luggage was checked to Italy, so I did not have to go to baggage claim. Instead, I walked toward the airport doors. Checking my emails, I saw one from Dawn, but the attachment was not there.

I replied to her: "Dawn no attachment. Could you send it, please?"

I did not want to call anybody until I saw it with my own eyes. I wanted to read the ruling. I had a long list of people to call: my sisters, brothers and friends, but first on the list was my sisters.

They would explain to my mother better than I could over the phone.

I had a lot of texts besides the ones from the lawyers. Among them was one from my daughter, Kamee. I called her to make sure everything was fine. She sounded as sweet as usual. She had just wanted to hear my voice. She missed me already. Out of this whole mess, the best reward was to have my children's love.

My dear friend, Alex, texted me asking: "Are you here already? Looking forward to seeing you."

Alex was in New York, and we had planned to get together for those six hours I had during the layover.

"Yes, I am already here. And we will probably celebrate big time."

"What? Tell me about it!"

"As soon as I have confirmation. Xoxo."

I checked my emails again, and there it was, another one from Dawn. I now had the attachment. Opening the attachment, I started to read the ruling, skipping over the regular header of every legal part: Case number... etc. In the Matter of the Marriage of...! And went to: "Court's Rendition of Judgment."

Finally, I could see it with my own eyes: Alejandro was at fault in the breakup of the marriage on the grounds of cruelty and adultery.

My eyes were now full of tears. I started to cry profusely. I had a feeling that I could not explain. The judge saw it. He was able to see the truth. They were not able to make their lies stand up in court.

All of the pictures and recordings with insults... The records from my doctors where I was so depressed that I wanted to end my life... They had tried to interpret statements written by the doctors in a way that had the meaning they wanted, but it was all too clear that I was a victim of abuse.

I was crying and praying, thanking God. "Thank you, God!" Sitting close to one of the doors at the airport, I started calling my sisters. My voice was so weak because I was crying.

"I won! I won! He is guilty of cruelty and adultery."

"What? I can't hear you," Laura said.

With my rusty voice, I repeated: "I won. I won," as tears rolled down my face. "I proved it. I proved he abused me. I proved his cruelty."

I was in my own world. I did not see anything around me. I just felt release and wanted the world to know that the truth came out. I could not contain myself. I was explaining the ruling and every few words I kept repeating, "I won, I won!" My voice was so weak.

Suddenly, security officers started gathering around me. I did not know why, until I remembered the cameras. It was New York. They were ready for disaster.

They must have seen me crying and came to check on me. A female officer walked up to me and asked: "Are you okay?"

"Yes, I am fine. I just got the greatest news."

I saw them, but I was not afraid anymore.

Photo Gallery

View the gallery of images in color by scanning the QR code
with your mobile device.

MY LIFE

My parents, the *maracucho* and the *llanera* during their first years of dating.
Maracaibo, Venezuela. Sometime in the 1960's. Personal file.

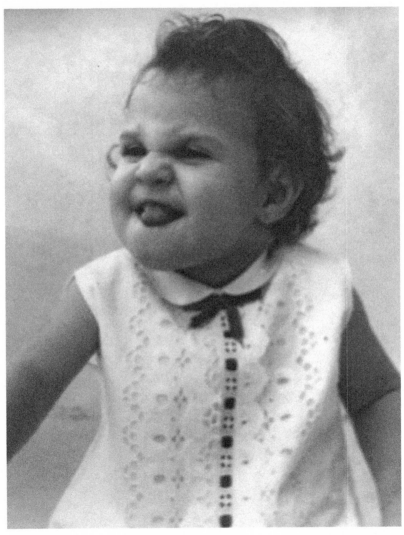

Always mischievous, always happy. My father captured this moment.
Maracaibo, Venezuela. Late sixties. Personal file.

When I see this picture, I see my two daughters. Puerto Azul Club, Caraballeda, Venezuela. Sometime in the 1960's. Personal file.

First Communion. Caracas, Venezuela. May, 1974. Personal file.

I always wanted to be a mother. I was always with my doll-baby. With my sister María Eugenia in Maracaibo, Venezuela. Sometime in the seventies. Private property.

There are friendships that become family. Here con Betzabé, Mercedes Mejía and my sister. Caracas, Venezuela. Sometime in the seventies. Personal file.

In this picture, with my mother, Mirna (my nanny), her husband and son.
Mirna moved with us to Caracas.
Caracas, Venezuela. Sometime in the seventies. Personal file.

Always the queen. Caracas,
Venezuela. 1979. Personal file.

With my cousin Omar Peña Ávila,
Aunt Marys' son. He got me my
first job at the store El Elefante
Rosa. Caracas, Venezuela. 1978.
Personal file.

Love and respect were the foundations of my parents' relationship. Eternal love.
Caracas, Venezuela. 1980. Personal file.

My first steps to be a model. Rome, Italy. 1980. Personal file.

First photographic session as model in Caracas, Venezuela. 1981.
Personal file.

Official picture as Miss Venezuela. Caracas, Venezuela. 1984.

During Miss Universe pageant, waiting for the score for the interview.
Miami, Florida, USA. July 1984. Personal file.

Official picture for Miss Universe as Miss Venezuela. Caracas, Venezuela. 1984.
Personal file.

The four runner ups with the new Miss Universe.
Miami, Florida, USA. July 1984.

Latinas competing in Miss Universe 1984. Miami, Florida, USA. 1984.

Last pictures as Miss Venezuela at my house.
Caracas, Venezuela. May 1985. Personal file.

Last pictures as Miss South America at my house.
Caracas, Venezuela. May 1985. Personal file.

Cover girl for *Venezuela Farándula*.
Caracas, Venezuela. 1984.

Cover girl for *Cosmopolitan*.
Miami, Florida, USA. 1984.

Cover girl for *Vanidades*.
Caracas, Venezuela. 1984.

Cover girl for *Caras*.
Caracas, Venezuela. 1984.

Cover girl for *Páginas*.
Caracas, Venezuela. 1984.

Cover girl for *Aboard* magazine.
Caracas, Venezuela. 1984.

Cover girl for *Auténtico*. Since then, I had to
deal with lies of the press. It reads: "Carmen
María got married pregnant." I had my first
child almost eight years after I got married.
Caracas, Venezuela. 1988.

Programing
for Venevisión Network.
Caracas, Venezuela. 1986.

The years of *Complicidades*. Here with Maite Delgado.
Caracas, Venezuela. 1986. Personal file.

We were three and then we were four. At the set of *Complicidades* with
Viviana Gibelli, Eva Gutiérrez and Maite Delgado. Caracas, Venezuela. 1987.
Photo Courtesy of Venevisión.

We worked live every day for three hours. Here in our set with
Miss Universe 1986. Caracas, Venezuela. 1986. Photo Courtesy of Venevisión.

He knew how to make me pretty, but more than that he looked after me,
Julio César Arráiz. Caracas, Venezuela. 1985.
Photo Courtesy of *Venezuela Farándula*.

We were the original trio that revolutionized the mornings in Venezuela.
Here with Maite Delgado and Eva Gutiérrez.
Caracas, Venezuela. 1986. Photo Courtesy of Venevisión.

Live from the set of *Complicidades* every morning.
Caracas, Venezuela, between 1986 and 1988.

Always helping since I was a teenager. Charity event for Granjas Infantiles.
Photo Courtesy of Granjas Infantiles. Caracas, Venezuela. 1986.

Factory Opening of Opalux make up line. Caracas, Venezuela. 1987.
Photo Courtesy of Opalux.

In that Venezuela that was in progress with successful business. Here with
Oswaldo Álvarez Paz. Caracas, Venezuela. 1986-1987. Photo Courtesy of Opalux.

Belly dancing at the Greensboro University with students.
Greensboro, North Carolina, USA. May 1989. Personal file.

At the GOP Convention of 1992 as a journalist.

Houston, Texas. Personal file.

Anchorwoman at the GOP Convention.

Houston, Texas. 1992. Personal file.

Making a wish after the GOP Convention was over, from the podium where President George Bush spoke. One day, I will be a speaker there. Houston, Texas, USA. July 1992. Personal file.

My mother, my rock, my role model.
Houston, Texas, USA. 2006. Personal file.

Always active. At my children's school for the International Fair,
representing Venezuela with a *manta guajira*. Houston, Texas. April 2006.
Personal file.

Official portrait for Woman of Distintion, event that recognizes women for their charity work in Houston for the Crohn and Colitis Foundation. Houston, Texas. 2010. Personal file.

Award for the Best-Dressed Women in Houston.
Westin Hotel. Houston, Texas. March 2011. Personal file.

Miss Venezuela 1984 and Miss Venezuela 1986.
Houston, Texas. May 2016. Personal file.

A month before the trial for the divorce, I participated in my first
charity event after years of break—this time raising money for back to school
supplies for children in need. Houston, Texas. 2016.
Photo Courtesy of Martínez-Arpin Foundation.

THE VIOLENCE

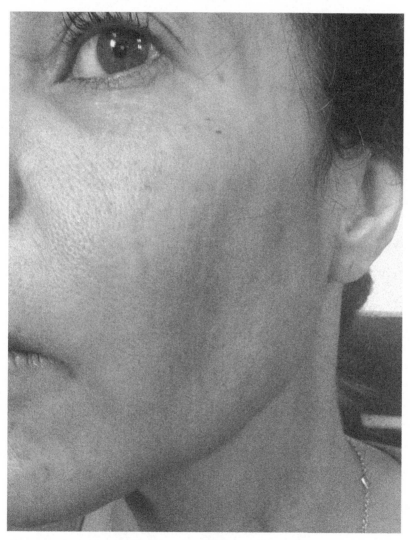

One more blow. Houston, Texas. 2012. Personal file.

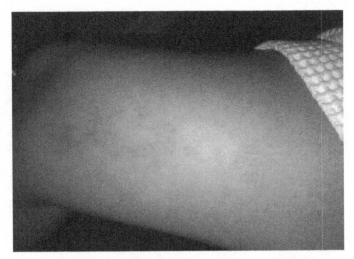

After assault on December 2011. Houston, Texas. Personal file.

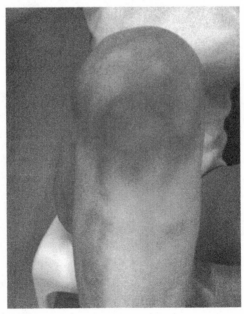

Result of the attack described in the Chapter "Get back on the Horse."
Houston. February 2013. Personal file.

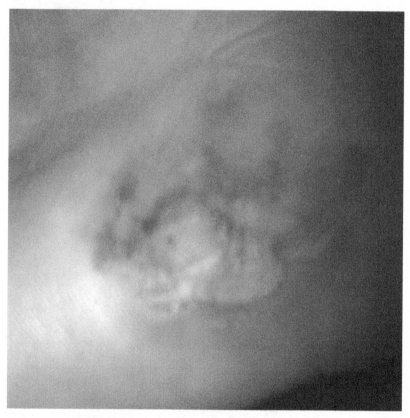

Infected bite described in the Chapter "The Silence."
Houston, Texas. February 2012. Personal file.

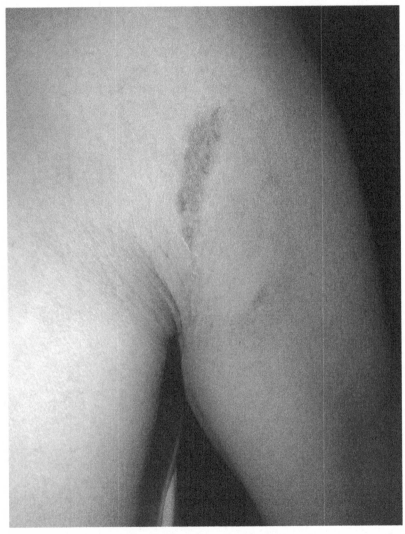

Bite described in the Chapter "The Silence."
Houston, Texas. 2012. Personal file.

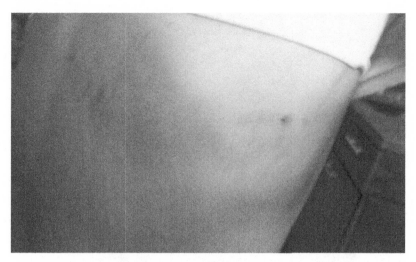

Attack described in the Chapter "The White Stuff."
Houston, Texas. June 16, 2012. Personal file.

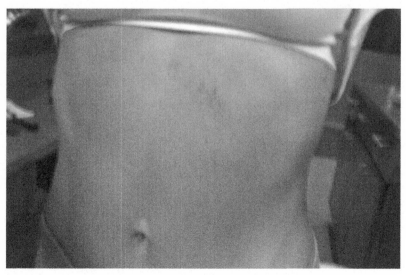

Attack described in the Chapter "The White Stuff."
Houston, Texas. June 16, 2012. Personal file.

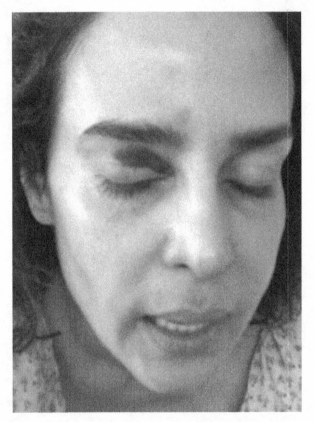

Attack in Miami during Eastern Week.
Brickel Key, Florida. March 2013. Personal file.

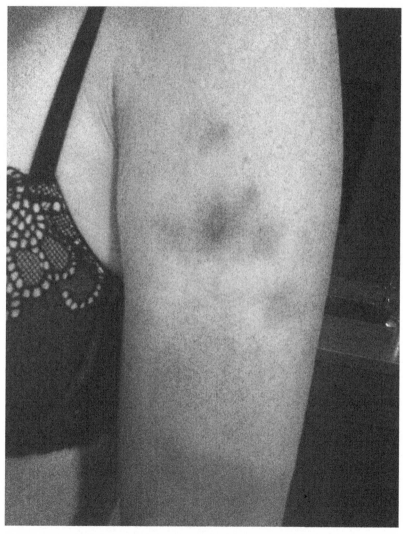

Attack described in the Chapter "Get Back on the Horse."
Houston, Texas. February 28, 2013. Personal file.

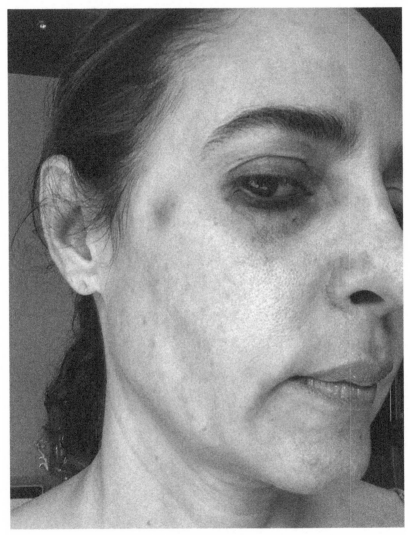

Attack during Houston-Bogota flight. June 6, 2013. Personal file.

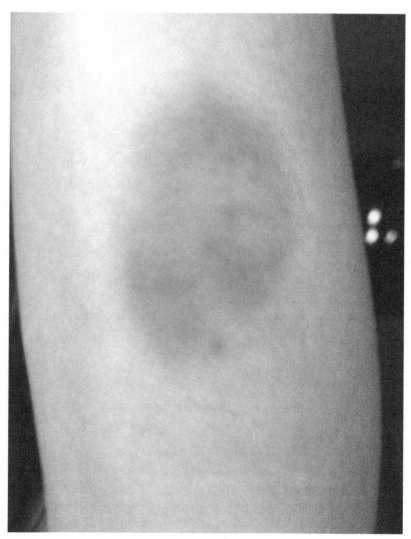

One of many assaults. Houston, Texas. 2012. Personal file.

My daughter Carmen (Kamee) and I embracing after her testimony in the
airline trial. October 1, 2015. Photo Courtesy of María Eugenia Montiel.

Table of Contents

Made in the USA
Coppell, TX
28 July 2021

59621838R00301